Clothing Technology

....from fibre to fashion

Second Edition

VERLAG EUROPA-LEHRMITTEL   Nourney, Vollmer GmbH & Co.
Düsselberger Straße 23   42781 Haan-Gruiten

Europa-Nr.: 62218

Authors:

Hannelore Eberle,	Senior Lecturer, Gewerbliche Schule, Ravensburg, Germany
Hermann Hermeling,	Principal, Frankfurter Schule für Bekleidung und Mode, Germany
Marianne Hornberger,	Lecturer, Meisterschule für Mode, Munich, Germany
Dieter Menzer,	Lecturer, Hubert-Sternberg-Schule, Wiesloch, Germany
Werner Ring,	Senior Lecturer, Fachschule für Bekleidung, Metzingen, Germany

Editor and Team Leader: Roland Kilgus, Principal, Fachschule für Bekleidung, Metzingen, Germany

Reprographics and Photography: Hans Mengel, Eningen, Germany

Fashion drawings: Studio Salo-Döllel, Aufkirchen bei Erding, Germany

Picture processing: Design Department, Verlag Europa-Lehrmittel, Leinfelden-Echterdingen, Germany

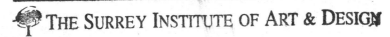
This book was produced according to the latest German Industrial Standards (DIN-Blätter). Conformance is strictly limited to the DIN-Blätter. The DIN-Blätter are published by: Beuth-Verlag GmbH, Burggrafenstrasse 6, 10787 Berlin.

Fifth German Edition 1998
Print 5 4 3 2 1
All prints of the same edition are interchangeable, excepting correction of printing errors.

Second English Edition 1999
Translation: Cotton Technology International, Dale House, 204 London Road, Hazel Grove, Stockport SK7 4DF, UK

ISBN 3-8085-6222-6   331197   687 CLO

© 1999 by Verlag Europa-Lehrmittel, Nourney, Vollmer GmbH & Co., 42781 Haan-Gruiten
Setting and printing: IMO-Großdruckerei, 42279 Wuppertal

Preface
to 1st and 2nd Editions

This is a vocational book, directed primarily at students of the clothing industry: sewing, cutting, garment assembly, men's and women' tailoring. However, it will also be found useful in courses for supervisors and technicians, and as a general reference work.

A key feature of the book is its concise and compact design - a prerequisite for summarising such a wide range of material in a single volume. Each page is complete in itself. Particular emphasis has been laid on providing a simple layout and straightforward language which students will find easy to grasp. Numerous colour diagrams are an effective aid to the comprehension of some of the more difficult topics. The colour pictures are a particularly useful feature of the chapters on Fabric Descriptions and History of Clothing.

The book is organised largely according to technological sectors, but teaching requirements have also been kept in mind. It is divided into thirteen chapters:

Fibres, Yarns, Textile Fabrics, Textile Finishing, Fabric Descriptions, Leather and Fur, Functions of Clothing, Clothing Manufacture, Organisation of Clothing Manufacture, Garment Sizing, Clothing Design, Clothing Styles, History of Clothing.

This arrangement of topics conforms to the educational guide-lines and the current curricula for courses in vocational technology for the German Federal States. For Bavaria, the book covers all of the course material in "technical theory" as well as parts of other courses. An important objective of this publication was to present the extensive material as a coherent whole. The importance to clothing of leather and fur is recognised by devoting a separate chapter to this topic. At all stages, account is taken of the latest scientific findings and the practical experience of the industry, as well as any relevant DIN standards.

At this point we would like to give special thanks to the companies and associations listed on page 256 for their assistance in the clarification of questions and for the provision of pictorial material. We are also indebted to *Ludwig Brauser* and *Malte Lütjens* for their support on the chapter on Leather and Fur, and to *Erich Stürner* for valuable advice in the section on knitted fabrics.

The authors and the publisher would welcome any suggestions for augmenting or improving the book.

Metzingen, Autumn 1989   Editor and authors

Preface
to 3rd to 5th Editions

In the light of many suggestions and new technical developments the whole book has been revised. The chapters on Fibres, Yarns, Functions of Clothing, and Clothing Manufacture have been expanded and partially reorganised. New topics, introduced because of their recent rise in importance, are the **microfibres**, and modern **all-weather protective clothing** as well as the **ecological aspects** of the textile pipeline. Topics which have been augmented significantly include **production planning and control**, and the **use of computers**.

The chapter on Fabric Descriptions has been expanded around the themes Fabric Examination, Linings, and Interlinings. To provide a rapid and concise guide, a **comparison of textile fabrics** and a **glossary of special terms** in the History of Clothing have been included.

We are especially indebted to *Professor Tuula Salo*, who has remodelled the **fashion drawings** in the chapter on Clothing Styles, and to *Mrs Langer-Korsch* for her valuable contribution in the revision of the section on leather.

As a result of these extensions and improvements, "Clothing Technology" is now even more appropriate for use in fashion schools as well as technical colleges and in the textile trade.

Metzingen, Spring 1998   Editor and authors

Contents

1
2
3
4
5
6
7
8
9
10
11
12
13

Preface
English Edition

"Fachwissen Bekleidung" is now in its fifth edition and has been a firm favourite in the German-speaking area of Europe since it first appeared in 1989. So far as we are aware, the book is unique in its scope and presentation, so it was perhaps natural that a demand should arise for an English-language version.

Although this English edition follows quite faithfully the general content and layout of the German, it is not always a precise translation. There are several instances in the original where the treatment of the subject matter naturally has a distinctively central-European bias. In the English, an attempt has been made to present a more international perspective. Wherever possible, ISO standards have been referenced rather than DIN.

For an international readership, there is always the problem of whether to use British or North American terminology. For this edition, wherever there is a conflict between the British and American traditions, the British has generally been selected, although the American is often acknowledged and occasionally preferred. The translators would be pleased to hear from readers about how the terminology might be improved, in this respect, for future editions.

The German approach to Work Measurement has been retained, as a valid and comprehensive example of the technique. Section 10, on Garment Sizing has been completely rewritten for the English edition.

The translators are grateful to the staff of the Manchester Metropolitan University Hollings Faculty, the British Leather Confederation, and the London College of Fashion for reviewing various parts of the manuscript; any errors which remain should not be laid at their door.

Special thanks are due to Alison Beazley, Jeni Bougourd, Howard Davies, Alex Lam, Axel Landmann, and Helen Rowe. In addition, the following literature has been consulted to verify various aspects of language, terminology and technology.

Cassel's New German Dictionary
H.T. Betteridge, *Cassel*, London, 1970
Circular Knitting
C. Iyer, B. Mammel & W. Schach, *Meisenbach*, Bamberg, 1992
Cotton
R.J. Kohel & C.F. Lewis, *American Society of Agronomy, Crop Science Society of America, Soil Science Society of America*, Madison, 1984
Cotton: World Statistics
International Cotton Advisory Committee, Washington, 1998
Dictionary of Art & Artists
P. & L. Murray, *Penguin Books*, Harmonsworth, 1968
Dyeing of Cellulosic Fibres
C. Preston, *Dyers Company Publications Trust*, Bradford, 1986
Encyclopedia of Fashion Details
P.J. Ireland, *Batsford*, London, 1993
Encyclopaedia of World Costume
D. Yarwood, *Batsford*, London, 1988
Fachwörterbuch der Maschenwaren-Produktion
E. Lesykova, *Meisenbach*, Bamberg, 1991
Fachwörterbuch Textil
J. Lösch, *Josef Lösch*, Frankfurt am Main, 1975
Fachwörterbuch Textil
D. O. Michelson, *Deutscher Fachverlag*, Frankfurt am Main, 1967
Fairchild's Dictionary of Textiles
S.S. Marks, *Fairchild Publications*, New York, 1959
Fashion in the Western World
D. Yarwood, *Batsford*, London, 1992
Fusing Technology
G. Cooklin, *Textile Institute*, Manchester, 1990
Handbook of Textile Fibres, Vol 1 Natural Fibres
J.G. Cook, *Merrow Publishing*, Watford, 1968
Handbook of Textile Fibres, Vol 2 Man-Made Fibres
J.G. Cook, *Merrow Publishing*, Watford, 1968
History of Art
H.W. Janson, *Thames and Hudson*, London, 1968
Illustrated Dictionary of Fabrics
M. Hardingham, *Studio Vista*, London, 1978
Illustrated Encyclopaedia of Costume and Fashion
J. Cassin-Scott, *Studio Vista*, London, 1994
Introduction to Clothing Manufacture
G. Cooklin, *BSP Professional Books*, Oxford, 1991
Introduction to Clothing Production Management
A.J. Chuter, *BSP Professional Books*, Oxford, 1990
ITS Textile Dictionary
International Textile Service Ltd., Zürich, 1989
Knitting Technology
D.J. Spencer, *Pergamon Press*, Oxford, 1989
Leather Clothing, Its Manufacture and Maintenance
British Leather Confederation, Harrogate & *Fabric Care Association*, Northampton, 1989
Leather Technician's Handbook
J.H. Sharphouse, *Leather Producer's Association*, Northampton, 1989

Lexikon der Textilen Raumuasstattung
D.C. Buurman, *Deutscher Fachverlag*, Frankfurt am Main, 1992
Man-Made Fibres
W. Meyer-Larsen, *Rowohlt Taschenbuch Verlag*, Reinbeck bei Hamburg, 1972
Man-Made Fibres
R.W. Moncrieff, *Heywood Books*, London, 1969
Manual of Textile Technology, Short-Staple Spinning Series, Vol 1 to 5
W. Klein, *Textile Institute*, Manchester, 1987 & 1993
Materials Management in Clothing Production
D.J. Tyler, *BSP Professional Books*, Oxford, 1991
Modern Sizing and Pattern Making for Women's and Children's Garments
P. Kunick, *Philip Kunick Publications*, London, 1984
Oxford-Duden German Dictionary
W. Scholze-Stubenrecht & J.B. Sykes, *Clarendon Press*, Oxford, 1993
Practical Introduction to Fibre and Tow Coloration
G. Clarke, *Society of Dyers and Colourists*, Bradford, 1982
Practical Introduction to Yarn Dyeing
J. Park, *Society of Dyers and Colourists*, Bradford, 1981
Reverse Dictionary
Readers Digest, London, 1989
Story of Art
E.H. Gombrich, *Phaidon Press*, London, 1964
Technisches Taschenwörterbuch
H.G. Freeman, *Max Hueber Verlag*, Ismaning, 1995
Technology of Textile Properties
M.A. Taylor, *Forbes Publications*, London, 1990
Technology of Threads & Seams
J & P Coats Ltd., Glasgow
Textile Printing
L.W.C. Miles, *Society of Dyers and Colourists*, Bradford, 1994
Textile Terms and Definitions
Textile Institute, Manchester, 1991
Watson's Textile Design and Colour
Z. Grosicki, *Newnes-Butterworths*, London, 1975
Watson's Advanced Textile Design
Z. Grosicki, *Newnes-Butterworths*, London, 1977
Wirkerei- und Strickerei- Fachwörterbuch
G. Sammler, *Prost & Meiner Verlag*, Coburg, 1976
Wool Handbook, Vol 1
W. von Bergen, *Interscience Publishers*, New York, 1963
Wool, Its Chemistry and Physics
C. Earland, *Chapman & Hall*, London, 1963
Woven Cloth Construction
A.T.C. Robinson & R. Marks, *Textile Institute*, Manchester, 1973

Stockport, Summer 1998

Allan Heap and Jill Stevens
Cotton Technology International

The Textile Pipeline
Clothing from Fibre to Consumer

FIBRES

Natural
Man-made
Blends

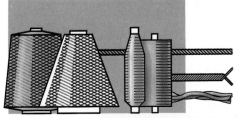

YARNS

Staple Fibre
Continuous Filament

TEXTILES

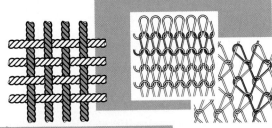

Wovens
Knits
Nonwovens

TEXTILE FINISHING

Colouration
Mechanical Finishing
Chemical Finishing

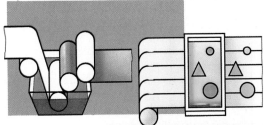

CLOTHING MANUFACTURE

Bespoke
Industrial

RETAILING

Chain Stores
Independents

CONSUMER

Use
Aftercare

DISPOSAL/RECYCLING

Recovery
Incineration
Landfill

TEXTILE FIBRES [1]	

NATURAL FIBRES

Group Sub-group	Name or Generic Name

Vegetable (cellulose)	
Seed	Cotton Kapok Coconut
Bast	Flax Hemp Jute Ramie
Leaf	Sisal Manila

Animal (protein)	
Wool	Wool Virgin wool
Fine hair	Alpaca Llama Vicuna Guanaco Camel Rabbit Angora Mohair Cashmere Yak
Coarse hair	Cattle Horse Goat
Silk	Cultivated Wild (Tussah)

Mineral	
Rock fibres	Asbestos [2]

MAN-MADE FIBRES

Group Sub-group	Name or Generic Name

Natural Polymers	
Cellulosic	Viscose Modal Lyocell Cupro Acetate Triacetate
Alginate	Alginate
Rubber	Rubber

Synthetic Polymers	
Elastomeric	Elastane Elastodiene
Fluorofibres	Fluoro
Polyacrylics	Acrylic Modacrylic
Polyamides	Nylon Aramid
Chlorofibres	Vinyl chloride Vinylidene chloride
Polyesters	Polyester
Polyolefins	Polyethylene Polypropylene
Vinylal	Polyvinyl alcohol

Inorganics	
Glass Carbon Metallic	Glass Carbon Metal

[1] Standards for generic names are in ISO 2076 and ISO 6938
[2] Asbestos is classified as a hazardous substance; the appropriate health and safety regulations must be observed.

Sources of Textile Fibres

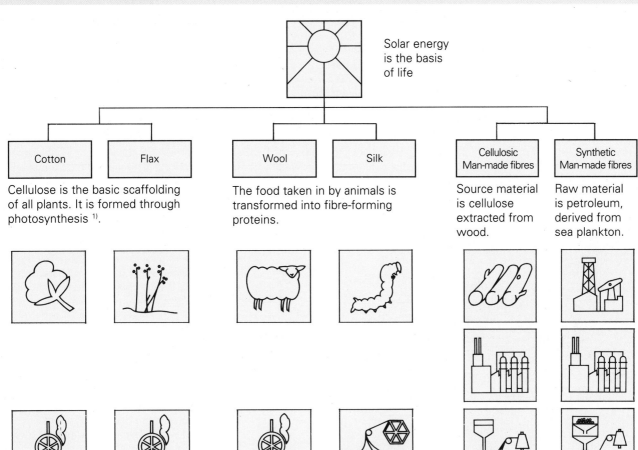

Solar energy is the basis of life

Cotton | Flax | Wool | Silk | Cellulosic Man-made fibres | Synthetic Man-made fibres

Cellulose is the basic scaffolding of all plants. It is formed through photosynthesis [1].

The food taken in by animals is transformed into fibre-forming proteins.

Source material is cellulose extracted from wood.

Raw material is petroleum, derived from sea plankton.

Fibres from plants and animals are constructed from natural polymers. Polymers are very large molecules (see page 27).

Cellulosic man-made fibres are formed from the natural polymers of plants (cellulose). The cellulose is dissolved and then forced through spinning jets.

Synthetic man-made fibres are derived from petroleum products. Their polymers are formed synthetically (artificially).

The common feature of all fibres is that they are constructed from large polymer molecules which lay alongside each other and are bonded together.

Production of Textile Fibres

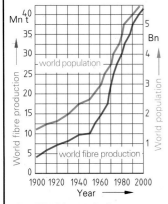

1: **World population and fibre production**

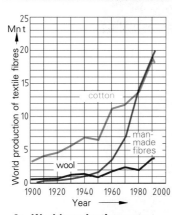

2: **World production: man-made fibres, wool, cotton**

The demand for **textiles**, and therefore for textile fibres has increased rapidly due to growing prosperity in the industrialised countries and the large increase in world population **(Figure 1)**. Because they possess certain desirable properties, production of synthetic man-made fibres has grown considerably since they became freely available in the late 1940's **(Figure 2)**.

Apparel fabrics satisfy the basic requirement of the population for clothing.

Household textiles, e.g. bed and table linen, decorative fabrics, furnishings and blinds, curtains and floor-coverings are utilised in dwellings.

Industrial textiles are used in increasing volumes for protective clothing, in medicine, packaging, engineering, house and road building, as well as in all forms of transport (including space travel).

[1] Synthesis of carbohydrates by green plants from carbon dioxide using solar energy.

Cotton   German: Baumwolle   French: Coton   Spanish: Algodon

History

Archeological findings at Mohenjo-Daro, in modern Pakistan, and in the Tehaucan valley in Mexico, both dating from about 3000 BC, suggest that the cotton plant was already domesticated and being used for making textiles over 5000 years ago. Cotton fabrics from India, of outstanding fineness and quality, were traded in the Mediterranean area from the time of Alexander, who had established the trade routes to the East. Alexandria became the major dispersal point for these goods. Later the rise to power of the city state of Venice is said to have been built largely on trade in Indian cotton cloth.

In the 8th century, cotton growing and fabric manufacture was introduced into Spain by the Moors, where it thrived until the expulsion of Islam in the 15th century. Thereafter, the opening of the sea route to India promoted Portugal to the prime source of cotton fabrics.

During the 17th century textile manufacturing expertise, and sea power, began to concentrate in Britain which then became the dominant centre of textile manufacture. Meanwhile cotton growing was expanded in North America and the Caribbean. These trends were reinforced in the late 18th century by the invention of the cotton gin in America, and by the development of spinning and weaving machinery, plus the harnessing of water and steam power, in Britain.

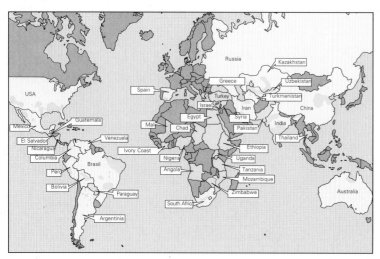

1: **Cotton growing regions**

Production and Sources

By 1930 cotton accounted for 85% of the world consumption of textile fibres but, between 1950 and 1980, its market share fell to 48% due to the introduction of synthetic fibres. Since then cotton's market share has been steady at 44 to 49%, with a current annual production of about 19 million tonnes.

Although cotton production has tripled in recent decades, the amount of land utilised has not increased. This is a result of constant improvements in cotton varieties and farming techniques.

Cotton is grown in about 80 different countries world-wide. The most important producers are the following:

1	China	6	Turkey
2	USA	7	Australia
3	India	8	Brazil
4	Pakistan	9	Greece
5	Uzbekistan	10	Argentina

The Cotton Plant

Cotton is a member of the Mallow family. Its height ranges from 25 cm to over 2 m, depending on variety, climate, and agronomy. It is normally grown as an annual shrub but, in parts of South America and the Caribbean, it is cultivated as a perennial shrub (tree cotton).

From planting to maturity takes between 175 and 225 days. At planting and during its growth, cotton needs plenty of water. For ripening, it needs heat. Therefore, the world's cotton belt is located mainly in the tropics and sub-tropics.

After flowering, the fruit nodes, located in the calyx (bracts), grow into capsules (bolls) which eventually crack open to reveal the seed hairs. In each boll there are about 30 seeds. The number of hairs on each seed ranges from fewer than 1000 to more than 10000, depending on the variety.

2: **Cotton field**

3: **Cotton flower**

4: **Fruit capsule**

5: **Open bolls**

Like any agricultural product, the way that cotton is grown in different countries varies widely, depending on the level of development: in the southern states of the USA large machines are utilised; in poorer countries, oxen or buffalo may be used for traction, and manual labour is the rule.

Harvesting

Harvesting is either by hand or by picking machines.

Hand picking extends over several weeks. In principle, it has the advantage that only the fully ripened bolls are collected and no leaves are included.

A picking machine will usually harvest the whole crop in one passage. It has a tendency to include some unripe bolls, together with various quantities of dead leaves, and other plant parts.

Drying

If the newly-harvested seed-cotton is wet, then it may have to be dried, using warm air, before it can be stored in large piles to await ginning. In many countries, drying is an integral part of the ginning process.

Ginning

Ginning is the separation of the fibres from the seeds. It is done by special machines. The separated fibres, called **lint**, have a staple length of between 15 and 50 mm, depending on the variety.

On many types of seed, there are some very short fibres, called **linters**. They are made of cellulose and they find many uses, including the production of man-made fibres. The **seeds** can also be utilised for the production of edible oil.

100 Kg of clean seed-cotton yields about 35 Kg of fibre, 62 Kg of seed and 3 Kg of waste.

Utilisation

Cotton fibres are made into staple fibre yarns either by ring spinning or rotor spinning.

Commercial Quality

Commercially, cotton is usually designated according to its variety and origin. Different varieties are grown in different countries - about 40 in the USA alone. Thus the country of origin is only a partial guide to quality. The famous Giza cottons of Egypt are in fact a range of various long-staple varieties. Sea Island cotton, from the West Indies, is a very high quality type produced in very small quantities. The most common type world-wide is the American Upland cotton.

Recently, naturally-coloured cottons, mostly in brown shades, have been adapted for commercial production on a limited scale.

1: Hand picking

2: Machine picking

3: Seed with fibres

4: Seeds with linters (left)
Seeds without linters (right)

5: Cotton staple length standards

Staple length	This is the most important aspect of quality. It generally lies between 20 mm and 40 mm. Spinnable fibres have a staple length greater than 16 mm. Sea Island cotton can be as long as 50 mm. Giza and Pima are about 36 mm, Upland is about 28 mm.
Fineness, Handle	Cotton fibres are fine. Their weight per unit length is between 1 and 4 dtex. Generally, the longer the fibre, the finer it is and the softer its handle.
Preparation, Impurities	Large amounts of contaminants, such as leaf or boll fragments, or of very short fibres, or of immature and "dead" fibres are severely detrimental to quality.
Strength	A high quality cotton will have a high strength relative to its fineness.
Colour and Lustre	The colour of cotton varies, according to the variety, from white (Upland) through creamy (Giza, Pima) to light yellow or brown. The lustre is usually matt. High quality types, such as Giza and Pima have a silky lustre.

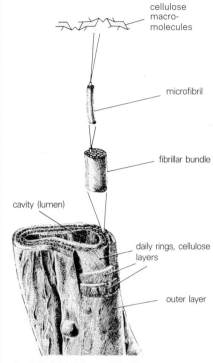

cellulose macro-molecules

microfibril

fibrillar bundle

cavity (lumen)

daily rings, cellulose layers

outer layer

1: Model of the cotton fibre

Construction of the Cotton Fibre

Cotton is composed of cellulose, the foundation of all plants.

Whilst it is growing inside the boll, the fibre is circular in section. When the boll opens, the fibre begins to dry and it collapses to a kidney-shaped cross-section. At very strong magnification in the electron microscope a suitably prepared cross-section shows daily growth rings, comparable with the annual rings in wood. These are the result of daily deposits of layer upon layer of fresh cellulose, proceeding from the outside inwards. The first-formed outer layer is composed of an especially tough kind of cellulose. At the end of the growth period, a cavity remains at the centre. This is called the Lumen. During drying the fibre twists backwards and forwards along its length axis and looks like a flattened, twisted tube. A layer of natural wax coats the surface.

Each cellulose layer is formed from fibrillar bundles composed of individual fibrils (fibril = tiny fibre). The fibrils are made of cellulose macromolecules (see page 27). The fibrillar bundles of succeeding cellulose layers, are inclined at an angle to the length axis of the fibre. Spaces between the ordered lattice of the fibrillar structure, as well as the hollow fibre centre, are easily penetrated by water. Moisture can be stored in the cavities. Sweat can be absorbed and can later be rinsed out again during washing. Cotton is stronger when it is swollen by water. This is because the presence of water promotes a more uniform distribution of stresses across and along the cellulose layers.

The high strength of the cotton fibre is a consequence of its construction from highly organised cellulose chain molecules in the fibre interior (crystalline regions). Its low elasticity is due to slippage between the crystalline regions.

Clothing Comfort (cf. pages 128, 129)

Thermal insulation	Cotton fibres are relatively fine and flexible. Therefore they are often made into textiles which have a low proportion of entrapped air (low specific volume). Warmer, more voluminous materials can be made, however, by appropriate choice of yarn and fabric constructions and through roughening (raising) the surface.
Moisture absorption	Cotton can absorb up to 20% of water vapour without feeling wet. Cotton fabrics absorb liquid very rapidly and can contain up to 65% of their own weight without dripping. Cotton dries slowly.
Next-to-skin comfort	Cotton is very comfortable next to the skin because of its fineness and softness.

Other Important Properties (cf. pages 43, 44, 45)

Strength	The strength of cotton is good. It is stronger when wet than when dry. Abrasion resistance and durability are good.
Extensibility	The extensibility is relatively low, at about 6...10%.
Elasticity	Cotton has a very poor elasticity and therefore it creases easily.
Electrostatic charge	It develops scarcely any electrostatic charge because it always contains moisture which conducts the charge away.
Fineness, Handle	Cotton fibres are fine and soft, they have a pleasant handle.

Improvement of Properties by Finishing (cf. Chapter 4)

Mercerizing	Treatment of cotton under tension with caustic soda solution causes the fibre cross-section to become more circular. This results in higher strength and lustre.
Crease-resist / Easy-care finish	The elasticity of cotton, and hence its resistance to creasing, can be improved by cross-linking the cellulose chains, using synthetic resins. However, there is a consequent reduction in its strength and absorptivity, although it will dry more quickly.
Anti-shrink finish	Shrinkage is deliberately induced in the fabric to avoid such shrinkage appearing after subsequent wet treatments. This process is important for improving the laundering characteristics of cotton textiles - especially when a household tumble dryer is used.
Water repellent finish	Cotton textiles can be made water repellent by impregnating them with special chemicals (e.g. silicones).

Fibre Identification

Microscopy	Burning Test	Tearing Test	Solubility Test
longitudinal view mature immature dead mercer-ized cross-sections	**Combustion:** Quick, bright, with afterglow **Smell:** Like burnt paper **Residue:** Pale grey, powder ash.	**Dry tearing:** Short fibres appear at the torn edges (cf linen). **Wet tearing:** If a spot of water is applied, the yarns will not tear across the wet area (cf viscose).	**Sulphuric acid:** Dissolves; cotton is destroyed (cf wool). **Alkalis:** Safe in washing liquors. Caustic soda is utilised in finishing (cf wool).

Typical Cotton Fabrics

Batiste	Cambric	Damask	Gaberdine	Plain rib
Buckram	Chintz	Denim (jeans)	Interlock	Poplin
Bedford Cord	Corduroy	Drill	Oxford	Terry towel
Calico	Cretonne	Flannelette	Piqué	Velvet

Fibre Blends   (cf page 41)

Fibre blending allows the disadvantages of one fibre to be offset by the advantages of another, or special effects to be achieved. Cotton is usually blended with polyester and polyamide as well as with viscose and modal fibres. Blending with synthetic man-made fibres improves the easy-care and durability of clothing. Blending with viscose and modal fibres is for their lustre and uniformity, whilst preserving good moisture absorption, and also to reduce the cost. Modal fibres are a good match for cotton in their strength and extensibility. Blends with other fibres are also possible. The most common blend ratios are 50:50, 60:40, and 70:30. Note that different varieties of cotton are frequently blended together in 100% cotton yarns.

Applications

Apparel Fabrics	Accessories	Household Textiles	Industrial Textiles
Shirts, blouses, underwear, nightwear, outerwear, rainwear (water-repellant finishes), trousers (jeans), leisure wear, professional clothing	Handkerchiefs, laces, ribbons, trimmings, umbrellas	Bed clothes, table and kitchen cloths, decorative fabrics, furniture coverings, hand and bath towels	Workwear and protective clothing, awnings, tarpaulins, sewing threads

Aftercare Properties and Labelling

Washable, boilable, dries slowly, can be ironed, not wrinkle-resistant.

Following are the most severe conditions that can be used; limitations may be imposed by fabric and garment construction, or finishing.

Washing	Chlorine	Ironing	Dry Cleaning	Drying
[95] [60] [40] white colours dark colours Cotton can be boiled. Lower temperatures for coloured items.	[Cl] Can be bleached with chlorine. Chlorine bleaching is less common nowadays.	[iron ···] Ironing temperature 200 °C; the goods should be damp.	(A) Cotton is not sensitive to solvents. (A = all normal solvents can be used).	[⊙] Can be dried in a tumble dryer. Exception: fabrics liable to shrinking.

Textile Labelling

The laws governing product descriptions allow the name "Cotton" to be applied only to fibres obtained from the seeds of the cotton plant.

International Cotton Emblem

The Cotton Emblem is registered internationally. It serves clearly to identify textiles made from pure cotton and implies good quality. It may not be applied to fibre blends.

1: **International Cotton Emblem**

1.2.2 Vegetable Fibres: Flax[1] (1)

Flax   German: Leinen   French: Lin   Spanish: Lino

1: **Egyptian woman in fine linen fabric**

History

Linen[2] has been known in civilised societies for thousands of years. Flax was already being cultivated systematically by ancient Egyptians, Babylonians, Phoenicians, and other civilisations between 5000 and 4000 BC.

Mummies from the pyramids of Egypt are wrapped in linen; cotton was unknown in ancient Egypt until about 400 BC.

The Romans laid down precise procedures for processing flax fibres which were hardly different, in principle, from those used today.

Linen was especially popular in the Middle Ages. It remains to this day a highly valued natural product.

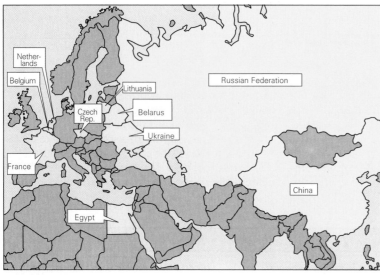

2: **Flax growing countries**

Production and Sources

World production of flax has been almost constant for the last 25 years at between 600 000 and 700 000 tonnes. This represents about 1.5% of world fibre production.

The main producing countries are:

1	China	6	Netherlands
2	Russian Federation	7	Egypt
3	Ukraine	8	Belgium
4	France	9	Czech Republic
5	Belarus	10	Lithuania

Altogether, there are about 20 countries that grow flax.

In recent years, attempts have been made to expand flax production in Europe.

The Flax Plant

Flax fibres are extracted from the stalks of the flax plant, which may be grown either for its fibres or for its seed. For fibre extraction, tall varieties with white to light blue flowers and a height of 80 to 120 cm are grown. The shorter types are grown for linseed oil.

Flax is an annual plant, it must be re-seeded every year. It thrives in temperate climates. Regions with a maritime climate grow the best flax qualities.

Planting is in March and April, and growth takes 90 to 120 days. The plant has side branches only at the top of the stem, from which the flowers grow. After flowering, the mature plant develops seed capsules the size of peas. The seeds are about 2 mm long and are very rich in oil.

Harvesting is in July and August.

4: **Flowering flax**

3: **Flax plant**   5: **Ripe flax**

[1] Flax: fibres extracted from the flax plant
[2] Linen: yarns made from flax fibres and fabrics made from linen yarns

1: Flax harvesting

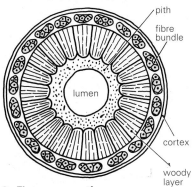

2: Hackled flax

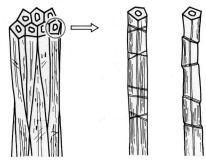

3: Flax cross-section

4: Fibre bundle and fibre ultimates

Harvesting and Fibre Extraction

Pulling. Traditionally, the plant is harvested whole, including the roots, in order to preserve the full length of the fibres. Nowadays, machine harvesting methods are also used.

Roughing out removes the seeds and other extraneous material from the stems.

Retting degrades the woody part of the stems so that the fibres are loosened. The flax is placed in tanks of warm water where it lays for 5 to 8 days.

Drying of the flax stalks is by means of warm air ovens.

Breaking and Scutching: after loosening the fibres from the wood by retting, the flax straw is broken and the woody parts are removed by scutching. The products are line fibre, with a length of 45 to 90 cm, and scutcher tow, with a length of 10 to 25 cm.

Hackling is the process of combing out the bast fibres into spinnable fibre bundles. The remaining woody particles, and short fibres are removed at the same time. The main product is line flax, the by-product is hackle tow.

Processing

The line tow is spun into yarns using the linen process.

Cross-section of a Flax Stalk

The cross-section of a flax stalk is composed of several layers which have to be removed in order to release the fibre bundles. The fibre bundles extend all the way to the plant roots. They are made up from individual fibres (ultimates) of about 25 to 40 mm in length which are cemented together by a mixture of lignins, pectins and hemicelluloses. This cement comprises about 30% of the dry weight of flax, with the remainder being mainly cellulose. The typical properties of flax are a consequence of this composition.

Cottonization of flax is when the fibre bundles are broken down to their ultimates by mechanical or chemical means. The product, called cottonized flax, can be blended with cotton (infrequent nowadays).

Construction of a Flax Fibre

Like cotton, flax fibres are constructed primarily from cellulose chain molecules. Flax is stiffer, partly because of the cement which holds the fibre ultimates together. It has a smoother surface and a darker colour than cotton.

Clothing Comfort (cf pages 128, 129)

Thermal insulation: Yarns and fabrics made from the smooth flax fibres do not enclose much air and have relatively poor insulation properties. Linen fabrics feel fresh and cool, a distinct advantage for Summer clothing.

Moisture absorption: Linen is highly absorbent. It takes up water rapidly and releases it quickly again to the surroundings. In hot weather this helps in regulating the microclimate between body and clothing.

Next-to-skin comfort: Flax fibres are stiffer and harder than cotton and are therefore less supple.

Other Important Properties (cf pages 43, 44, 45)

Strength: Flax has very good tenacity and durability. It is stronger wet than dry.

Extensibility: The extensibility of flax, about 2%, is the lowest of all apparel fibres.

Elasticity: Flax has a low elasticity; it creases very badly.

Electrostatic charge: This is practically nil, since the fibre always contains moisture.

Surface, Lustre: Because of its smooth surface, linen fabric has a subdued lustre, does not soil easily, and does not shed lint.

Fineness, Handle: The coarse fibre bundles give linen a firm handle.

Improvement of Properties by Finishing (cf Chapter 4)

Like cotton, linen fabrics can be given an easy-care treatment (cf page 12)

1 **Fibres** 1.2 Natural Fibres	**1.2.2 Vegetable Fibres: Flax (3)**	

Fibre Identification

Microscopy	Burning Test	Tearing Test	Light Test, Oil Test
fibre ultimate fibre bundle (cross-section)	**Combustion:** Quick, bright, with afterglow. **Smell:** Like burnt paper. **Residue:** Pale grey, powdery ash.	**Dry tearing:** The torn edges are much longer than with cotton. Linen Cotton	When held up against the light, pure linen fabrics show thick places in both warp and weft. An oil spot on a linen fabric is more transparent than on cotton.

Typical Linen Fabrics   (with typically irregular yarns)

Crash	Filter cloth	Holland	Interlining
Duck	Half linen (Union)	Huckaback	Mattress ticking

Fibre Blends   (cf page 41)

The most important mixtures are with cotton. "Half linen" or Union is a fabric with cotton warp yarns and linen weft (see Textile Labelling and Linen Seal, below). Flax is also mixed with other bast fibres, such as hemp and sisal, and with cellulosic or synthetic man-made fibres, such as modal, polyamide, polyester, or polyacrylics. The linen look (yarn structure, colour and lustre) can be imitated to some extent by synthetic fibres, but without the typical linen properties.

Applications

Apparel Fabrics	Accessories	Household Textiles	Industrial Textiles
Leisure and Summer wear: blouses, shirts, skirts, trousers, jackets, suits, interlinings for stiffening.	Pockets, bags, shoes, trimmings.	Bed clothing, table cloths, drapes, furniture and wall coverings, mattress lining.	Tarpaulins, ropes, sewing thread.

Aftercare Properties and Labelling

Washable, boilable, quick-drying, easily ironed, not wrinkle-resistant

Following are the most severe conditions that can be used; limitations may be imposed by fabric or garment construction, or finishing.

Washing	Chlorine	Ironing	Dry Cleaning	Drying
white 95 colours 60 Linen can be boiled. Lower temperatures for coloured items.	Can be bleached with chlorine.	Can be ironed up to 220 °C. The goods should be damp.	Linen can be cleaned with all of the usual solvents.	Can be tumble dried.

Textile Labelling

The laws governing product descriptions allow the name linen to be used only for fibres originating from the stems of the flax plant. Textiles made from 100% linen may be described as pure linen. The term "half linen" may be used for fabrics in which the warp is made only from cotton, the weft is only linen, and the overall linen content is at least 40%.

Linen Seal

The linen industry of Western Europe has created a Linen Seal for its products and has registered the mark world-wide. The seal may be used to identify pure linen and half linen textiles. Linen industry regulations specify that the linen content of blends must be at least 50%.

The Linen Seal is a guarantee of quality.

1: Linen Seal

Fibre Name	Source	Appearance	Properties and Applications
Kapok	**Hair cells** from the Kapok fruit **Origin:** Brazil, India, Indonesia, Mexico, East and West Africa		Kapok fibres can not be spun into yarns because they are very weak. Their density is only 0.35 g/cm³, due to the large air-filled lumen. The fibres are water repellent, fine, soft, and lustrous. Kapok fibres are used as stuffings and waddings for e.g. cushions, bolsters, and mattresses. In addition, Kapok is suitable as filling for life-jackets.
Hemp	**Bast fibre** from the stems of the hemp plant **Origin:** Italy, Poland, former Yugoslavia, former USSR, Romania, Spain, Algeria		Hemp fibres are very strong. Extensibility and elasticity are similar to flax. The fibres are coarse and stiff. They rot only slowly. Cultivation of hemp was banned for a while but nowadays specific varieties are allowed for fibre production. Hemp is used for ropes, tarpaulins, and as backing for carpets. Apparel uses are being developed.
Jute	**Bast fibre** from the stems of jute plants **Origin:** India, Bangladesh, Pakistan		Jute fibres are very woody and irregular. Strength is lower than flax but extensibility and elasticity are similar. Jute has a strong aroma and is susceptible to rotting. Jute is manufactured into packaging fabrics, wall coverings (Hessian), and base cloths for belts and tapestries. Jute can also form the backing cloth for floor coverings.
Ramie	**Bast fibre** from the stems of the ramie plant, "oriental linen" **Origin:** Far East, former USSR, USA		Ramie fibres are strong and high grade bast fibres, similar to flax. They are smooth and uniform, easy to dye and resistant to light. The fibres are white, with a durable lustre. Absorbency is good but the handle is somewhat harder than cotton. Ramie is used to make fine, light and durable fabrics for kitchen and table cloths, belts and ribbons. Short, waste fibres may be included in banknotes.
Sisal	**Hard fibres** from the leaves of the sisal plant **Origin:** Brazil, Indonesia, Mexico, East Africa		Sisal fibres have a high strength and abrasion resistance. They are easy to dye and are resistant to water. They are white in colour. Sisal is used for ropes, carpets, nets and matting.
Manila	**Hard fibres** from the leaves of a type of banana **Origin:** Philippines (capital: Manila), North America		Manila fibres are stronger than sisal. They are very resistant to sea water. They have a relatively low density. They are used for marine cables and other ropes, also for nets and matting.
Coir	**Hard fibre** from the coconut **Origin:** India, Indonesia, Sri Lanka		Coir fibres have a very high abrasion resistance, are very durable and have good elasticity. They do not soil easily and are good insulators. Coir is used primarily for stair carpets, floor coverings, ropes, stuffed furniture backings, and brushes. They are often used in raw form.

17

Wool   German: Wolle   French: Laine   Spanish: Lana

History

Wool felts were known 7000 years ago in China, in Babylon, and in Egypt. Shearing of the wool, rather than pulling, was made possible by the invention of cutting tools in the Iron Age. The Merino sheep, which has the finest wool, was bred in the 14th century, in Spain. Sheep breeding began in Australia at the end of the 18th century. Today, Australia rears about 160 million sheep - about 14% of the world sheep population.

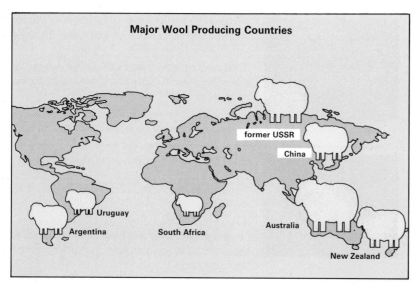

1: Wool producing countries

Production and Sources

Since the turn of the century, the production of wool has roughly doubled. Production of scoured wool is about 1.5 million tonnes; unscoured wool is about 2.5 million tonnes. This represents about 3% of total world fibre production. Sheep are to be found in almost every country in the world.

The most important wool producers are:

1	Australia	6	Uruguay
2	Former USSR	7	South Africa
3	New Zealand	8	Turkey
4	China	9	Great Britain
5	Argentina	10	Pakistan

Wool Production

Shearing: The sheep are shorn using electric shears. Care must be taken to avoid injuries and to ensure that the coat is separated intact. This coat is called the fleece. Wool from the legs is short and coarse. Because of its lower quality, it is separated from the fleece during shearing.

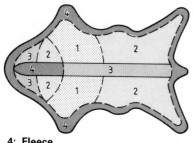

2: Merino ram

3: Examination

4: Fleece

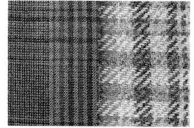

5: Worsted and woollen fabrics

Classing: After shearing, the fleece is graded into essentially four qualities (1 = best, 4 = worst). The grader classifies the wool according to fineness, crimp, length, impurities, and colour. Heavy contamination is found in the belly area.

Scouring: An unscoured fleece weighs between 1 and 6 Kg. The average Australian fleece weighs 4.5 Kg. About 40% of this weight is grease (lanolin), dirt, and burs. The dirt and most of the grease are removed by a gentle scouring.

Carbonising: Vegetable impurities are removed, when necessary, by treatment with sulphuric acid.

Processing: Wool fibres are spun into fine, smooth yarns by the Worsted process, and into coarser, more bulky yarns by the Woollen process.

1.2.4 Animal Fibres: Wool (2)

Pure New Wool

Classification of Wool

There are hundreds of different types and breeds of sheep. They are classified according to their wool into five basic types:
Fine, Medium, Crossbred, Long, and Coarse.

Wool Type	Fine	Medium, Crossbred	Long, Coarse
Breed (examples)	Merino, Rambouillet	Southdown, Corriedale	Lincoln, Romney, Karakul
Fineness, Diameter	finest wools, 15...23 µm[1]	medium fine, 24...30 µm	coarse, over 30 µm
Length	50...120 mm	120...150 mm	over 150 mm
Crimp, Waviness	highly crimped	normal crimp	low crimp, straight
Sources (examples)	Australia, South Africa, ex USSR	Argentina, Uruguay	New Zealand, Great Britain
Applications	fine outerwear, knitted and woven, shawls, socks	heavier, more robust, sporting clothing	carpets, traditional furniture coverings

[1] $1 \text{ µm} = \dfrac{1}{1\,000\,000} \text{ m} = 10^{-6} \text{ m}$

Apart from its fineness, length, crimp, and breed, wool can also be classified according to:

Shearing **Lambswool:** From the first shearing, after six months. It is fine, not very strong, and has fine tips.
Yearling wool: From the first or second shear after 10-12 months.
Six-month, Eight-month, Twelve-month wools: shorn at intervals of 6, 8, or 12 months.

Source **Australian, New Zealand, Cape** etc.

Origin **Virgin wool**: fibres shorn from living, healthy sheep or lambs. **Dead wool, Fallen wool:** wool taken from sheep that have died from natural causes. **Skin wool:** wool removed from the skin of slaughtered sheep. **Recovered wool**: wool that has been recovered mechanically by teasing apart production waste and second-hand clothing. Recovered wool is damaged and is of low quality.

Spinning **Worsteds:** usually fine Merino, spun into fine, smooth, uniform, combed yarns. **Woollens:** heavier, more voluminous yarns prepared on the woollen spinning system. **Carpet wools:** long, coarse wools for carpet yarns.

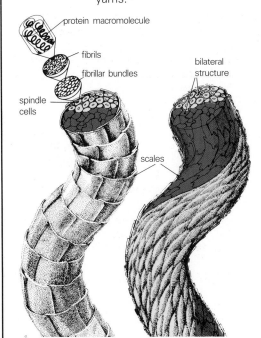

protein macromolecule
fibrils
fibrillar bundles
bilateral structure
spindle cells
scales

1: Model of the wool fibre

Construction of the Wool Fibre

The wool fibre is made of protein molecules (**keratin**). It is very similar to human hair. The long-chain protein molecules are formed into fibrils. These combine into fibrillar bundles which form the mass of the spindle cells. This construction gives the wool fibre an extraordinary elasticity. The bulk of the fibre is made from two separate components. These have different chemical constitutions, and they wind in a spiral around each other (bilateral structure). Moisture and temperature have different effects upon the two components, which swell to different extents, causing changes in the overall fibre shape. It is the bilateral structure which causes the fibres to be crimped. Heat and moisture together can relax bonds between the protein chains. The bonds are re-formed during cooling and drying and this is the source of the good smoothing and shaping properties of wool.

Wool absorbs moisture (is hygroscopic). It can absorb about $1/3$ of its mass of water vapour without feeling wet. The moisture is released only slowly. In spite of the strong affinity for water of the fibre interior, its surface is water repellent (hydrophobic) because it is covered by an extremely thin skin, the epicuticle. This skin causes liquid water to roll up into droplets whilst allowing the passage of water vapour.

The **scales** on the fibre surfaces are capable of hooking onto one another to cause felting, under the influence of water, heat, and mechanical action.

1.2.4 Animal Fibres: Wool (3)

Pure New Wool

Clothing Comfort (cf pages 128, 129)

Thermal insulation	In smooth, combed yarns, the fine wool fibres are tightly constrained; they can scarcely crimp. Fine combed yarns enclose less air and therefore provide less insulation ("Cool Wool"). Bulky woollen yarns have a looser structure. The fibres can develop their crimp inside the yarn and, due to the large amount of entrapped air, offer excellent protection against cold.
Moisture absorption	Wool is hygroscopic. It can absorb up to a third of its weight in moisture vapour without feeling wet. Perspiration (weak acids, alkalis, salts) will be chemically bound, and neutralised. Water vapour is absorbed very rapidly, but water droplets are repelled. Liquid water is absorbed only very slowly. Such behaviour is called "hydrophobic". Wet wool dries very slowly.
Next-to-skin comfort	The softness of wool depends on its fineness. Lambswool and fine Merino wool are especially soft. Wools which are coarser than about 30 μm can irritate the skin.

Other Important Properties (cf pages 43, 44, 45)

Strength	Wool has adequate strength which, nevertheless, is lower than that of most normal apparel fibres. Textiles made from wool are not particularly durable.
Extensibility	The fibres have very good extensibility, which is greater when wet than dry. Dripping wet wool garments should be laid flat to dry, to avoid stretching.
Elasticity	Elasticity and "springiness" are excellent. Creases soon drop out of wool clothing (especially under the influence of steam).
Formability	The molecular chains in the wool fibre can be re-oriented under the influence of heat and moisture. In this way, wool fabrics can be more or less durably shaped.
Felting	Felting is the matting together of fibres, under the influence of mechanical action, heat and water. It is facilitated by the scales on the fibre surface which can hook onto each other. The effect is utilised for the production of felts but it is a disadvantage in the aftercare of wool clothing.
Fineness, Handle	Wool fibres may be fine or coarse, depending on the type. The very finest Merino wools (less than 16 μm) are designated as Super 100's. They are sold at special auctions and made into extremely fine, soft fabrics.
Electrostatic charge	Wool fibres develop only small electrostatic charges, because they always contain some moisture which conducts the charge away.
Flammability	Wool does not burn easily. It is suitable for protective clothing.

Improvement of Properties by Finishing (cf Chapter 4)

Anti-felting treatment	Wool can be made machine-washable by chemical treatments which greatly reduce the tendency of the fibres to felt.
Carbonising	Removal of vegetable impurities using sulphuric acid.
Decatizing	Application of heat, moisture, and pressure stabilises and smoothens wool textiles. Fabrics have improved handle and lustre, and are then ready for making into clothing.
Flame retardance	Protection against heat and flames can be improved by treatment with chemicals which combine with the wool protein molecules.
Fulling	Deliberate felting of wool materials. The material shrinks and becomes denser.
Moth proofing	Impregnation of the fabric with chemicals which make the fibres inedible and to which the moths are averse.
Permanent creasing	Ironed creases can be durably fixed through heat, pressure and chemicals (Siroset process).
Raising	Fibre ends are teased out of the textile material. The weave structure is obscured. Often follows fulling.
Water repellency	Wool textiles may have their water repellancy enhanced by treatment with chemicals.

1.2.4   Animal Fibres: Wool (4)

Pure New Wool

Fibre Identification

Microscopy	Burning Test	Rubbing Test	Solubility Test
Cross-section: round **Appearance:** overlapping scales, like roof tiles	**Combustion:** small, sputtering flame, self-extinguishing **Smell:** like burning hair **Residue:** black, friable cinder	If a wool fibre is held between thumb and forefinger (parallel to them), and thumb and finger are rubbed together, then the fibre will travel in one direction. If the fibre is turned around, then it travels in the opposite direction.	**Sulphuric acid:** Cold, concentrated sulphuric acid has scarcely any effect (cf cotton). **Alkalis:** Boiling 5% caustic soda, and lithium hypochlorite solutions will dissolve wool (cf cotton).

Typical Wool Fabrics

Afgalaine	Charmelaine	Donegal	Flannel	Fresco	Saxony	Shetland	Tricotine
Baize	Cheviot	Felt	Fleece	Loden	Serge	Tartan	Tweed

Fibre Blends   (cf page 41)

Wool is excellent for blending with synthetic fibres, such as polyester, acrylic, and nylon. Both fibres are complemented in the mixture; the tendency to felting is reduced and the aftercare characteristics are enhanced. In addition, the durability is improved. So long as the proportion of wool is greater than 50%, then its good clothing comfort properties are retained. Common blend ratios are 50:50, 55:45, 60:40, and 70:30. Wool is also blended with silk, with cotton, and especially with fine hair fibres.

Applications

Apparel Fabrics	Accessories	Household Textiles	Industrial Textiles
Suits, costumes, pullovers, waistcoats, overcoats, dresses, winter blouses	Ties, scarfs, hats, socks, stockings	Blankets, carpets, drapes, furnishings	Fire protection clothing, industrial felts

Aftercare Properties and Labelling

Washable (with care), very slow drying, can be ironed, not wrinkle-resistant.

Following are the most severe conditions that can be used; limitations may be imposed by fabric and garment construction, or finishing.

Washing	Chlorine	Ironing	Dry Cleaning	Drying
Washable wool can be machine-washed. Use wool detergents.	Should not be chlorine bleached	Iron at 150 °C, with steam or a damp cloth.	Can be cleaned using Perchloroethylene.	Should not be dried in a tumble dryer, or in direct sunlight, or over direct heat.

Textile Labelling

The regulations governing product labelling allow the terms **New Wool** or **Virgin Wool** to be used only for fibres shorn from a living sheep or lamb. Virgin Wool products must be made from wool fibres which have not previously been spun into yarn or felted, nor previously been incorporated into a finished product. Textiles made from **100% virgin wool** may be labelled as **Pure New Wool**, or Pure Virgin Wool. An allowance may be made for 0.3% of adventitious foreign fibres, and of 7% for visible ornamental effects. New Wool and Virgin Wool descriptors may also be used in blends where there is only one other fibre present, and where the proportion of virgin wool is at least 25%. The term **Pure Wool** may also be used for products made from recovered wool.

PURE NEW WOOL

1: Wool Mark

NEW WOOL BLEND

2: Wool Blendmark

Wool Mark and Wool Blendmark

The **Wool Mark (Figure 1)** is applied to Pure New Wool. As well as the fibre content, the mark guarantees a certain product quality level: colour fastness, strength, and dimensional stability. The **Wool Blendmark (Figure 2)** is applied to blends where there is only one other fibre, and a virgin wool content of at least 60%. It guarantees the same quality levels as for the Wool Mark. Both the Wool Mark and the Wool Blendmark are strictly regulated and controlled.

Fine Animal Hairs

Fibre Name	Appearance	Description
Alpaca **Llama** **Vicuna** **Guanaco**		Alpaca, llama, vicuna, and guanaco are all types of llama, both wild and domesticated, which live in the Andes mountains of South America. They are shorn every two years and the hairs are sorted by colour and fineness. They are fine, soft, lightly crimped, and very warm. They are used in expensive knitted fabrics, jackets, over-coats, and blankets.
Camel		Camel hair is the downy undercoat of the bactrian (two-humped) camel. It is moulted every year, is very fine, soft, lightly crimped and beige in colour. Camels under one year old are blonde, almost white. Their "baby hair" is especially soft and valuable. Camel hair is used for outerwear. The coarser guard hairs, and those of the one-hump camel are used for interlinings.
Cashmere		The cashmere goat lives in Mongolia and the Himalayan mountains at altitudes of up to 5000 m. To withstand the cold, it has an unusually fine undercoat. At the yearly coat-change, the underhairs are separated from the coarser guard hairs and are sorted by colour. Textiles made from cashmere are very soft, light and lustrous; it is the most expensive hair fibre.
Mohair **Yak**		Mohair is the hair of the angora goat, which may be shorn twice each year. The best quality comes from Texas, South Africa, and Turkey. The hairs are long, lightly curled, and have a silky lustre. They are white, and do not felt easily, and are well suited for dyeing. Mohair is used for outerwear. Yak is the hair of the domesticated Tibetan ox.
Angora **Rabbit**		Angora fibre is the hair of the angora rabbit, which is farmed in Europe and East Asia. The name derives from Ankara, in Turkey. The rabbits are shorn up to four times each year. The fine, very light hairs are very good at absorbing moisture vapour. They are used for thermal underwear and ski underwear. In outerwear, inclusion of the coarse guard hairs gives angora fabrics their typical spiky appearance.

Within the Wool Mark, and the textile labelling regulations, fine animal hairs have equivalent status to wool, because they have similar properties. So long as they conform to the quality requirements, fine hairs can be labelled with the Wool Mark.

Coarse Animal Hairs

Coarse hairs are used mostly for the manufacture of resilient and stable interlining materials. The most important are **Horse hair**, **Camel hair (guard hairs)**, **Cattle hair**, and **Goat hair**.

Silk   German: Seide   French: Soie   Spanish: Seda

History

According to legend, almost 5000 years ago the Chinese Empress Si Ling Shi (or Lei Zu) observed a silk caterpillar spinning itself into a cocoon. She unravelled the filaments and made a fabric from them.

The Romans paid one pound of gold for a pound of silk fabric. Caterpillar eggs were smuggled into Europe in about 555 AD and, from then on, it was possible to produce silk in the Mediterranean region.

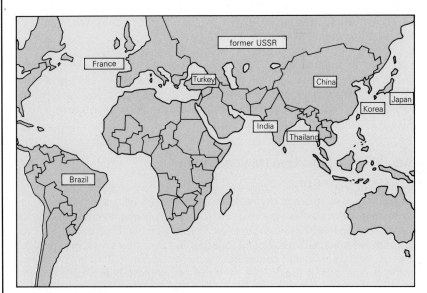

1: Silk producing countries

Production and Sources

The world production of raw silk is about 70000 tonnes. This is less than 0.2% of world textile fibre production.

Silk can be produced only where the mulberry tree grows.

The most important producing areas are:

1 China	4 former USSR	7 Thailand
2 India	5 Brazil	8 Turkey
3 Japan	6 Korea	9 France

The Mulberry Silkworm

On emerging from its egg, the mulberry silkworm is only about 2 mm long. It feeds on a large quantity of mulberry leaves.

After about 30 days, and after moulting four times, it will be as large as a middle finger and begins to pupate. Straw or twigs are supplied at this stage for the caterpillars to use. The silk fluid (**fibroin**, an animal protein) is extruded from a spinneret located under the lower lip. The spinneret is fed by two glands and the emerging filaments are coated with silk gum (**sericin**). Spinning takes about 3 days, during which a twin filament of about 3000 m is produced. The silkworm moves its head in a figure-of-eight pattern to create a **cocoon** about the size of a pigeon's egg. The tangle of loose silk with which the silkworm originally secured its position in the straw, is called **floss**, or **blaze**.

The transition from pupa to moth takes about 14 days. The moth dissolves a portion of the cocoon wall and crawls out. The moths mate, the female lays, and both die immediately.

The harvest from 50000 silkworms is about 1000 Kg of cocoons, which yield about 120 Kg of raw silk.

3: Caterpillar development

2: Egg-laying female

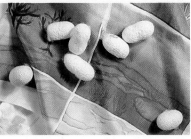

4: Spinning silkworm

5: Cocoons, anchored by floss

6: Newly-emerged moth

7: Cocoons on silk cloth

Wild Silk

Beside the mulberry silkworm, there are many wild species. The most important of these is the Tussah. So far, this type of silkworm has not been bred in Europe.

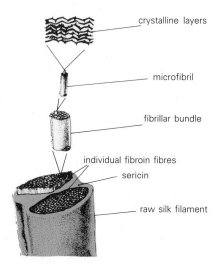

1: Model of a raw silk filament

crystalline layers

microfibril

fibrillar bundle

individual fibroin fibres

sericin

raw silk filament

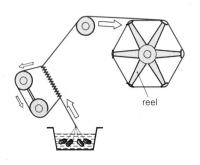

2: Silk reeling

reel

Construction of the Silk Filament

The basic fibre substance is **fibroin**. Like wool, it is made from long-chain protein molecules. Each of the two individual fibroin filaments is constructed from fibrillar bundles (tiny fibres) which themselves are made from microfibrils. The microfibrils are built from the protein chains.

The physical, chemical, and clothing-comfort properties of silk are determined by the molecular chains, and their orientation in the fibre interior. These are disposed in crystalline layers, somewhat like the leaves of a book. This results in high strength and good resilience.

The silk gum, or **sericin**, surrounds the two filaments and holds them together. It is a transparent, water-soluble protein, which may be more or less pigmented in the usual silk-cocoon colours of natural white to yellow or orange-yellow, for mulberry silk, or light brown to reddish-brown or dark brown, for tussah.

Production of Cultivated (Mulberry) Silk

Raw silk (Net silk): The silk cultivator needs to have undamaged cocoons. He kills the pupae with steam or dry heat. The cocoons are placed in hot water, to soften the gum, and the filament ends are found. The filaments are then wound up onto a reel. An individual filament is too fine to be wound separately, so 7 to 10 of them are collected and wound together to form the **raw** or **greige silk**. The reeled silk is a bundle of continuous filaments, about 1000 m long, coming from the middle part of the cocoon, and still cemented together by the gum. Later, several of these bundles will be twisted together in the silk throwing process.

Spun silk: Unwindable remnants from the cocoons, together with other waste silk, are converted into spun yarns by the usual methods. Spun yarns are made from the longer fibres, separated at a combing machine. They are fine, smooth and regular. Also known as **Schappe** silk.

Noil silk: The shorter waste fibres, in the form of comber noils from spun silk processing, are spun into coarser, irregular, neppy yarns using the woollen spinning system. Also known as **Bourette** silk.

Recovery of Wild Silk (Tussah Silk)

The wild Tussah cocoons are gathered from trees and bushes. Wild silk is not easy to degum and usually can not be reeled. Therefore, it tends to retain its natural reddish or brownish colouring. The filaments exhibit variations in their fineness, which may look like irregular penciled streaks.

Wild silk has a different cross-sectional shape from cultivated silk (cf page 26).

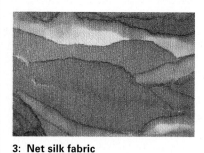

3: Net silk fabric

4: Knitted fabric from spun silk

5: Noil (Bourette) silk fabric

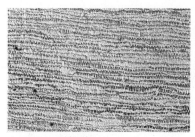

6: Wild silk fabric

Clothing Comfort (cf pages 128, 129)

Thermal insulation	Silk is seen as both cool and warm. Filament silk is made into fine fabrics, with a small volume of enclosed air, which lie smoothly on the skin. This gives a cooling effect. Nevertheless, these fine, compact silk fabrics are good insulators because the layer of warm air, which lies between fabric and skin, is not able to escape very easily.
Moisture absorption	Like wool, it can absorb and hold about 1/3 of its weight of water vapour without feeling wet. Liquids are absorbed rapidly into the non-crystalline regions of the fibre interior.
Next-to-skin comfort	Silk is very pleasant to wear, because of its fineness and softness.

Other Important Properties (cf pages 43, 44, 45)

Lustre, Fineness, Handle	The most important properties of degummed silk are its typical lustre, its fineness, and its pleasant handle.
Strength	Silk has a very good tenacity.
Extensibility	Extensibility is very good; it lies between 10% and 30%.
Elasticity	Silk has outstanding resilience. With the exception of very fine, smooth, weighted woven fabrics, it does not crease badly and the wrinkles tend to fall out.
Electrostatic charge	It builds hardly any electrostatic charge, because it always contains moisture which conducts the charge away.
Sensitivity	Perspiration, deodorant sprays, and perfumes can cause colour changes, and can embrittle the fibre. Therefore arm linings should be used.
Scroop	When a silk fabric is compressed by hand, it makes a rustling sound somewhat like the crunching of fresh snow.

Improvement of Properties by Finishing

Degumming	The natural silk gum makes knitted and woven raw silk fabrics harsh and rough. The sericin gum is removed by a gentle boiling in mild soap solution.
Weighting	The degummed silk is made heavier and firmer again by the addition of metallic salts, or other chemicals.

Properties of Different Types of Silk (summary)

The properties given above apply mainly to degummed net silk. These properties may vary according to the source (cultivated or wild) the fibre type and processing (net, spun, bourette) and the finishing (raw, degummed, weighted). The table gives an overview of the most important differences.

Degummed, Cultivated Silk	Weighted, Cultivated Silk	Wild Silk
• wrinkles little • supple • fine lustre **Net:** • smooth, finest **Spun, Schappe:** • fine, smooth, regular **Noil, Bourette:** • coarser, neppy, irregular	• full • heavy • stiff • wrinkles • less durable • stronger lustre The burning test will indicate whether silk has been weighted with metallic salts (cf page 26)	• coarse (thicker fibre, different cross-section) • is seldom degummed • harsh handle • heavier than cultivated silk • darker, duller colours • dull lustre • not so uniform • more sensitive to perspiration

In addition, as with all textile materials, fabric properties are influenced by the weave type and density, and by further processing.

1.2.6 Animal Fibres: Silk (4)

Fibre Identification

Microscopy		Burning Test	Appearance, Handle	Solubility Test
Cultivated degummed	Wild degummed	**Combustion:** small flame, slowly self-extinguishing **Smell:** like burning horn or hair **Residue:** black, friable cinder, weighted silk leaves a crystalline ash.	Degummed cultivated silk is supple, smooth, and lustrous. Net silk: very fine Spun silk: fine Bourette: coarse, neppy Weighted silk: smooth, stiff Wild silk: firm, irregular	**Sulphuric acid:** Dissolves, destroyed (cf wool) **Lithium hypochlorite** dissolves

Typical Silk Fabrics

Bourette	Crêpe de chine	Organza	Satin crêpe	Wild silk: Doupion
Chiffon	Damask	Pongé	Taffeta	Honan
Crêpe	Duchesse	Satin	Twill	Shantung

Fibre Blends (cf page 41)

Silk is usually processed as the pure fibre. It can be blended with practically all apparel fibres - primarily as staple fibre blends. Blends with wool and fine (high quality) animal hairs are valued highly.

Applications

Apparel Fabrics	Accessories	Household Textiles	Industrial Textiles
Dresses, blouses, sophisticated lingerie, ski underwear, formal dress	Scarfs, squares, gloves, ties, hats, artificial flowers, handbags, umbrellas	Drapes, wall coverings, carpets, lampshades, bed clothes	Sewing threads, embroidery threads, typewriter ribbons, racing bicycle tyres

Aftercare Properties and Labelling

Must be washed carefully, can be ironed, not wrinkle-resistant, dry cleaning recommended

Following are the most severe conditions that can be used; limitations may be imposed by fabric and garment construction, or finishing.

Washing	Chlorine	Ironing	Dry Cleaning	Drying
Gentle detergents, minimum agitation, cool rinse, a dash of clear vinegar in the last rinse.	Do not bleach	Iron on the back at 120 °C to 150 °C. Do not press seams. Steam and water can leave stains.	Coloured and sensitive articles should be dry cleaned.	Do not tumble dry. Do not dry in direct sunlight.

Textile Labelling

The regulations governing the labelling of textiles stipulate that the word "silk" may be used only for fibres obtained from the cocoon of the silk moth. Phrases such as "artificial silk" and "man-made silk", or the use of "silk jersey" and "silk damask" for cotton fabrics are not permitted.

The Silk Seal

The internationally recognised Silk Seal stems from the European Silk Secretariat. It stands for pure silk and good quality.

1: Silk Seal

1.3.1 Composition of Textile Fibres

Chemical Elements - Building Blocks of all Materials

All substances (not just textile materials) are constructed out of about 100 basic chemical elements. The smallest individual component in chemistry is the **atom**. Atoms can not be subdivided by chemical means; they are the basic building blocks of chemical compounds. The most important atoms in fibre-forming materials are Carbon (C), Hydrogen (H), Nitrogen (N), and Sulphur (S) (**Figure 1**).

1: Atoms

Chemical Compounds

Atoms combine to form **molecules**, the smallest units of a compound. The best-known chemical compound is water (H_2O). Its molecule is a combination of two atoms of hydrogen and one of oxygen (**Figure 2**).

Manufacture of a chemical compound is called **synthesis**.

Separation of a compound into its constituents is called **analysis**.

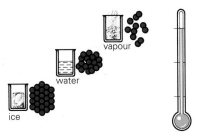

2: Water molecules

Molecular Aggregation

The different physical forms of a compound are called its states (**Figure 3**).

Solid: The molecules are arranged in fixed positions, as for example in crystals of ice. They have very little independent motion.

Liquid: The molecules are held together much more loosely, and can move relatively freely, as in water. The compound is amorphous[1].

Gaseous: The molecules are free to move independently, as in water vapour.

3: Different states of water

Macromolecules

Very large molecules are called macromolecules[2]. When macromolecules are constructed in the form of long chains of small units (**Figure 4**), then they are called long-chain macromolecules, or linear **polymers**[3]. All fibres, whether vegetable, animal, or man-made, are constructed from linear polymers which lie alongside each other and are bonded together.

Textile fibre-forming materials are made either from natural or from synthetic linear polymers.

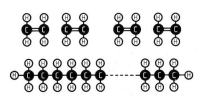

4: Building a molecular chain from small molecules

Construction and Internal Structure of Fibres

The bulk of the fibre is constructed from fibrillar bundles[4]. The individual fibrils are made from long-chain macromolecules. In vegetable fibres, the molecular chains are primarily those of cellulose; in animal fibres they are proteins. Vegetable cellulose is the raw material for the manufacture of cellulosic man-made fibres. Synthetic man-made fibres are made from synthetic polymers, whose basic raw materials are derived from petroleum. Thus fibre-forming substances can be classified according to the source of their basic raw materials - which also are responsible for many of the basic fibre properties.

amorphous region

crystalline region

molecular chain

fibril

fibrillar bundle

fibre

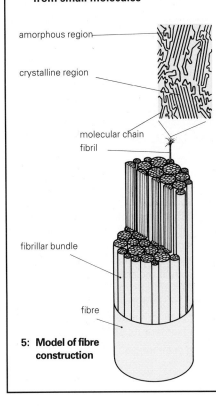

5: Model of fibre construction

Amorphous and Crystalline Regions

The fibre bulk contains amorphous and crystalline[5] regions, depending on the arrangement of the chain molecules (**Figure 5**). The crystalline regions give the fibre its strength, while the amorphous areas allow flexibility. Small molecules, such as water or dyestuffs, can penetrate the amorphous areas but not the crystals. The properties of fibres are governed by the constitution and the organisation of the macromolecules, and by the amorphous and crystalline regions.

[1] amorphous: without form
[2] makros (Grk.) = large
[3] poly (Grk.) = many, meros (Grk) = part
[4] fibril: tiny fibre
[5] crystalline: having regular arrangement of atoms

1.3.2 Fibre-forming Materials

The principles of man-made fibre production are grounded on three basic steps: conversion of the fibre-forming substance into a fluid - by solution or melting, extrusion of the fluid through spinnerets, solidification of the extruded filaments.

Cellulosic Man-made Fibres

Cellulosic man-made fibres are made from natural cellulose polymers, extracted from plants. The macromolecule which has been synthesized by nature may be used as such, or may be chemically modified. To enable cellulose to be spun, it has to be dissolved. There are many different ways to do this, but only four are used in practice.

- **the viscose process**   - **the cuprammonium process**   - **the acetate process**   - **the lyocell process**

Synthetic Man-made Fibres

Synthetic fibre-forming materials, are made in two steps:

1. Synthesis of reactive precursors. These are small molecules, which are called **monomers**[1]. Petroleum is the main raw material for their production.

2. Coupling of thousands of monomers to form macromolecules. The macromolecules are called linear **polymers**, because they are built from many monomers into long chains. Two different types of polymerization reaction, namely, **addition** and **condensation**, are utilised to synthesize fibre-forming polymers. Homopolymers are made from a single species of monomer; copolymers are made from two or more different species. In copolymers, the two (or more) monomers may be pre-formed into blocks which, when polymerised, form a **block copolymer**.

Addition Polymerization

Addition polymers are made by direct coupling of two, usually identical, reactive monomers to form long chains, without by-product. Typical addition polymers are polyacrylics, polyvinyl chloride, and polypropylene.

A +	A +	A +	A +	A +	A	→	A A A A A A
monomer	monomer	monomer	monomer				homopolymer

Condensation Polymerization

Condensation polymers are made by coupling two, usually different, reactive monomers, with the elimination of a small by-product molecule (often water). Typical textile condensation polymers are polyesters and polyamides.

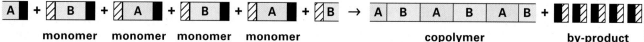

A + B + A + B + A + B →	A B A B A B	+ by-product
monomer monomer monomer monomer	copolymer	by-product

Block Copolymers

The starting reactive monomers are pre-formed into blocks, which are then polymerised, usually by condensation. Elastomeric fibres are made from block copolymers.

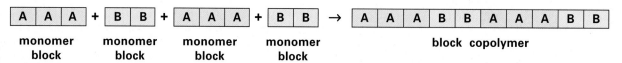

A A A +	B B +	A A A +	B B	→	A A A B B A A A B B
monomer block	monomer block	monomer block	monomer block		block copolymer

Drawing

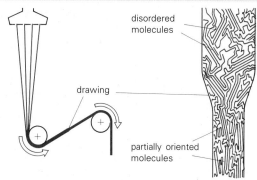

disordered molecules

drawing

partially oriented molecules

1: Orientation of microfibrils by drawing

The spinning fluid solidifies as it emerges from the spinneret. Inside the filament, the microfibrils are not very well ordered. Drawing the filament down to a thinner section causes the disordered microfibrils to become oriented more in the direction of the filament axis. Crystalline regions are formed within the microfibrils through individual molecular chains bonding together along their length. Amorphous regions are between and at the surfaces of the microfibrils. The formation of crystalline microfibrils, and their orientation along the filament axis is what gives the filament its strength.

Drawing may be done during spinning and also in a separate, subsequent process.

[1] monos (Grk.) = alone

1.3.3 Spinning Man-made Fibres

Man-made Fibre Spinning Processes

There are three major types of process for spinning man-made fibres. They have several basic elements in common: a reservoir and a metering pump for the fibre-forming material, a spinning jet (spinneret), a fluid in which the filaments are formed, and a take-up mechanism which draws the filaments and winds them onto a package.

Wet Spinning	Dry Spinning	Melt Spinning
Spinning from a polymer solution		Spinning from a polymer melt
The polymer solution is extruded into a bath containing chemicals which neutralise the solvent and coagulate (solidify) the filaments.	The polymer solution is extruded into a stream of warm air which evaporates the volatile solvent and solidifies the filaments.	The molten polymer is extruded into a cold air stream which cools the melt and solidifies the filaments.
Examples: viscose, acrylics	Examples: acrylics, acetate	Examples: nylon, polyester

After the filaments have been extruded and solidified, they are drawn out between rollers having different speeds. Drawing can also be a separate process. Spinneret size, plus spinning and drawing conditions, determine the final filament diameter.

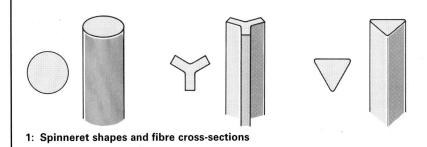

1: Spinneret shapes and fibre cross-sections

The holes in the spinneret may be circular or some other shape, according to requirements. This enables the production of filaments having different cross-sections.

The filament cross-section, and the optional inclusion of delustrants, influences the lustre and handle.

It is also possible to extrude two different polymers, side-by-side, from single spinneret to form **bicomponent fibres**.

Terminology of Extruded Filaments

Filaments: The continuous strands of man-made fibres.
Monofilament: When the spinneret has only a single hole.
Multi-filament: The bunch of filaments from a multi-hole spinneret.
Textured: Thermoplastic multi-filament yarns which have been given a permanent crimping (bulking) treatment.

The filaments from several spinnerets can be combined into a tow and then chopped or broken into **staple fibres**. These are classified as **wool type** or **cotton type**, according to their staple length and crimp. Man-made staple fibres may be spun into yarns, either alone or as blends with other man-made or natural fibres.

There are three main types of **natural polymer** man-made textile fibres; **cellulosics**, **alginates**, and **rubber**. Fibres can also be made from proteins. Of these, the only ones of real commercial significance are the cellulosics - made from natural cellulose. For practical purposes, natural polymer man-made fibres means the cellulosics. **Alginate** fibres are made from seaweed. They are not very stable; they dissolve in soapy water. At one time they found use as soluble fibres (for making temporary joins) but have been replaced by polyvinyl alcohol. **Rubber** fibres are made from latex; they are being extensively replaced by the elastomerics.

History of Cellulosic Man-made Fibres

1: Advertising for "Artificial Silk" textiles (1928)

There has always been a desire to find a cheap substitute for silk. Robert Hooke speculated on the idea in 1664 but it was not until about 100 years ago that scientists found a way to produce an artificial fibre which looked like silk.

The first soluble cellulose derivative with fibre-forming properties, cellulose nitrate, was prepared in 1832, by Braconnet. Later, it was found to be soluble in a mixture of alcohol and ether, and several more or less successful attempts were made to produce fibres but the processes were never fully developed. It was left to Count Hilaire de Chardonnet to solve the technical problems of "artificial silk"[2] production. His process was patented in 1885 and the product was named "Chardonnet silk". Yarns and fabrics of Chardonnet silk were shown at the Paris Exhibition in 1889. Commercial production of the first man-made textile fibres began in Chardonnet's factory in Besançon in 1891.

The solubility of cellulose in aqueous ammonia containing copper oxide was discovered in 1857. By 1897, the process had been developed to the extent that fibre production was possible. Commercial production of cuprammonium rayon[2] or "Bemberg silk" began in Wuppertal in 1904.

The viscose process was developed in England between 1892 and 1898. In this process, cotton was treated with sodium hydroxide and carbon disulphide to yield a thick (viscous) yellow fluid which could be extruded into a coagulation bath.

A further method of cellulosic man-made fibre production followed the laboratory discovery of cellulose acetate, in 1864. A patent application for the dry spinning of cellulose acetate was submitted in 1904.

Thus, the years leading up to 1900 can be seen as the birth of the man-made fibre industry. Artificial silk stockings, which arrived after the first world war, precipitated the short skirts of the "roaring twenties". A similar revolution took place in artificial silk lingerie. A new style in lingerie took over, based on soft, silky, drapable, colourful, and highly resilient locknit fabrics. At first, the cellulosics were produced only as "artificial silk" (continuous filament) yarns but, during the twenties, staple viscose rayon fibres were developed in Germany, where they were called "Zellwolle"[3]. Further developments of the viscose process led to cellulosic man-made staple fibres with properties very similar to cotton. In recent times a more environmentally friendly, organic solvent spinning process has been developed for cellulose.

Classification of Cellulosic Man-made Fibres

Cellulosic man-made fibres can be classified according to the solvent system which is used to convert the cellulose raw material into a spinnable solution.

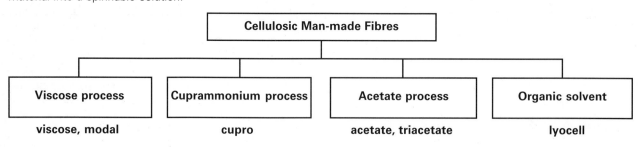

Cellulosic Man-made Fibres			
Viscose process	**Cuprammonium process**	**Acetate process**	**Organic solvent**
viscose, modal	cupro	acetate, triacetate	lyocell

Production of Cellulosic Man-made Fibres

The man-made cellulosics have never captured a very large share of the world market for textile fibres. In 1996, world production was about 2.7 million tonnes; about 6% of all textile fibres.

The most important of the cellulosics is viscose.

---

[1] The international man-made fibre symbol signifies the products of members of the Man-made Fibres Federation.
[2] artificial silk, rayon: former names for cellulosic filament yarns   [3] Zellwolle (Ger.) = cellulose wool

Viscose, Modal

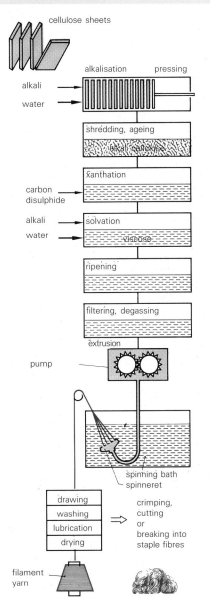

cellulose sheets

alkalisation — pressing

alkali →
water →

shredding, ageing
alkali cellulose

Xanthation
carbon
disulphide

alkali → solvation
water → viscose

ripening

filtering, degassing

extrusion

pump

spinning bath
spinneret

drawing
washing
lubrication
drying

crimping,
cutting
or
breaking into
staple fibres

filament
yarn

1: The classic viscose process

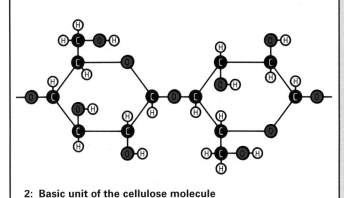

2: Basic unit of the cellulose molecule

Manufacture

The raw material for viscose is extracted from eucalyptus, pine or beech wood which, after removing the bark, is chipped into fragments the length of matches. Resins and other impurities are extracted in a rather expensive procedure. The cellulose is purified and bleached, then pressed into solid sheets.

For fibre production, the cellulose must be dissolved. Using the 100 year old viscose process (**Figure 1**), the cellulose sheets are first steeped in sodium hydroxide solution. This penetrates into the molecular bundles and loosens their structure, to form soda cellulose. After pressing off excess liquor, the soda cellulose is shredded, and then allowed to age. Ageing causes a reduction in the length of the cellulose molecules, which makes them easier to dissolve. Addition of carbon disulphide (Xanthation) converts the cellulose to a form which is soluble in dilute sodium hydroxide to yield the spinning fluid, the viscose, which looks like honey. Delustrants or pigments may be added. The viscose is degassed and filtered and, after ripening, is extruded through fine spinnerets which are immersed in the coagulation bath. The cellulose is regenerated in the spinning bath and solidifies into filaments which are drawn, gathered into a filament yarn, and wound onto a spool. This is followed by a thorough washing, to remove all process chemicals, lubrication (addition of oils) for suppleness, and drying. Staple fibres are made by cutting the filaments to a given length.

Fibre Composition

Viscose: Chemically, the cellulose is scarcely altered by the viscose process. After fibre formation it is again cellulose (**Figure 2**), and is called **regenerated cellulose**. Thus the chemical structure of viscose is comparable to cotton. Nevertheless, the cellulose molecules are shorter than those of cotton, and their organisation in the fibre is different. This is the main reason for the lower strength of viscose fibres.

Modal fibres are made by a modified viscose process. The spinning conditions are different and the coagulation bath contains additional chemicals. These modifications result in longer cellulose molecules and an improvement of the structure and orientation of the crystalline areas. This yields a higher strength, both wet and dry, and better textile performance properties.

Clothing Comfort (cf pages 128, 129)	
Thermal insulation	Viscose filament yarns are made into smooth textiles with a low volume of entrapped air (low specific volume). Staple fibre yarns made from viscose or modal can yield textiles with varying specific volumes, so that the insulation properties can be controlled to some extent. The fibre itself has only a small influence on insulation.
Moisture absorption	Viscose and modal are very absorbent. In normal conditions, they absorb 11 to 14% of water vapour. In liquid water, they swell and can absorb 80 to 120% of water. They are more absorbent than cotton.
Next-to-skin comfort	Viscose and modal fibres are fine and soft. They are very comfortable to wear.

Other Important Properties (cf pages 43, 44, 45)

Strength	Viscose has a significantly lower dry strength than cotton. The wet strength is low; it is only 40 to 70% of the dry strength.
Extensibility	The breaking extension is 15 to 30% - more than double that of cotton.
Elasticity	Poor resilience is a feature of all cellulose fibres. Viscose and modal wrinkle easily.
Electrostatic charge	Very low, because the fibres always contain moisture.
Fineness, Handle	Fabrics may be fine and soft, or firm, depending on the fibre fineness and the fabric construction.
Colouration	Viscose and modal are excellent substrates for dyeing and printing. Colours are very bright.
Lustre	Can range from high lustre to matt, depending on the fibre cross-section and the addition of delustrants.

Improvement of Properties by Finishing

Easy-care treatments	Viscose fibres swell in water; they become thicker. This causes viscose fabrics to shrink. Swelling and shrinkage can be reduced by treatment with synthetic resins. The treatment also improves wrinkle recovery but moisture absorbency is reduced. Modal fibres swell less and fabrics shrink less than viscose so that, in the absence of chemical finishing, the fabrics are more stable.

Applications

Filament viscose is used to produce lustrous fabrics, for effect yarns in woven and knitted fabrics, and for crêpe fabrics. More than half of all lining fabrics are viscose. Other applications are blouses, shirts, dresses, drapes, lingerie, ribbons and trimmings.

Staple viscose fibres are mostly used in blends with other fibres, where their uniformity, lustre, and absorbency are useful. Cotton, wool, and linen type fabrics can be made.

Modal is produced almost exclusively as staple fibre and is used primarily in blends with cotton or polyester because of its strength, uniformity, and absorbency. The blended fabrics are used in underwear and outerwear.

Fibre Identification

Microscopy: cross-section is usually serrated; depends on spinning conditions.

Burning Test: Combustion: rapid, bright, with afterglow. Smell: like burning paper. Residue: pale grey, powdery ash.

Wet Tearing Test: Tears straight through a wet spot (cf cotton).

Solubility Test: Sulphuric acid dissolves viscose and modal.

Aftercare Properties and Labelling

Viscose and modal are washable, easy to iron, not wrinkle-resistant

Following are the most severe conditions that can be used; limitations may be imposed by fabric and garment construction, or finishing.

Washing Viscose Modal	Chlorine	Ironing	Dry Cleaning	Drying Viscose Modal

Textile Labelling

The term **viscose** is reserved for regenerated cellulose fibres produced by the viscose process.

Modal is used for regenerated cellulose fibres with a defined high breaking strength and wet modulus (ISO 2076).
Examples: Avril®, Danufil®, Enka-Viscose®, Koplon®, Lenzing-Modal®, Prima®.

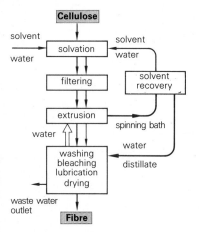

1: The new Lyocell process

Lyocell

Recently, a new process has been developed. This utilises an organic (amine oxide) solvent which, together with water, is capable of dissolving the cellulose in a single step (**Figure 1**). Since almost all of the solvent can be recovered and re-used, and since the use of carbon disulphide is avoided, the new process is much more environmentally friendly. The resulting fibres have a structure and properties significantly different from the viscose types, so a new generic name, **Lyocell**, has been specified for the products of this new process.

Properties: (cf page 45)
Tenacity: 32 ... 38 cN/tex dry, 26 ... 36 cN/tex wet. Breaking Extension 10 ... 16%. Elasticity: poor, like all cellulosic fibres. Moisture Absorption: less than viscose but greater than cotton.

Applications: Similar to Modal

Examples: Tencel®, Lenzing Lyocell®, NewCell®

Cupro, Cupra

Manufacture and Fibre Composition	Properties, Applications, Identification
Copper oxide and other copper compounds dissolve in aqueous ammonium hydroxide to give blue solutions which are capable of dissolving cellulose. Upon dilution, the cellulose precipitates (solidifies). Use of this mechanism to produce a spinnable fluid is called the cuprammonium process. It is a wet spinning process which has been discontinued in some countries for cost and environmental reasons. Cupro is a regenerated cellulose fibre.	As a regenerated cellulose, the important fibre properties are similar to those of viscose. Cupro's pleasant handle and good absorbency are especially prized, but it is not a very important textile fibre. The main outlets are in lining fabrics.

Aftercare Properties and Labelling	Textile Labelling
Cupro is machine washable, ironable, not wrinkle-resistant. Following are the most severe conditions that can be used; limitations may be imposed by fabric and garment construction, or finishing.	The Cupro (Cupra) label is used for regenerated cellulose fibres which have been produced by the cuprammonium process.

Washing	Chlorine	Ironing	Dry Cleaning	Drying

Acetate, Triacetate

Manufacture and Fibre Composition	Properties, Applications	Fibre Identification
Acetate: Cellulose acetate is a (partial) chemical combination of cellulose and acetic acid. It is a dry, granular substance which can be dry spun from solution in acetone. Its properties are quite distinct from those of viscose, modal, and cupro. For example, it reacts differently in burning and solubility tests. **Triacetate**: The completely-reacted cellulose triacetate is not as soluble in acetone; the spinning solvent is dichloromethane. This results in a different range of properties. Acetate and triacetate are **cellulose derivatives**; the hydroxyl (-OH) groups of cellulose are more or less substituted with acetyl groups. Triacetate represents full substitution of the hydroxyl groups.	**Acetate** has a sophisticated, subdued lustre, full handle, and elegant drape. It is the closest approach to natural silk. Elasticity and stability are better than viscose. Acetate is thermoplastic and sensitive to dry heat. It has low moisture absorption so that it dries rapidly, but is susceptible to electrostatic charging. **Triacetate** has better resistance to heat than acetate, and lower moisture absorbency. It is also thermoplastic; it can be textured, and permanently creased or pleated. The other fibre properties are similar to acetate. Acetate and triacetate are produced as both filament and staple fibres, for dresses, blouses, and lining fabrics.	**Solubility Test:** Cellulose acetate is soluble in acetone, dichloromethane, glacial acetic acid, and formic acid. It is sensitive to both acids and alkalis. **Burning Test**: Acetates melt in a flame; they burn rapidly, with an acidic smell. The residue is hard and black.

Aftercare Properties and Labelling	Textile Labelling
Acetate must be washed and ironed carefully. It is not wrinkle-resistant. Triacetate is machine washable and ironable. It is quite wrinkle-resistant. Following are the most severe conditions that can be used; limitations may be imposed by fabric and garment construction, or finishing.	The textile labelling regulations reserve the terms **Acetate** and **Triacetate** for fibres which have been produced from cellulose acetate. Examples: Arnel® (acetate), Tricel® (triacetate).

Washing Acetate Triacetate	Chlorine	Ironing Acetate Triacetate	Dry Cleaning	Drying
		  without steam		

History of Synthetic Fibres

1: Sheer nylon stockings (1952)

In 1925 it was proposed, by the German chemist Staudinger, that textile fibres were formed from linear polymers: very long chain molecules built up from large numbers of simple, small molecules. In natural fibres, the linear polymers are made by plants and animals. Staudinger's insight provided the stimulus for humans to attempt to synthesize linear polymers in the laboratory.

The years between 1931 and 1941 saw the synthesis of polyvinyl chlorides, polyacrylonitriles, polyamides, and polyurethanes. 1941 saw the patent application for polyester; currently the most important synthetic fibre. The commercial breakthrough for synthetic fibres came in the early 1950's, with the successful introduction, world-wide, of nylon stockings. Up to that time, sheer stockings for formal wear had been made from silk or artificial silk. A few years later, the knitted, easy-care nylon shirt was launched. The first elastomeric fibre, Lycra, was developed in the USA and was brought to the market in 1959. Nowadays, synthetic fibres represent about 47% of world textile fibre consumption.

Cellulosic fibres can be regarded as the first generation of man-made fibres; synthetics are the second generation. The third generation, represented by aramids, carbon fibres, and ceramic fibres, have emerged in the last 20 to 25 years.

Classification of Synthetic Fibres

One way of classifying synthetic fibres is according to the general chemical mechanisms used for building the linear polymers from small molecules. The two basic mechanisms are condensation polymerization and addition polymerization. Textile polymers are usually homopolymers (repetition of relatively simple basic units) but may be block copolymers (alternation of blocks, each with different basic units).

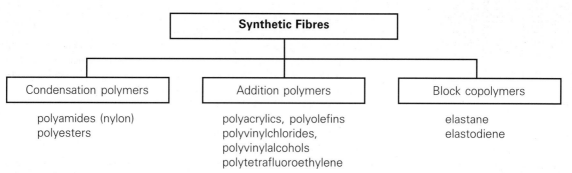

```
                    ┌─────────────────────┐
                    │   Synthetic Fibres   │
                    └─────────────────────┘
          ┌──────────────────┼──────────────────┐
┌─────────────────────┐ ┌─────────────────────┐ ┌─────────────────────┐
│ Condensation polymers│ │  Addition polymers   │ │   Block copolymers   │
└─────────────────────┘ └─────────────────────┘ └─────────────────────┘
```

polyamides (nylon)	polyacrylics, polyolefins	elastane
polyesters	polyvinylchlorides,	elastodiene
	polyvinylalcohols	
	polytetrafluoroethylene	

Polycaprolactam (nylon 6), is classified as a condensation polymer, even though it is formed by an addition mechanism, because its molecular structure conforms to the condensation polymer type.

Production of Synthetic Fibres

In 1996, the total production of all textile fibres was about 44 million tonnes. Of this, about 20 million tonnes were synthetic fibres and 2.7 million tonnes were cellulosic man-made fibres.

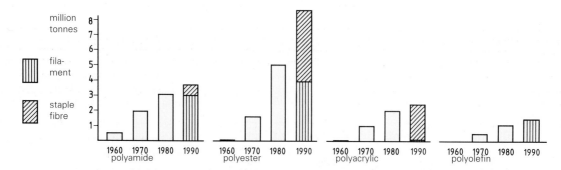

2: Growth of world synthetic fibre production: million tonnes

Acrylic, Modacrylic

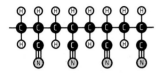

1: **Section of a polyacrylonitrile molecule**

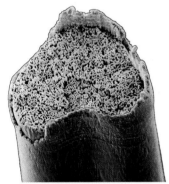

2: **Porous acrylic fibre**

3: **Warm acrylic clothing**

Manufacture

Acrylonitrile, made from propylene and ammonia, is polymerized to form polyacrylonitrile powder. It is dissolved in dimethylformamide or dimethylacetamide, and either wet or dry spun to acrylic filaments. Polymerization of the acrylonitrile can also be effected in the solvent, to form the spinning solution directly.

Fibre Composition

The polyacrylic linear chain molecule is built from repeating units of CH_2CHCN (**Figure 1**). There are three broad types of acrylic fibres: normal acrylics, modacrylics (modified acrylics), which are highly resistant to burning, and the porous fibre Dunova® (**Figure 2**).

Properties (cf pages 43, 44, 45)

Acrylics are produced almost exclusively as staple fibres. They have a wool-like handle, low density, and good resistance to light and chemicals. Like all synthetic fibres they are thermoplastic and wrinkle-resistant (though they are susceptible to deformation in steam or hot water).

Acrylic yarns are usually voluminous, and are very soft, and warm; somewhat similar to wool in character (**Figure 3**). Heat will cause the fibres to shrink strongly. By mixing such fibres with stabilised fibres in a spun yarn, a subsequent heat treatment will induce bulking in the yarn, due to the shrinkage of the unstabilised fibres. Acrylic yarns have a high specific volume, due partly to the low density of the fibres.

Applications

Acrylics are spun into staple yarns, either alone or blended, especially with wool. The yarns are made into knitted fabrics, outerwear, blankets, imitation fur, drapes and furnishings, carpets and awnings.

Modacrylics are modified acrylic fibres. Their properties include flame resistance. They are made into protective clothing and drapes.

Porous acrylic fibres contains many micro-capillaries which are able to absorb liquids. They are used for warm and absorbent underwear.

Fibre Identification

Burning Test:
Acrylics shrink and burn with a sooty flame, with melting and dripping. The smell is pungent; the residue is hard and unbreakable.

Solubility Test:
Solvents are dimethylformamide, dimethylacetamide, and nitric acid.

Aftercare Properties and Labelling

Acrylics are wrinkle-resistant, machine washable and will dry quickly. They are susceptible to heat and must be ironed carefully.

Following are the most severe conditions that can be used; limitations may be imposed by fabric and garment construction, or finishing.

Washing	Chlorine	Ironing	Dry Cleaning	Drying
40		without steam	Ⓟ	

Textile Labelling

The textile labelling regulations reserve the name **acrylic** for fibres which have been made from at least 85% acrylonitrile. The label must show the generic name acrylic. Trade names may also be given.

Examples: Courtelle®, Dolan®, Dralon®, Dunova®, Wolpryla®.

For **modacrylics**, the proportion of acrylonitrile must lie between 50% and 85%.

Polyamide, Nylon

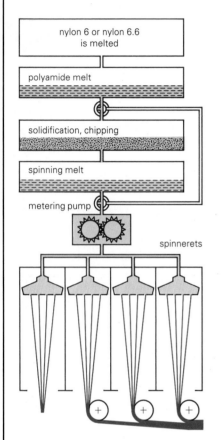

drawing, oiling

texturing

tow formation, drawing, oiling, bulking, cutting or breaking into staple fibres

filaments

staple fibres

1: Melt spinning of nylon

2: Repeat unit of nylon 6

3: Repeat unit of nylon 6.6

Manufacture

The most important polyamides are nylon 6 and nylon 6.6. Nylon 6 is made by polymerizing caprolactam (a cyclic amide derived from a particular amino acid) to polycaprolactam. Nylon 6.6 is made by condensation polymerization of hexamethylene diamine and adipic acid, through the intermediate "nylon salt", to poly(hexamethylene adipamide).

The nylon 6 or 6.6 is melted and either extruded directly, or converted into nylon chips for later use. After emerging from the spinneret, the filaments are cooled in a cold air stream and drawn by three to fourfold in length (**Figure 1**).

Fibre Composition

Polyamides are linear macromolecules containing amide groups (-CO-NH-) at regular intervals. Different types of polyamide are made by using starting materials (monomers) of different sizes (different numbers of carbon atoms). Nylon 6 has six carbons in the repeating unit (**Figure 2**); Nylon 6.6 has two sets of six carbons (**Figure 3**).

Applications

Nylon 6 and nylon 6.6 are used in apparel, household, and industrial fabrics. There are special nylon types for particular end uses. Examples are high-bulk, antistatic, and high-lustre fibres. In recent years, a new type has been developed for industrial textiles; the **aramids**. These are aromatic polyamides, in which a large proportion of the recurring amide groups are joined to aromatic rings. Such fibres tend to have more highly oriented molecules and better crystallinity; they are therefore stronger and more resistant to high temperatures.

Clothing Comfort (cf pages 128, 129)	
Thermal insulation	Insulation properties depend on whether the fibre is produced as flat filament, textured filament, or staple yarn. Flat filaments entrap very little air and have low insulation. Texturing increases the specific volume and allows more air to be enclosed for better insulation. Staple yarns may be either fine and smooth or more voluminous.
Moisture absorption	Nylons absorb little water; between 3.5 and 4.5%. In textured yarns, the capillary spaces are capable of transporting liquid water effectively.
Next-to-skin comfort	Fine and soft nylon fibres are utilized for apparel fabrics.

1: Nylon sportswear

2: Kevlar® aramid fencing suits

Other Important Properties (cf pages 43,44,45)

Strength	**Nylon** is very strong and has excellent abrasion resistance. The wet strength is 80 to 90% of the dry. **Aramid** fibres have about five times the tensile strength of apparel fibres.
Extensibility	Breaking extension is very high, either wet or dry. Depending on the fibre type it may be from 20 to 80%.
Elasticity	Nylon is very resilient and wrinkle-resistant.
Electrostatic charge	Very susceptible, but can be reduced by special anti-static treatments.
Fineness, Handle	Fineness ranges from microfibres to coarse fibres (cf page 44). Fabrics may be fine and soft or firm, according to fibre fineness, fabric construction, and finishing.
Lustre	From matt to high lustre, depending on fibre cross-section and addition of delustrants.
Formability	Is thermoplastic; can be permanently shaped under the influence of heat. This property is utilized for texturing and heat setting.
Chemical resistance	Nylon is resistant to alkalis and many solvents. It is attacked by concentrated acids.
Light resistance	Nylons will yellow and lose strength on long exposure to sunlight. Resistance can be improved by including special chemicals in the spinning melt.
Biological resistance	Nylon is resistant to moulds and fungi. It does not decompose.
Heat resistance	Nylon is sensitive to dry heat.

Applications

Filament yarns, usually textured, are about 80% of nylon production. They are utilized in sheer stockings, lingerie, foundation garments, swimming, sports and leisure wear (**Figure 1**), linings, dresses, and blouses, weather-proof clothing and umbrellas, reinforcing yarns for knitted fabrics, and carpets. Monofilaments are used for sewing yarns.

Staple fibres are blended with wool, cotton, or other man-made fibres for apparel fabrics. They are used in knits, plush, carpet pile, and drapes. They are also used for fleece fabrics.

Aramids are used mostly for fibre-reinforced plastics. They are also utilized in protective clothing such as bullet-proof vests, fencing suits (**Figure 2**), and clothing for forestry workers, racing drivers, and fire fighters.

Fibre Identification

Microscopy: usually circular but depends on the spinneret.

Burning Test: shrinks and melts away from the flame with fibre-forming drips. Residue is hard and uncrushable.

Solvent Test: Destroyed by 80% formic acid and concentrated mineral acids. Slightly degraded by dilute organic acids.

Aftercare Properties and Labelling

Nylon is machine washable, quick drying, and wrinkle-resistant but should be ironed with care.

Following are the most severe conditions that can be used; limitations may be imposed by fabric and garment construction, or finishing.

Washing	Chlorine	Ironing	Dry Cleaning	Drying
		without steam		

Textile Labelling

The labelling regulations stipulate the use of the generic name **polyamide**, or **nylon**, without type designation. Trade names can be added.

Examples of **nylon**: Antron®, Bayer-Perlon®, Enka-Perlon®, Tactel®, Rho-Sport®.

Examples of **aramids**: Kevlar®, Nomex®.

Polyester

1: Polyester chips

2: Flat filaments

3: Textured filaments

4: Staple fibre

5: Repeat unit of the polyester macromolecule

Manufacture

Terephthalic acid combines with ethylene glycol to form dihydroxyethyl terephthalate. At high temperature and vacuum, condensation polymerization proceeds to form poly(ethylene terephthalate), polyester, which is cast and cut into chips. The chips (**Figure 1**) are melted at about 280 °C and extruded (melt spinning process). After drawing, the flat filaments (**Figure 2**) are usually textured (**Figure 3**) or cut into staple fibres (**Figure 4**).

Fibre Composition

The polyester macromolecule contains the ester group (-CO-O-) at regular intervals (**Figure 5**). Esters are produced by the reaction of an organic acid with an alcohol, with the elimination of water.

Types

In addition to standard polyester fibre, there are special types for particular end-uses. Examples are high strength, flame resistant, heat resistant, high shrink, high crimp, antistatic, low pill, low melting adhesive fibres, and profiled fibres.

Clothing Comfort (cf pages 128, 129)	
Thermal insulation	Flat filament yarns enclose little air; textured yarns are better insulators. Staple yarns may be fine and smooth or very bulky, with corresponding poor or good insulation.
Moisture absorption	Polyester scarcely absorbs water. Transport of liquid water in the yarn capillaries is good.
Next-to-skin comfort	Fine and soft fibres are used for apparel fabrics.

Other Important Fibre Properties (cf pages 43, 44, 45)	
Strength	Polyester and nylon have the highest tensile strength and abrasion resistance of all textile fibres. The wet strength of polyester is the same as the dry.
Extensibility	The breaking extension is between 15 and 50%; somewhat lower than nylon.
Elasticity	Is very good, it is very wrinkle-resistant.
Electrostatic charge	Is very high, but can be reduced by antistatic treatments.
Fineness, Handle	Fibre fineness ranges from microfibres to coarse fibres (cf page 44). Fabrics are fine and soft, or stiff depending on the fibre fineness, fabric construction, and finishing.
Lustre	From bright to matt, depending on fibre cross-section and addition of delustrants.
Formability	Polyester is thermoplastic; it can be textured.
Chemicals	Unaffected by most acids, alkalis, and solvents. Can be degraded by strong, concentrated acids and alkalis and a few solvents.
Light resistance	Very good
Biological resistance	Resistant to moulds and fungi; does not decompose.
Heat resistance	Polyester has the best heat resistance of all synthetic fibres used for apparel fabrics.

1: Rainwear in polyester microfibres

2: Principle of modern rainwear

3: Fleece fabric in polyester microfibres

4: Textured (bulked) polyester sewing thread

5: Sail cloth in high tenacity polyester filament yarn

Applications

Polyester is the most versatile of the man-made fibres and, therefore, finds the widest range of uses. About 60% of polyester production is in the form of staple fibres (cotton or wool type)

Staple fibres are used primarily in blends with other fibres, especially wool, cotton, viscose, and modal. The blending level depends on the end use and the other fibre. Common blending ratios are 70:30, 65:35, 55:45, and 50:50, though other blend ratios, and other fibres are also used. The most important applications are in suits, costumes, dresses, shirts and blouses, leisure wear, rainwear, workwear, and bed clothing. 100% polyester staple yarns are used for high strength sewing threads, and staple fibres are made into waddings for interlinings or used as filling material for quilted articles.

Filament yarns for apparel fabrics are usually textured. These are used in dresses and blouses, ties and scarfs, rainwear and linings. Bulked yarns are used for edge overlocking, because they have good covering power. Almost all net curtains are made from filament yarns.

Flame resistant variants are used in hotel bedding, children's nightwear, and furnishings and upholstery in theatres and transport.

High tenacity variants are used for tent-roofing, tarpaulins, and tyre cords, in geotextiles, and many other industrial end uses.

Fibre Identification

Microscopy:
Cross-section usually circular, but depends on the spinneret. Profiled fibres may be triangular or five-point star (for modified lustre, handle, and soil-hiding properties).

Burning Test:
Melts and shrinks from the flame to form a brownish mass which may drip filaments. Residue is hard and uncrushable.

Solubility Test:
Polyester is soluble only in concentrated sulphuric acid, concentrated potassium hydroxide, tetrachloroethane, and phenols.

Aftercare Properties and Labelling

Polyester textiles are machine washable, quick drying, and wrinkle-resistant.

Following are the most severe conditions that can be used; limitations may be imposed by fabric and garment construction, or finishing.

Washing	Chlorine	Ironing	Dry Cleaning	Drying
60	⊠	⌐	Ⓟ	⊡

Textile Labelling

The generic name **polyester** should be used. Trade names may be added.

Examples of the many trade marks are: Dacron®, Diolen®, Tergal®, Trevira®.

Synthetic Fibres: Elastomerics, Fluorofibres, Chlorofibres, Olefins, Vinylals

Generic Group	Sub-group	Form	Special Properties	Applications	Trade Marks (examples)
Elasto-merics	**Elastane** Elastane is manufactured from at least 85% of **polyurethane.** **Elastodiene** is scarcely used for textile purposes.	Filament	Very highly extensible (up to 800%), and elastic; easily dyed. Compared to rubber: can be made finer, more washable, more resistant to light and oxidation.	Usually in combination with other fibres for swimwear, foundation fabrics, stockings, stretch clothing.	Lycra° Dorlastan° Elastan° Enkaswing°
Fluoro-fibres	**Poly(tetrafluoro-ethylene)** PTFE	Filament Staple Film	Water repellent, outstanding chemical resistance, heat resistant, can scarcely be dyed.	Microporous membranes for weather-proof clothing.	Teflon°, Hostaflon° membranes in Gore-Tex° weather-proof clothing.
Chloro-fibres	**Poly(vinyl chloride)** PVC **Poly(vinylidene chloride)** is used only for industrial materials.	Filament Staple	Voluminous fabrics are very warm; high chemical resistance.	Thermal underwear, protective clothing (rarely nowadays).	Clevyl° Rhovyl° Leavil°
Olefins	**Polyethylene**	Monofilament Split film	Low density, low softening temperature, absorbs no water.	Industrial textiles: ropes, cables, nets, filters.	Fibrite° Leolene° Vestolan°
	Polypropylene	Filament Staple	Absorbs no water but good capillary action.	Sports undergarments (rapid wicking of perspiration).	Meraklon° Vegon°
Vinylals	**Poly(vinyl alcohol)** PVA	Filament Staple	Water soluble and insoluble types.	Adhesives, separation yarns, industrial textiles.	Kuralon°

Inorganic Man-made Fibres: Glass, Carbon, Metal

Generic Group	Sub-group	Form	Special Properties	Applications	Trade Marks (examples)
Glass	**Glass**	Filament Staple	Non-flammable, low moisture absorption, low extensibility, brittle.	Furnishing, wall coverings, reinforced plastics.	Fibreglass°
Carbon	**Carbon**	Filament Staple	High heat resistance, high strength, stiff.	Reinforced plastics (machine parts, sports equipment).	Asgard° Grafil° Panox°
Metal	**Metal**	Wire-drawn Flat-drawn Filament Staple Metallised, plastic ribbons	Wire-drawn are very finely drawn out metal; flat-drawn are like fine ribbons. Lurex is a very thin sheet of metal, sandwiched between films of acetate or polyester.	Metal fibres and Lurex are used as effect yarns in trimmings and brocades. Inclusion of a small percentage of metal fibres inhibits the formation of static charge.	Lurex°

Fibre blending is used either to improve the quality, by compensating a weakness in the properties of a given fibre type, or to achieve special optical effects. Blending will also influence processing efficiency, yarn fineness, and cost.

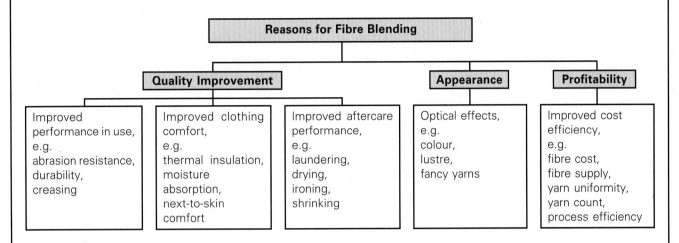

Typical Blends and Blending Ratios

Blending can be effected at either of two stages in textile manufacture:

During staple yarn production, by blending different types of fibres.

During fabric production, by mixing yarns made from different fibres or filaments. Any combination of natural fibre and man-made fibre yarns is possible, in principle.

1: Combination of two natural fibres

2: Blend of natural and man-made fibres

It is especially advantageous to blend natural fibres with man-made fibres. In this way, the most desirable properties of both fibre types can be exploited, whilst some of their disadvantages can be partially offset.

The most popular blends are those of wool with polyester, nylon, and acrylics, and of cotton with polyester, nylon, viscose, and modal. The superb clothing comfort properties of the natural fibres are supplemented by the high strength, abrasion resistance, and resilience, and the good aftercare characteristics of the synthetic man-made fibres to make textiles with excellent all-round performance. The cellulosic man-made fibres are valuable blending materials because of their softness and high moisture absorption, and because they can be produced with the ideal length and fineness for making fine yarns.

Special effects can be obtained with man-made fibres through controlling their lustre and shrinking potential. The best staple fibre blends are obtained when the different fibres are closely matched in their extensibility, length, and fineness.

The most common blending ratios are between 70:30 and 50:50.

Aftercare

In principle, aftercare has to be based on the properties of the weakest component. Nevertheless, wool which has not been given an anti-felting treatment can be made machine washable by blending with a high proportion of a synthetic fibre.

Labelling of Blended-fibre Fabrics

3: Label for polyester-cotton blend fabric

The labelling regulations require that the components of the blend, and their proportions be stated in rank order. Natural fibres are indicated by their common names. Man-made fibres must be designated by the generic terms, such as polyester, nylon, etc. Trade marks of individual manufacturers and quality marks may also appear (see page 46).

Inclusion of aftercare symbols is optional.

Aftercare Characteristics of Apparel Fabrics

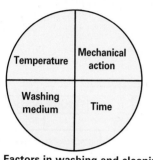

1: **Factors in washing and cleaning, after Sinner**

Aftercare requirements form part of the utility value of textiles. If clothing demands laborious and expensive laundering, then its value is so much the less. Aftercare may include airing, washing, bleaching, dry cleaning, drying (laid flat, hanging on a line, or in a tumble dryer) and ironing.

Four factors are important in washing or dry cleaning; temperature, time, washing medium, and mechanical action **(Figure 1)**. These four have to be optimised.

Particular laundering procedures have to be chosen according to the type of fibre and its properties, such as strength and sensitivity to chemicals and temperature. Additional limitations may be imposed by yarn and fabric construction, or special finishes. Clothing with linings and interlinings, such as suits, costumes, jackets and overcoats, must usually be dry cleaned. Aftercare characteristics can be established by means of laundering tests.

Aftercare Symbols	Applications

The provision of washing symbols is optional. They indicate a recommended procedure which, if followed, should avoid the risk of damage to the textile product. They always indicate the most severe procedure which is acceptable. For fibre blends, the recommendation should be based on the most sensitive component. (ISO 3758; ASTM D5489). The precedence of the symbols on the care label is: Washtub, Triangle, Iron, Circle, Square.

 Washing (symbol: wash tub)

The symbol indicates that water washing, either by hand or by machine, is acceptable. The number in the wash tub indicates the maximum temperature. A line underneath the wash tub indicates a less severe process (gentle wash, low water level). A broken line indicates an especially gentle treatment.

Standard (built) detergents include water-softening, bleaching and optical brightening agents, anti-redeposition agents and fillers. **Gentle** detergents are used for wool, silk and other sensitive fabrics. They are active at low temperature, have low alkalinity, and do not contain bleaching or optical brightening agents. Bleaches and water-softening agents can often be purchased separately, so that a gentle detergent can be "built" by the consumer according to the level of soiling of the wash load and the hardness of the water. This can result in a lower environmental impact. **Compact** detergents contain no fillers and are active at low temperatures. This saves energy and reduces the environmental impact.

 Chlorine (symbol: triangle)

The chlorine symbol is important for domestic stain removal and for commercial laundries, where chlorine bleach may be used.

 Ironing (symbol: iron)

The dots in the iron symbol indicate the maximum temperature: ••• 200 °C, •• 150 °C, • 110 °C.

 Dry Cleaning (symbol: circle)

The letters indicate acceptable cleaning and stain removal solvents. A line under the circle means reduced mechanical action, temperature, and added water.

 Drying (symbol: square)

A circle inside the square indicates tumble drying. A line under the square indicates gentle treatment. The dots in the tumbler symbol indicate the temperature: • low, •• normal, ••• hot.

	Hot wash: white cotton or linen without special finishes
	60 °C: cotton, linen, modal, polyester and their blends where colours and finishes are fast at 60 °C
	40 °C: cotton or polyester in deep colours
	40 °C, gentle program: delicate fabrics of modal, viscose, lyocell acrylics, polyester, nylon
	30 °C, gentle program: shrink-resistant wool, acetate
	Hand wash: normal wool, silk
	Do not wash: very delicate wool and silk fabrics
	May be chlorine bleached
	Do not use chlorine bleach
	cotton, linen
	wool, silk, polyester, viscose
	acrylic, nylon, acetate
	do not iron: polypropylene
	A = All normal solvents may be used without restriction.
	P = Perchloroethylene and Fluorohydrocarbons. These are the most common solvents for normal cleaning.
	F = Fluorohydrocarbons and white spirit. These are used for sensitive articles.
	Do not dry clean
	The divisions are similar to those for washing and ironing. Fabrics made from wool, silk and acrylics, and knitted fabrics susceptible to shrinking or stretching are not suitable for tumble drying.
	Do not tumble dry

In the absence of proper labels, the fibre type can be established by simple tests.

Microscopy: A good microscope is needed. Cotton and wool have distinctive appearances.

Burning test: A specimen of fibres, yarn, or fabric is held horizontally with tweezers. Its behaviour as it approaches the flame, how it burns, the smell and the residue are all observed.

Dry Tearing test: A piece of fabric is snipped and then torn by hand. The length of the broken fibre ends is observed.

Wet Tearing test: A drop of water is applied and the behaviour of the wet place is observed during tearing.

Solubility test: Used mainly to identify fibre blends. The material is immersed in various chemicals for several hours. Acids are used in concentrated form.

	Fibre Type	Fibre Composition Polymer type	Microscopy Longitudinal and cross-sectional appearance	Burning Test (untreated fibre) B = burning S = smell R = residue	Other Tests So = solubility test Td = dry tearing Tw = wet tearing
NATURAL FIBRES / vegetable	**cotton**	cellulose	kidney or bean-shape	B: rapid, bright, afterglow S: like burning paper R: pale grey powder	So: dissolved by sulphuric acid Td: short fibre ends, cf linen Tw: high wet strength, cf viscose
	linen	cellulose	irregular polygon	B: rapid, bright, afterglow S: like burning paper R: pale grey powder	So: dissolved by sulphuric acid Td: long fibre ends, cf cotton
NATURAL FIBRES / animal	**wool**	keratin (protein)	round to oval	B: slow, sputtering S: burning hair R: friable cinder	So: lithium hypochlorite dissolves animal proteins So: strong alkalis dissolve wool
	silk, degummed	fibroin (protein)	rounded triangle	B: slow, sputtering S: burning hair R: friable cinder	So: lithium hypochlorite dissolves animal proteins So: sulphuric acid dissolves silk
MAN-MADE FIBRES / cellulosic	**viscose, modal**	regenerated cellulose	dep. on spinning conditions	B: rapid, bright, afterglow S: like burning paper R: pale grey powder	So: dissolved by sulphuric acid So: viscose is attacked by hydrochloric acid Tw: low wet strength, cf cotton
	acetate	cellulose acetate	dep. on spinning conditions	B: melts, burns, drips S: pungent, vinegar R: sets hard	So: acetate is soluble in acetone and acetic acid So: triacetate is soluble in dichloromethane
MAN-MADE FIBRES / synthetic	**polyester**	poly(ethylene-terephthalate)	depends on spinneret	B: shrinks, melts, burns, drips in filaments R: sets hard	So: soluble in dichlorobenzene and sulphuric acid
	nylon	polyamide	depends on spinneret	B: shrinks, melts, burns, drips in filaments R: sets hard	So: soluble in formic acid and hydrochloric acid
	acrylic	polyacrylo-nitrile	dep. on spinning conditions	B: shrinks, melts, burns (sooty), drips R: sets hard	So: soluble in dimethylformamide and nitric acid
	polypropylene	polypropylene	depends on spinneret	B: shrinks, melts, burns, drips R: sets hard	So: soluble in xylol
	elastane	polyurethane	fibrillar	B: shrinks, melts, burns, drips R: sets hard	So: soluble in cyclohexanone and dichlorobenzene

Fibre Fineness (linear density)

Linear density, or titre, is the fibre weight per unit length. The units are tex or dtex (decitex).

tex	=	mass	in	grams	of	one	kilometre	of	fibre	(yarn)
dtex	=	mass	in	grams	of	ten	kilometres	of	fibre	(yarn)

The smaller the number, the finer is the fibre. A fineness of 2 dtex indicates that 10 km of fibre has a mass of 2 grams.

Fibre	Fineness range dtex	Micro fibres	Fine fibres							Coarse fibres										
			1 2 3	4 5	6 7	8	9 10 11	12 13	14 15	16	17 18 19									
			Fibre fineness in dtex																
Cotton	1…4																		
Flax	10…40																		
Wool, Hairs	2…50																		
Silk	1…4																		
Viscose, Modal	1…22																		
Acetate	2…10																		
Polyester	0.6…44																		
Nylon	0.8…22																		
Acrylic	0.6…25																		
Polypropylene	1.5…40																		
Elastane	20…5000																		

magnification 250 times

1: **Fabric from nylon 78 dtex yarn; 98 filaments of 0.8 dtex**

2: **Fabric from nylon 78 dtex yarn; 23 filaments of 3.4 dtex**

Textile fibres can be classified into **Coarse**, **Fine**, and **Microfibres**. Apparel fabrics are usually made from fine fibres and microfibres. Finer fibres make softer, denser, and more comfortable fabrics, with better drape **(Figures 1 and 2)**.

Microfibres are generally man-made fibres with a linear density of less than 1 dtex. They are predominantly nylon or polyester filament or staple fibres. Microfibre yarns allow the production of fine and dense fabrics.

Applications for microfibre fabrics are in all-weather clothing and for soft, flowing outerwear materials. Their surface characteristics can be modified in several ways; velvety, crêpe, brushed.

Trade marks for microfibre fabrics include Belseta®, Diolen Mikro®, Meryl®, Setila®, Tactel 24 Carat®, Tactel Micro®, Trevira Finesse®, Trevira Micronesse®.

1.6 Fibre Properties, Fibre Identification (3)

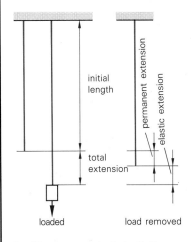

1: Measurement of tenacity and breaking extension

2: Measurement of elasticity

Fibre properties can only be assessed comparatively. Therefore they have been summarised in tabular form. From the wide range of available data, only those properties which are of importance for apparel fabrics are presented.

Fibre Length (staple)

Long fibres allow the production of yarns with low hairiness. The shorter the fibres, the greater the frequency of protruding fibre ends.

Fibre Density

The density of a fibre affects the weight of its fabrics. In general, fibres with a low density allow the production of light, voluminous fabrics.

Moisture Absorption

Most fibres will absorb a certain amount of water from the atmosphere. The amount absorbed depends on the relative humidity of the air. Moisture absorbed by clothing can conduct away electrostatic charges.

Biological Resistance

Cellulose and protein fibres are decomposed; synthetic fibres are not.

Tenacity

Tenacity is the breaking force per unit of fineness, expressed in cN/tex (cN = 1/100 Newton). The higher the value, the better is the strength, and the durability of the corresponding fabrics.

Breaking Extension and Elasticity

Together with the fabric construction, fibre extensibility and elasticity influence the general comfort, the formability, the dimensional stability and the wrinkle resistance of clothing.

Breaking extension is given in percent, based on the initial length.

Elasticity is the property which allows a fibre to recover its length after it has been extended. Fibres never return completely to the original length; they always retain a greater or lesser part of the extension.

Fibre	Fineness dtex	Length mm	Density g/cm³	Moisture Absorption		Biolo-gical Resist-ance	Tenacity		Breaking Extension		Elas-ticity
				standard condition[1] %	high humidity[2] %		standard condition cN/tex	wet % of dry value	standard condition %	wet % of dry value	
Cotton	1...4	10...60	1.50...1.54[3]	7...11	14...18	poor	25...50	100...110	6...10	100...110	poor
Flax	10...40	450...900	1.43...1.52	8...10	...20	poor	30...55	105...120	1.5...4	110...125	poor
Wool	2...50	50...350	1.32	15...17	25...30	poor[4]	10...16	70...90	25...50	110...140	good
Silk	1...4		1.25[5]	9...11	20...40	poor	25...50	75...95	10...30	120...200	very good
Viscose	1...22	38...200	1.52	11...14	26...28	poor	18...35	40...70	15...30	100...130	poor
Modal	1...22	38...200	1.52	11...14	26...28	poor	35...45	70...80	15...30	120...150	poor
Acetate	2...10	40...120	1.29...1.33	6...7	13...15	good	10...15	50...80	20...40	120...150	good
Polyester	0.6...44	38...200	1.36...1.38	0.2...0.5	0.8...1	very good	25...65	95...100	15...50	100...105	very good
Nylon	0.8...22	38...200	1.14	3.5...4.5	6...9	very good	40...60	80...90	20...80	105...125	very good
Acrylic	0.6...25	38...200	1.14...1.18	1...2	2...5	very good	20...35	80...95	15...70	100...120	very good
Polypropylene	1.5...40	38...200	0.90...0.92	0	0	very good	15...60	100	15...200	100	good
Elastane	20...4000		1.15...1.35	0.5...1.5	0.5...1.5	good	4...12	75...100	400...800	100	highest

[1] 20 °C and 65% RH   [2] 24 °C and 96% RH   [3] cell wall: whole fibre is less dense   [4] attacked by moths   [5] degummed
Values extracted from the Denkendorf Fibre Chart

Textile Labelling Regulations

Label

Selvedge

Packaging

1: Location of labelling information

The Textile Labelling Regulations in various countries constrain trade and industry to display information about the raw materials on their products, so that the consumer shall be able to determine which fibre types have been used to make the product. In the European Union, for example, the regulations stipulate the descriptors which must be used for the different fibre types and what additional information is important or is permitted. In addition, textiles, designs, samples and illustrations in catalogues must also be labelled, though not newspaper advertisements. In clothing, fibre content information must be provided on sewn-in labels; in piece goods the information may be woven into the selvedge. If the product is sold in a package (stockings and tights), then the information may be placed on the packaging **(Figure 1)**.

2: Example of a label

Trade marks, brand names, or company names may be placed beside the fibre content, but must be clearly separate. It is recommended, though not prescribed that the aftercare symbols should also be provided **(Figure 2)**.

The Textile Labelling Regulations stipulate the fibre descriptors which may be used. These are given in the raw materials overview on page 8. For man-made fibres, the generic names are used e.g. polyester, viscose. The specific names for linen, wool, and silk are given under the descriptions of the individual fibres.

	100% Silk
	Pure Silk
3:	All Silk

Materials which are made 100% from only one raw material may be described as "pure" or "all"; an allowance of 7% for visible decoration material is given **(Figure 3)**. Interlinings used for shaping need not be identified.

4:	80% Nylon 20% Elastane

With blended products, the percentages by weight of the constituent fibres must be given. The fibres must be listed in decreasing order **(Figure 4)**.

5:	minimum 85% Silk

For textiles which are made from several fibres, one of which is at least 85%, it is sufficient to say "85% minimum content" **(Figure 5)**.

6:	60% Silk, 25% Wool Viscose

If no one fibre in a blend is as much as 85%, then it is sufficient to give the percentage share of the two dominant fibres with the other components listed in decreasing order with or without percentage shares **(Figure 6)**.

7:	85% Cotton 15% other fibres

If one or more components are present in an amount of less than 10%, then they may be designated as "other fibres" **(Figure 7)**.

8:	Outer fabric: 100% New Wool Lining: 100% Silk

With lined clothing, the fibre content of the main lining material must be given **(Figure 8)**.

Brand Names, Quality Marks, Registered Trade Marks

9: Examples of Registered Quality Marks & Trade Marks

Brand names are used by manufacturers to advise the consumer of special, high quality products. In addition, there are **Quality Marks** which indicate that the products, which may be supplied by different manufacturers, conform to certain written quality standards.

Brand names and logos can be officially registered at national or regional patent or registration offices. These are **"Registered Trade Marks"** which are usually indicated by a superscript R in a circle. National and international regulations govern the use of these marks, and protect them against misuse.

Examples of Trade Marks are e.g. Dolan, Dunova, Trevira. Examples of Quality Marks are the Cotton Emblem, the Linen Seal, The Woolmark, the Silk and the Man-made Fibre Seals **(Figure 9)**.

2 Yarns   2.1 Fundamentals

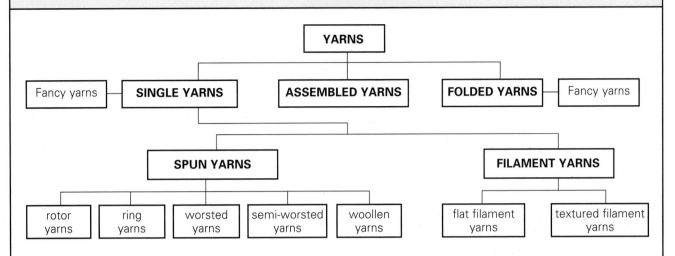

Definition

The word yarn (or thread) is used in common parlance to cover all of the linear textile structures given below. Yarns can be either "single" or "folded". Thus a yarn is an assembly of fibres or filaments having a substantial length and relatively small cross-section, with or without twist, being the end-product of a spinning and winding process.

Assemblies of fibres or filaments which are intermediate products in a spinning process are given special names such as "sliver", "roving", "bave", "top", or "tow", depending on the process and the particular intermediate stage.

Terms

	Spun yarns are made by mechanical assembly and twisting together (spinning) of staple fibres.
Flat filament	**Filament yarns** are made by the assembly of continuous filaments, made from silk or man-made fibres.
Twisted multi-filament	A **multi-filament yarn** is a filament yarn made from multiple filaments, assembled with or without twist.
Monofilament	A **monofilament** yarn consists of only a single continuous filament.
	Two or more yarns which are wound side by side onto the same package, but without twisting around each other, are called **assembled yarns**.
	Folded or **Plied yarns** are yarns made by twisting together two or more single (and/or folded) yarns of the same or different types.

Composition

Staple yarns	Filament yarns	
	Multi-filament	**Monofilament**
From staple fibres such as cotton, flax, wool, spun and noil silk, broken or cut man-made fibres.	reeled silk man-made fibre	man-made fibre

Production of Spun Yarns

Fibres from the compressed bales are first opened up and then assembled into a yarn in the following stages.

| loose stock | opening & cleaning | orientation | sliver formation | drawing | roving formation | yarn formation (spinning) |

1: Principle of spinning

Formation of the roving can be accomplished either by dividing a web into ribbons **(Figure 2)** or by several stages of doubling and drafting of slivers **(Figure 3)**, depending on the type of raw fibre stock and the desired yarn properties.

Formation of a Roving (slubbing) by Partitioning a Web

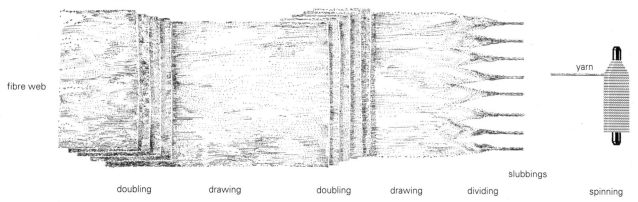

fibre web

slubbings

| doubling | drawing | doubling | drawing | dividing | spinning |

2: Principle of the woollen (or condenser) spinning system

Formation of a Roving by Doubling and Drafting of Slivers

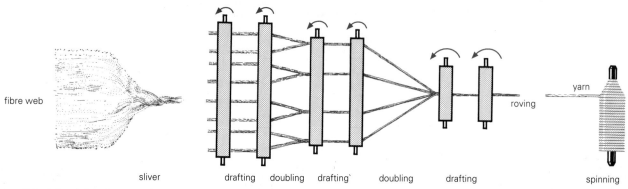

fibre web

roving

| sliver | drafting | doubling | drafting | doubling | drafting | spinning |

3: Principle of the short staple and worsted spinning systems

Spinning is the last processing stage in the formation of yarns. Normally, the spinner will rewind the yarn from the spinning cops onto cross-wound cones in order to facilitate quality control and to obtain larger packages.

Twist

The term twist stands for both the direction of twisting and the number of turns in a yarn.

Twist direction

 If the direction of inclination of the fibres appearing at the surface of a yarn (or of the single yarn components of a folded yarn) is to the right, when the yarn is held vertically, then this is called Z twist.

 If the direction of inclination of the fibres appearing at the surface of a yarn (or of the single yarn components of a folded yarn) is to the left, when the yarn is held vertically, then this is called S twist.

Twist level is the number of turns of twist, in single or folded yarns, per unit of length; e.g. turns per metre. Highly twisted yarns are used for smooth and dense fabrics. Low twist yarns have greater volume and are used for rougher and thicker fabrics.

Spinning Systems for Different Types of Fibres

Group	Spinning system	Fibre type	Fibre length
Long staple systems	Woollen system Semi-worsted system Worsted system	Wool Man-made fibres (wool type)	18... 60 mm 60...120 mm
Short staple systems	Condenser system (similar to woollen system) Cotton system (ring spinning) Rotor spinning	Cotton Man-made fibres (cotton type) Mainly cotton	10... 25 mm 20... 50 mm 10...100 mm
Bast fibre systems	Flax system Hemp system Jute system	Flax Hemp Jute	up to 1000 mm
Silk systems	Spun silk (schappe) Noil silk (bourette)	Silk	up to 250 mm up to 60 mm
Man-made fibre systems	Converter Direct spinning	Man-made fibres	continuous

Woollen System

Almost any spinnable fibre can be processed on the woollen system. The starting material is usually compressed bales of washed and sorted raw wool, recovered wool, or other fibres. The material is taken from the bales in layers and fed to a carding willow for opening.

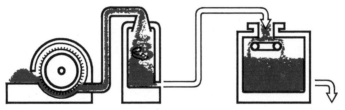

1. Willowing	**2. Mixing and oiling**
Opening and cleaning of the loose stock.	Mixing of fibre types and colours. Composition of a spinning lot. Oiling to improve processing characteristics.

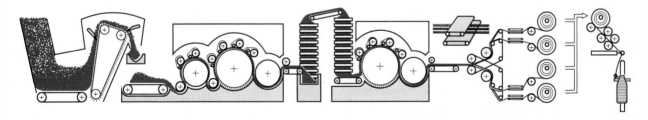

3. Weighing	**4. Carding**	**5. Dividing the web and rubbing**	**6. Spinning**
Opening up the stock. Feeding portions of equal weights to the card.	Individualising the fibres. Orientation. Removal of impurities. Formation of a web.	Dividing the web into ribbons. Rubbing the ribbons between reciprocating aprons to form the slubbing.	Drafting to the required fineness. Twisting. Winding.

Woollen yarns have a coarse, hairy, rustic appearance.

2.2.2   Wool Spinning

Worsted System

The worsted system is used to produce smooth, uniform yarns from the longer types of wool fibres.
The raw wool is first prepared at the top-makers where it is washed, combed, and formed into a sliver.

Worsted Preparation

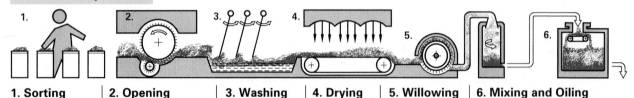

1. Sorting	2. Opening	3. Washing	4. Drying	5. Willowing	6. Mixing and Oiling
Sorting the fleece wool according to fibre quality	Separating the stock into tufts and removal of coarse impurities	Removal of dirt and grease with alkaline soap solution	Drying with warm air	Opening up and cleaning the loose stock	Mixing fibre types and colours. Composing a spinning lot. Oiling to improve the processing characteristics

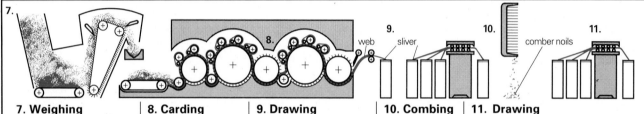

7. Weighing	8. Carding	9. Drawing	10. Combing	11. Drawing
Opening up the loose stock Feeding portions of equal weights to the card	Individualising the fibres Orientation Removing impurities	Doubling and drafting to improve regularity Mixing of fibre types and colours	Combing out the short fibres	Further regularity improvement. After the final drawframe, the contents of the cans are compressed and these "bumped tops" delivered to the spinner.

Spinning

The bumped tops from the combing mill are fed to the worsted drawframes.

 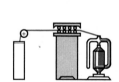 

12. Drawing	13. Roving preparation	14. Spinning
Further regularity improvement and mixing of different fibres	Drafting and twisting into a roving	Drafting to the required fineness Twisting Winding

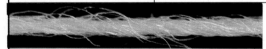

Worsted yarns are particularly smooth and regular because of the repeated doubling and drafting, and the combing.

Semi-worsted Spinning

The designation semi-worsted means that the worsted process is followed with the exception that there is no combing stage. Instead of a combed top, the drawframes are fed with card sliver.

Semi-worsted yarns have a character between woollen and worsted yarns. Usually they are made from coarse fibres and are quite hairy but they are also quite regular due to the doubling and drafting.

2.2.3 Cotton Spinning

The cotton spinning system is sometimes known as the three-cylinder system. This is because the drafting zone of the ring spinning machine normally contains three pairs of drafting rollers.

At the drawframes a group of six or eight slivers are laid together (doubled) and are drawn out by the effect of the different rotation speeds of successive pairs of rollers. For example if the surface speed of the delivery rollers is eight times that of the feed rollers, then the slivers will be drawn out to eight times their original length.

The regularity of the yarn will depend on the number of drawframe passages and on whether or not a combing process is used.

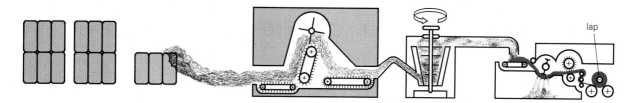

1. Bale lay-down, Mixing	2. Bale opener	3. Opener	4. Scutcher or Picker[1]
A spinning lot is composed by laying out a fairly large number of bales, in order to achieve a good mixing of the raw stock.	Preliminary opening of the bales	Opening up into tufts, cleaning	Further opening and cleaning; pneumatic[2] transport of the material to the card or formation of a lap.

[1] no longer used in modern lines [2] by means of air

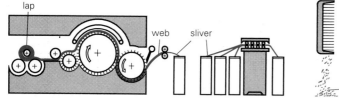
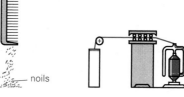

5. Card	6. Drawframe	7. Comber	8. Roving frame	9. Ring spinning frame
Individualising the fibres Cleaning Orientation Sliver formation	Improvement of regularity in 1 to 3 passages Cross-mixing of slivers; blending	Removal of the short fibres (up to 25%) Cleaning used only for high quality yarns	Drafting to a roving Slight twisting	Drafting to the required fineness Twisting Winding

Ring spun yarns are relatively smooth and regular (**Figure 1**). If the combing process is used to remove short fibres, then the regularity is improved further and the end product is called a combed yarn (**Figure 2**).

1. Carded cotton yarn

2. Combed cotton yarn

3: Principle of ring spinning

[1] n = rpm

The ring spinning principle is used to convert roving into yarn in both the cotton and the worsted systems.

The drafted strand is wound onto a spinning cop which is driven by a spindle at the same surface speed as the strand is delivered. Twist is inserted into the strand by the rotation of the traveller, which runs on a circular guide - the ring - and is dragged around by the strand. Thus the rotation of the spindle is transmitted to the yarn.

The twist level of the yarn is controlled by the relationship between the rotational speed of the spindle and the delivery speed of the front rollers.

The ring spinning system is capable of making very fine yarns.

Rotor Spinning

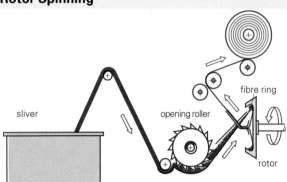

sliver | opening roller | fibre ring | rotor

1: Principle of rotor spinning

2: Rotor yarn

Rotor spinning **(Figure 1)** is growing in importance because it does not require the production of a roving and it is capable of producing yarn up to seven times faster than ring spinning.

The rotor spinning frame is fed with card or drawframe sliver. The sliver is opened up practically to single fibres and simultaneously cleaned. The fibres are deposited as a consolidated ring of the required thickness in a spinning rotor by the centrifugal effect. The open end of a seed yarn is used to withdraw the ring continuously whilst the rotor inserts twist into the withdrawn strand. Spinning systems in which the yarn is assembled at such an open end are called Open-End or OE spinning systems.

Rotor yarns **(Figure 2)** have a different character from ring yarns. The fibres are not so well oriented and are frequently wrapped around the yarn in "belts". They are not as smooth and as strong as ring yarns but usually are more uniform in their properties. Rotor yarns can not be spun as fine as ring yarns.

Bast Fibre Spinning Systems

The hackled flax, or hemp is formed into a sliver on a spreading machine. This is then subjected to several passages of doubling and drawing on gill boxes to improve its regularity. A lightly twisted roving is made on a flyer frame and the roving is converted into yarn either on a wet or a dry spinning frame.

Dry spinning can be used only for medium and coarse yarns. It is not possible to draft the dry roving out to a fine strand because the fibre ultimates are held together by the natural cement.

During wet spinning, the natural cement is dissolved by hot water so that the roving can be drawn out much finer.

Silk Spinning

Spun Silk, Schappe Silk

Spun silk yarns are made from the waste from the silk reeling process. The best waste is sorted, washed and degummed, then spun by a combed yarn process into high quality yarns.

Noil or Bourette Silk

Waste from the spun silk process, perhaps mixed with small quantities of fibres recovered from fabric waste, are spun into relatively coarse, irregular yarns on the condenser system.

Man-made Fibre Spinning

Man-made fibres can also be spun on short staple spinning systems. The opening and cleaning processes are much shorter and less severe.

Converter System

The continuous filament tow is converted into a staple fibre top by breaking or cutting the filaments. The high degree of orientation of the fibres is preserved to a large extent and is further improved by drawing processes.

The resulting slivers can be spun, either alone or after mixing with other fibre types, by any of the spinning systems described above.

Direct Spinning

In this system the continuous filament tow is converted into a staple fibre yarn in a single process by drawing and breaking on a special drawframe, followed by twisting and winding.

Blended yarns can not be made on this system.

2 Yarns	2.3 Folded Yarns, Plied Yarns

Folded or plied yarns are made by twisting together at least two single yarns, in order to:

- improve the strength
- improve the regularity
- make heavier structures
- achieve special effects

The direction of twisting is designated as S or Z, just as in single yarns. Normally the folding twist is in the opposite direction to that of the single yarns.

Folding twist may be soft, normal, or hard, according to the number of turns per metre compared to that in the single components. Balanced twist is when the folding twist is approximately equal and opposite to the singles.

Cabled yarns are made by twisting together folded yarns.

1: Folded yarn

Folded Yarns

Folded yarns are made in a single process step, combining 2, 3 or more single yarns into one by twisting them together.

2: Two-fold or two-ply	**3: Three-fold or three-ply**	**4: Four-fold or four-ply**

Cabled Yarns

Cabled yarns require more than one twisting stage. Two or more folded yarns may be twisted together to form a cabled yarn.

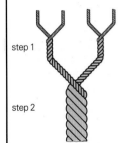   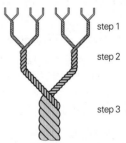

step 1
step 2
step 3

step 1
step 2

5: Two-fold, two-fold	**6: Two-fold, three-fold**	**7: Three-fold, two-fold**	**8: Two-fold, two-fold, two-fold**

Core Yarns

Core yarns are multi-component yarns in which one of the components, the core, stays at the centre of the yarn whilst the others cover it.

Core

Core yarns have long been used for burnt out effects in woven fabrics. The covering component is made from a different material from the core and can be selectively removed, according to a printed pattern.

Stretch fabrics can be made from core yarns in which the core is an elastane filament and the covering is made from natural fibre yarn.

Core-spun yarns are made by covering a core filament yarn with staple fibres in a single spinning process.

Sewing threads are often made from core yarns or core-spun yarns. The synthetic filament core gives high strength whilst the cover yarn or covering fibres prevent the needle from overheating and protect the core from softening or melting at the needle during high-speed sewing.

9: Core yarn

2 Yarns	2.4 Fancy Yarns

In the design of textile products, yarns are first selected on the basis of their mechanical properties such as strength, extensibility, elasticity, etc. Choices may also be made on the basis of the so-called physiological properties such as vapour permeability and moisture transport. Mechanical and physiological properties are governed mainly by the type of fibre, the fibre length, and the spinning system.

However, yarns may also be selected for their appearance. Special types of yarns, both single and folded, can be created to give particular optical effects.

Colour Effects

Mixture or Ingrain yarns are made by mixing fibres of different colours during spinning. This results in a heather effect. Fabric example: marengo.

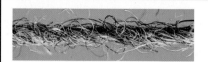

Melange or Vigoureux yarns are spun from combed sliver or top which has been printed with stripes. The appearance is somewhat like mixture.

Mottle or Marl yarns are made by spinning from two-colour rovings or from two rovings of different colours. The appearance is like mouliné but with less sharp contrast.

Jaspé or Mouliné yarns are made by folding two or more differently coloured yarns, or yarns made from different fibres with different dyeing behaviour. They give a mottled appearance. Fabric example: fresco.

Structure Effects

Slub yarns are single or folded yarns having long thick places, regularly or irregularly disposed. The slub effect is made either in spinning or in folding. Fabrics may have the character of linen or wild silk which is favoured in furnishings.

Bourette or Knop yarns are folded yarns containing short, often coloured bunches of fibres or yarn at regular or irregular intervals. The knops may be formed during carding, during spinning, or during folding. Fabrics have a structured surface. Example: Donegal tweed.

Bouclé or Loop yarns are compound yarns made by a special folding process which results in wavy or looped projections. Fabrics have a more or less grainy handle and a textured surface. Examples: bouclé, frisé, frotté.

Chenille is a cut pile yarn, it is soft and voluminous. These yarns are made by cutting special fabrics into strips. They are used in furnishing fabrics and knitwear.

Crêpe yarns are used to make fabrics with a wrinkled surface and a sandy handle. They are made from highly twisted yarns. Fabric examples: crêpe de chine, georgette, crepon, marocain.

Lustre Effects

Matt/Lustre effects are obtained by mixing matt and bright fibres. **Lustre and Glitter** effects can also be obtained by the use of metal fibres (uncommon today) or metallised plastic films (e.g. Lurex), or clear films, or man-made fibres with special cross-sections. Fabric examples: brocade, lamé.

Texturing

Flat continuous filament yarns made from thermoplastic (heat-formable) materials can be made permanently bulky by various processes. This is called texturing and it results in:

- increased volume
- increased extensibility and elasticity
- lower lustre
- better thermal insulation due to the enclosed air
- higher vapour permeability and moisture transport
- softer and more comfortable fabrics

Important Texturing Processes

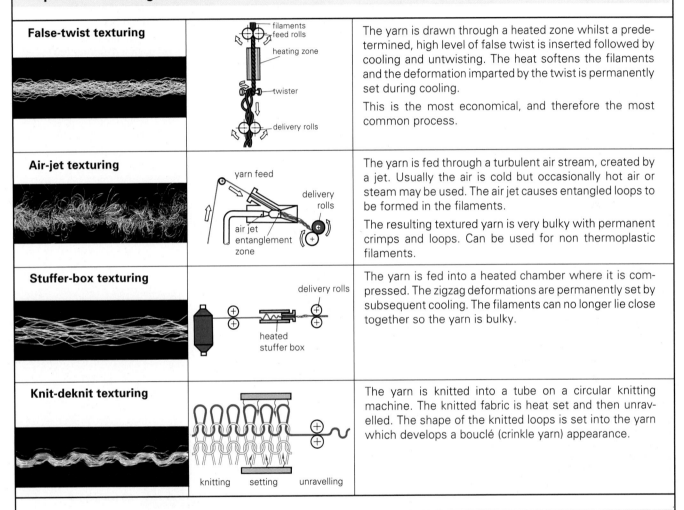

False-twist texturing	The yarn is drawn through a heated zone whilst a predetermined, high level of false twist is inserted followed by cooling and untwisting. The heat softens the filaments and the deformation imparted by the twist is permanently set during cooling.
	This is the most economical, and therefore the most common process.
Air-jet texturing	The yarn is fed through a turbulent air stream, created by a jet. Usually the air is cold but occasionally hot air or steam may be used. The air jet causes entangled loops to be formed in the filaments.
	The resulting textured yarn is very bulky with permanent crimps and loops. Can be used for non thermoplastic filaments.
Stuffer-box texturing	The yarn is fed into a heated chamber where it is compressed. The zigzag deformations are permanently set by subsequent cooling. The filaments can no longer lie close together so the yarn is bulky.
Knit-deknit texturing	The yarn is knitted into a tube on a circular knitting machine. The knitted fabric is heat set and then unravelled. The shape of the knitted loops is set into the yarn which develops a bouclé (crinkle yarn) appearance.

Types of Textured Yarns

Whatever the texturing process used, textured yarns can be classified into three groups:

Stretch yarns: Highly elastic yarns with a crimp extension of 150 to 300%.

Stabilized yarns: Yarns which have been given an additional setting treatment to reduce their elasticity and crimp extension.

Bulked yarns: Voluminous yarns with crimps and loops having normal extensibility and elasticity. The term bulked yarn is used generally to cover all continuous filament textured yarns and bulked staple fibre yarns.

High-bulk yarns

Man-made staple fibres can also be made into bulky, voluminous yarns. Such high-bulk yarns are usually made by blending acrylic fibres of high and low potential shrinkage. During a subsequent heat treatment, the high-shrinkage fibres contract causing the other fibres to buckle. A similar effect can be obtained by using bicomponent fibres.

Applications for Textured Yarns

Stockings and tights, swimwear, sportswear, outerwear, underwear, carpets, sewing and overedge stitching threads for extensible fabrics.

2 Yarns	2.6 Yarn Numbering

In textile and clothing manufacture, a wide range of yarns is used, from coarse to very fine. The appearance and the properties of fabrics are influenced by the fineness of the yarns. Yarn fineness is indicated by a number which is based on the relationship between weight and length.

This method of expressing fineness is called yarn numbering.

Numbering Systems			
Direct Systems		**Indirect Systems**	
Number of mass units per unit of length.		Number of length units per unit of mass.	
titre[1] tex Tt	**titre denier Td (den)**	**Metric Number Nm**	**English Number, cotton Ne$_c$**
mass in grams (g) length = 1 km	mass in grams (g) length = 9 km	length in metres (m) mass = 1 gram (g)	length in hanks[2] mass = 1 pound (lb)[3]

Tex System

Although all of the above yarn numbering systems (and many others) are used in certain areas, the tex system is the only one which is internationally standardised.

Tex is the mass of a yarn per km of its length. The unit g/km has been given the name tex.

20 tex means that 1 km of yarn has a mass of 20 g.
50 tex means that 1 km of yarn has a mass of 50 g.

$$Tt \text{ (tex)} = \frac{\text{mass (g)}}{\text{length (km)}}$$

the finer the yarn,
the smaller the number

Example: A yarn with a length of 2.5 km has a mass of 40 g.

$$Tt \text{ (tex)} = \frac{\text{mass (g)}}{\text{length (km)}} = \frac{40 \text{ g}}{2.5 \text{ km}} = 16 \text{ g/km} \rightarrow 16 \text{ tex}$$

For very fine or very coarse yarns, the prefixes **Deci** or **Kilo** can be used.

Examples: 50 dtex means that 1 km of yarn has a mass of 50 dg. $Tt = \dfrac{50 \text{ dg}}{1 \text{ km}} = 50 \text{ dtex}$

50 ktex means that 1 km of yarn has a mass of 50 kg. $Tt = \dfrac{50 \text{ kg}}{1 \text{ km}} = 50 \text{ ktex}$

For folded and cabled yarns, the individual yarns are indicated, followed by a multiplication sign and the number of components. **Examples:**

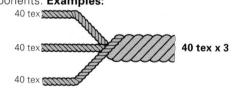

40 tex x 3

20 tex x 3 x 2

1: **Three-ply yarn made from 40 tex singles**   2: **Cabled yarn made from six 20 tex singles**

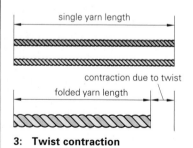

single yarn length

contraction due to twist

folded yarn length

3: **Twist contraction**

In the second example, the final yarn count might be estimated as 20 tex x 3 x 2 = 120 tex. However this answer would not be correct because the cabled yarn is shorter than the individual single yarns due to the effect of twisting. Depending on the twist density, the actual yarn number could be e.g. 132 tex. This is called the resultant yarn number and is indicated by the letter R. In this example, the designation would be R 132 tex/3/2; 20 tex or, alternatively 20 tex x 3 x 2; R 132.

[1] titre = linear density
[2] 1 hank = 840 yards; 1 yard = 91.44 cm
[3] 1lb = 454 g

2 Yarns	**2.6 Yarn Numbering**

Denier (Td)

Denier was originally used for silk yarn numbering but is now applied to all filament yarns.

Td is the mass (g) of 9 km of yarn. Td 12 means that 9 km of yarn has a mass of 12 g.

$$Td = 9 \; \frac{mass\ (g)}{length\ (km)}$$ or $Td = 9 \cdot Tt$ (tex)   the finer the yarn
the smaller the number

Example: A yarn with a length of 3 km has a mass of 5 g

$$Td = 9 \cdot \frac{mass\ (g)}{length\ (km)} = 9 \cdot \frac{5\ g}{3\ km} = 15\ g/km \rightarrow Td\ 15\ or\ 15\ den$$

Metric Number (Nm)

The metric number is the length in metres of 1 gram of yarn.

$$Nm = \frac{length\ (m)}{mass\ (g)}$$ the finer the yarn
the larger the number

Nm 40 means that 40 m of yarn has a mass of 1 gram; Nm 100 means that 100 m of yarn has a mass of 1 g.

For folded yarns the singles yarn number is usually followed by a solidus (/) and the number of components. **Examples:**

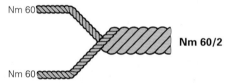

Nm 60
Nm 60
Nm 60/2

Nm 20
Nm 20
Nm 20
Nm 20
Nm 20
Nm 20
Nm 20/2/3

1: **Two-ply yarn made from Nm 60 singles**   2: **Cabled yarn made from six Nm 20 singles**

English Number, Cotton (Ne$_C$)

The English cotton number is the number of hanks, each of 840 yards, per pound (lb) of yarn.

$$Ne_C = \frac{length\ (hanks)}{mass\ (pounds)}$$

For folded yarns, the singles yarn number is followed by a solidus (/) and the number of components.

Numbering of Sewing Threads

Unfortunately there is no coherent and rationalised system of numbering for sewing threads.

Threads made from silk, man-made fibres and wrapped yarns are usually designated by metric number (Nm 70/3; Nm 80/3; Nm 120/3; Nm 120/2). If the number of components is not given, then it is always the most common, three-ply yarn.

With cotton threads the English number is used (Ne$_C$ 50/3; Ne$_C$ 40/3). The number of components often is not given but usually is three. If it is not three, then the yarn number given is chosen so that division by three will give the number of the single yarn component, e.g.:

Ticket number	Yarn number	Component
No. 60	Ne$_C$ 60/3	ca. Ne 20
No. 60/4	Ne$_C$ 80/4	ca. Ne 20
No. 60/2	Ne$_C$ 40/2	ca. Ne 20

3: **Sewing thread tickets**

2.7 Review of Yarn Types

	Yarn Type, Fibres	Features, Properties	Applications
Staple Yarns			
	Worsted wool, fine hairs, mixtures (longer fibres)	fine, smooth, regular, short fibres are combed out, harder twist, compact, strong	high quality, smart suits, costumes and dress-goods, e.g. gaberdine, Cool Wool, mousseline, fine knits
	Woollen wool, fine hairs, mixtures (shorter fibres)	rough, irregular, hairy, coarse, less well-ordered yarn structure, softer twist, voluminous, higher short fibre content	rustic suitings and costume fabrics, bulky jacket and coat fabrics, e.g. loden, fleece, shetland, tweed, heavy knits
	Ring spun, combed cotton and blends	fine, smooth, regular, short fibres are combed out, firm twist, compact, high quality	fine and superfine dresses, blouses and washable fabrics, e.g. batiste, damask, satin, zephyr; fine knits
	Ring spun, carded cotton and blends	less fine, relatively regular, voluminous, softer twist, matt, less well-ordered yarn structure, contains short fibres	medium to heavy weight washable fabrics, workwear, furnishings, e.g. calico, cretonne, drill; knitted fabrics
	Rotor-spun cotton and blends	textured surface due to less well-organised yarn structure, coarser, voluminous, harder twist, matt, contains short fibres	medium to coarse cotton fabrics, e.g. twills, denims
	Spun silk longer waste from the silk reeling process (5...10 cm)	similar to worsted yarns: long staple fibres, regular, fine, lustrous, strong	fine to heavy silk fabrics for shirts, blouses, nightwear, underwear and bedsheets, e.g. tulle, sewing threads.
	Noil silk (bourette) noils from the spun silk process	like woollen yarns: irregular, rough, neppy, dull, short fibres, voluminous	coarse and neppy silk fabrics for outerwear and furnishings, e.g. bourette
Filament Yarns			
	Raw silk, Net silk continuous filament silk from the central part of the cocoons; several cocoons are reeled together (multi-filament)	very fine, smooth, extremely regular, low twist (very lustrous) to high twist (matt); many fine filaments	fine fabrics for dresses, blouses, ties; e.g. pongee, organza, taffeta, satin, twill; folded for button-hole thread
	Monofilament single filament, spun from a single-hole spinneret; mainly nylon, polyester, or elastomeric	hard, stiff, smooth, fine to coarse (depending on spinneret size) usually colourless (transparent), lustrous; a single filament	transparent sewing yarns, mesh, bristles, nets, filter cloths, sieves
	Multi-filament, flat a group of filaments spun from one multi-hole spinneret; cellulosic or synthetic man-made fibres	smooth, compact, dense, regular, low twist (lustrous) to high twist (duller); many fine filaments	linings, dresses and blouses, ties, squares, lingerie, net drapes; e.g. taffeta, satin, locknit, duchesse, twill, voile
	Multi-filament, textured usually thermoplastic filaments of synthetic man-made fibres or triacetate	more or less crimped, bulky, voluminous, firm, elastic; many fine filaments	stretch yarns, bulk yarns for overedge sewing, socks, stockings, dresses and blouses, swimwear

Yarn Properties

The performance of textile fabrics and clothing is strongly influenced by the properties of the yarns from which they are made. Sewing threads require certain yarn properties.

Regularity Smooth fabrics should be sewn only with very regular yarns. In spun yarns, this is achieved by repeated doubling and drafting, and by combing out the short fibres.

Strength Yarn strength depends on the quality of the fibres, the yarn regularity and the twist. Folding increases the strength.

Hardness/Twist The twist density affects the hardness of a yarn and hence the handle and the appearance of textiles.

Extensibility/ Elasticity Extensibility and elasticity are very important during yarn processing and utilisation. They are determined mainly by the fibre type and the spinning system.

Sewing Threads

Yarn Type	Remarks	Applications
Cotton	Usually high quality, combed, ring spun, folded yarns; bleached, dyed, singed, mercerized and lubricated. Typically 7.4...84 tex.	Almost any sewings on cotton fabrics.
Silk	Doubled and folded silk filament yarns; dyed and lubricated. 14...80 tex.	Fancy button holes.
Spun silk	Folded spun silk yarns; dyed and lubricated. 8.2...33 tex.	Almost any sewings on wool and silk fabrics.
Polyester	Spun polyester folded yarns; heat set, dyed and lubricated. 7...33 tex.	Sewings on almost any fabric.
Monofilament	Usually transparent polyester. 7...100 tex.	Blind stitchings.
Textured yarns	Textured multi-filament yarns; dyed and lubricated. 18...80 tex.	Covering seams and cut fabric edges.
Core-spun yarns	Expensive threads with a core of continuous filament polyester wrapped by, or folded with cotton. The polyester is for strength whilst the cotton helps to keep the sewing needle cool. 6.6...33 tex.	All types of sewing, especially on high-speed machines.

Packaging

Sewing threads are offered on several different types of package. The type of package depends on the application area (home sewing, needlecraft, industry). Yarn length may be from 20 to 20000 metres.

Spools

Cross-wound cops

Cross-wound cones

Vicones

3 Textile Fabrics   3.1 Overview

Textile fabrics can be made from fibres by various routes.

```
                    ┌──────────────────┐
                    │ Textile Fabrics  │
                    └──────────────────┘
          ┌──────────────────┼──────────────────┐
    ┌───────────┐      ┌───────────┐      ┌──────────────┐
    │   Yarns   │      │  Fibres   │      │ Combinations │
    └───────────┘      └───────────┘      └──────────────┘
```

wovens
knits
braids
open-work
stitched

non wovens
(felted, needled,
adhesive-bonded)

stitch-bonded
laminated

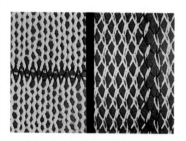

1: Woven fabric

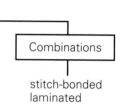

2: Knitted fabrics

Woven fabrics are made by the inter-leaving of two sets of yarns, disposed at right angles.

Knitted fabrics are made by the inter-locking of loops. In weft knitted fabrics, the loops are formed by yarns traversing across the fabric width. In warp knitted fabrics the loops are formed by a set of yarns disposed along the fabric length.

3: Open-work fabric

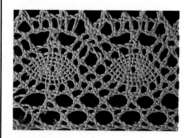

4: Braid

Open-work fabrics such as lace and net can be made by various techniques such as leno, bobbinet, and warp knit-ting.

Braid is made by the interleaving of at least three yarns in a diagonal pattern.

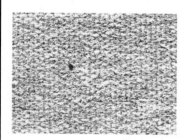

5: Needle felt

6: Wool felt

Nonwoven fabrics are made directly from fibres, with no intermediate yarn stage.

Webs, or batts are given strength by mechanical entanglement or adhesive bonding of the fibres.

Wool felts are made by the entangle-ment of wool or other animal hairs by the felting action of heat, moisture, and agitation.

7: Stitched fabric

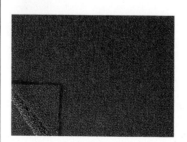

8: Laminated fabric

Stitch bonding can be used to make fabrics from several types of fibre as-sembly, including webs, slivers, rovings or yarns.

Laminated fabrics are made by the adhesive bonding of two or more fab-rics, or by bonding fabrics to foam, film, or paper.

3.2.1 Woven Fabric Manufacture

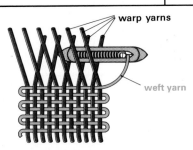

1: Principle of weaving

Weaving is the name given to the interleaving of two sets of yarns, warp and weft, at right angles.

The **warp** yarns are those which lie in the length direction of a fabric whilst it is being woven.

The **weft** or **filling** yarns are those which, during weaving, are introduced between the warp yarns, across the width direction of the fabric.

Warp yarns are usually stronger than weft because they have to sustain larger stresses during weaving.

Principle of Shaft Weaving

The warp sheet passes over the back rest roller and lease rods, through heald shafts and reed, and over the breast beam to the cloth roller. The heald eyes of each heald shaft are threaded in a set pattern (**Figure 2**) e.g. yarns 1, 3, 5, 7, 9 etc. or 2, 4, 6, 8, etc. By raising and lowering the healds a shed is formed in the warp yarns, through which the weft yarn can be drawn. For a plain weave at least two shafts are needed. After the weft has been introduced the reed beats it up into the fell of the cloth. The range of patterns which can be woven on a shaft loom is limited by the number of shafts which can be accommodated in the machine.

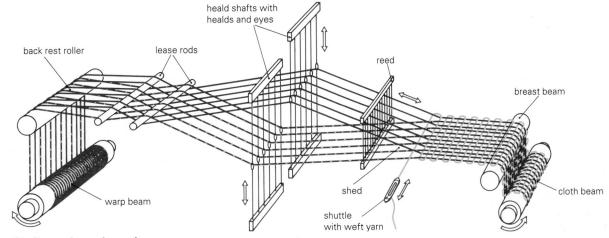

2: Shaft weaving: schematic

Principle of Jacquard Weaving

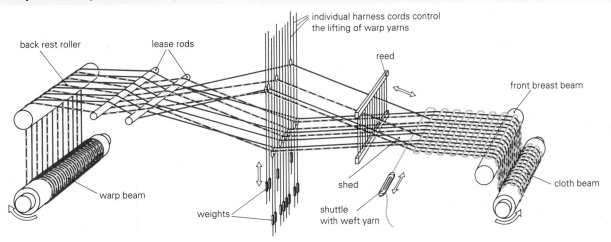

3: Jacquard weaving: schematic

The lifting of each warp yarn can be controlled individually. This is effected by either a punched card or an electronic control system, according to the required weaving pattern.

The technique is named after its inventor J.M. Jacquard (1755-1834), a silk weaver of Lyon. The name "jacquard pattern" is now often used for any woven or knitted design with a large or intricate figured pattern.

3.2.1 Woven Fabric Manufacture

Weaving Preparation

Before weaving, the warp and weft yarns are subjected to several preparation processes.

Winding	Warping	Sizing, Slashing	Drawing in
Large cross-wound cones can be prepared by the spinner; otherwise they are made in the weaving preparation room. Weft bobbins have to be wound if shuttle weaving machines are to be used.	A definite number of warp yarns is wound onto a beam with a defined width and density. Warping may be carried out directly (direct beaming) or indirectly, in sections (sectional warping).	Sizing is used to protect the warp from the rigours of weaving. The size is a film-forming polymer such as starch and is applied from a solution. The warp yarns are made smoother, stronger, and more resistant to abrasion.	The warp yarns are drawn, in the correct order, through the heald eyes or the jacquard harness, and then through the reed.

Weft Insertion

The weft can be introduced into the shed by means of a shuttle, a projectile, a gripper, an air jet or a water jet.

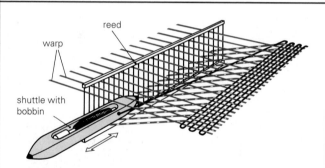

1: Weft insertion by shuttle

The weft bobbin is transported through the shed by a shuttle. The shuttle travels back and forth in both directions, thus forming a solid edge to the fabric.

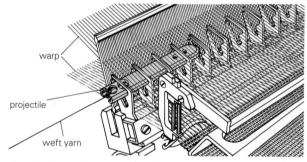

2: Weft insertion by projectile

The small gripper-projectile is supplied with yarn from a weft cone and carries it through the shed, always in the same direction. The weft has to be cut and separately secured at the fabric edge. The lower height of the shed and the smaller mass of the projectile allow an increase in production speed.

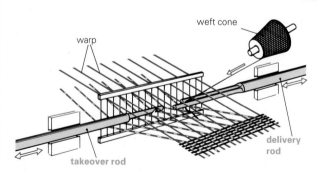

3: Weft insertion by rapier

A delivery rod with a gripper takes the yarn from the weft cone and transports it to the centre of the shed where it is accepted by a takeover rod and drawn to the opposite side. As with the projectile machine, the end of the weft yarn has to be secured at the selvedge.

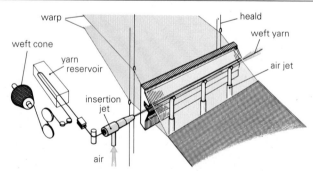

4: Weft insertion by jets

In this system the required length of weft yarn is held loosely in a reservoir and is projected through the shed by a jet of air or water. With air jet machines, there are several booster jets along the yarn path.

3.2.2 Principles of Cloth Construction

The pattern of interlacings of the warp and weft yarns is called the cloth **construction**.

The diagrammatic representation of a construction is called a **pattern draft** or **point paper design**. It is marked and read from bottom left to top right. The vertical columns represent the warp yarns; horizontal rows represent the weft. A mark placed in any cell indicates that the warp is lifted over the weft at that intersection. Absence of a mark indicates the reverse (warp remains below weft). Each cell represents one **interlacing** of warp and weft. The smallest number of cells which can specify a given construction is called the **repeat**. A pattern draft usually contains several repeats. The interlacing of the yarns may also be represented by a **fabric section**. When a yarn is not interlaced over several cells, it forms a **float**.

Basic Weave Constructions

	Plain Weave Each warp yarn is lifted over alternate weft yarns. Neighbouring warp yarns lift in the opposite sense.	**Twill Weave** This construction makes a pattern of diagonal lines. Each warp yarn lifts over (and/or remains under) more than one weft. Adjacent warp yarns make the same lifting pattern, but displaced by one cell.	**Satin Weave** The warp floats over four or more wefts and remains under only one. Adjacent warps have their floats arranged as randomly as possible, so no twill line is generated.
Interlacings			
Pattern draft Repeat			
New condensed notation after DIN 61 101 (suitable for EDP)	Pattern drafts can also be represented numerically. A new system of notation codifies information on the weave type, warp lifting pattern, number of ends lifting together, and move number. $\boxed{10} - \boxed{01\ 01} - \boxed{01} - \boxed{00}$ **Construction** 10 plain 20 twill 30 satin — **Lifting pattern** of the first warp yarn — **Number of adjacent warp yarns** with identical lifting pattern. — **Move number**. The number of weft yarns by which the lifting pattern of each subsequent warp yarn must be displaced, always reading from bottom left to top right. 00 means weaving oppositely.		
Old notation	$P\dfrac{1}{1}$	$T\dfrac{1}{2}Z$	$S\dfrac{4}{1}$ (3)
	The old notation starts with a code letter for the weave type, e.g. P = plain, T = twill, S = satin. The numbers above the line represent the warp lifting; below the line, the warp threads remaining under the weft. For twill weaves, a letter indicates the direction of the twill line, e.g. Z direction. A satin weave is supplemented by the move number in parentheses, showing by how many weft yarns the lifting pattern of the next warp yarn must be displaced.		

Plain Weave

10 – 01 01 – 01 – 00

1: Pattern draft

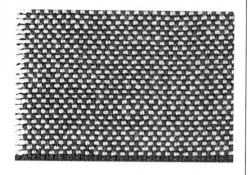

2: Plain weave fabric

Plain weave is the simplest and the tightest method of interlacing warp and weft. Each warp yarn passes alternately over and under each weft. The interlacing is opposite in all neighbouring cells. The repeat is over two ends and two picks. Opposite sides of the fabric are the same.

Plain weave allows the highest possible number of interlacings which, depending on the fibre and yarn type, the thread density and the finishing, can yield fabrics with high abrasion resistance and resistance to yarn slippage. Batiste, cambric, donegal, fresco, honan, muslin, taffeta, voile are all plain weave fabrics.

Elaborations of Plain Weave

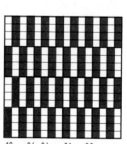

10 – 04 04 – 01 – 00

3: Pattern draft

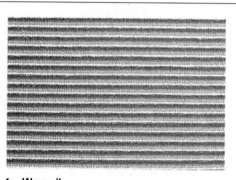

4: Warp rib

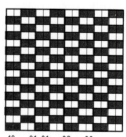

10 – 01 01 – 02 – 00

5: Pattern draft

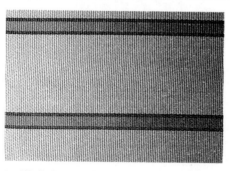

6: Weft rib

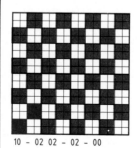

10 – 02 02 – 02 – 00

7: Pattern draft

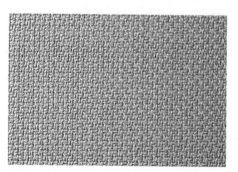

8: Hopsack

Ribs

A rib fabric is one whose surface shows raised lines or ridges.

Warp rib

A rib running across the fabric width is obtained with a high density of warp ends, when two or more weft picks are placed in each shed (**Figure 3**). The warp yarn is usually finer than the weft and covers the surface of the fabric. Hence the name warp rib (**Figure 4**).

A ribbed appearance can also be obtained in plain weave by using coarse weft and fine warp yarns.

The properties and the appearance are determined by the fibre and yarn qualities used in the warp, since this predominates on both sides of the fabric.

Commercial styles: ottoman, rib.

Weft rib

Ribs running the length of the cloth are obtained with a high weft density, by alternately raising and lowering two or more warp ends over and under the weft picks, with the same number of adjacent ends doing the opposite (**Figure 5**). The high density of weft results in a lower weaving production rate, so these fabrics are not very common.

The properties and appearance depend primarily on the nature of the weft yarns (**Figure 6**).

Hopsacks

Hopsacks have a checkered appearance, made by alternately raising and lowering two or more warp ends over and under the same number of weft picks, with the same number of adjacent ends doing the opposite (**Figures 7 and 8**).

Commercial styles: hopsack, matt, basket.

3.2.3 Basic Weaves and Variations

Twill Weave

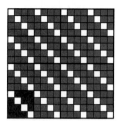

20 – 03 01 – 01 – 03

1: Pattern draft

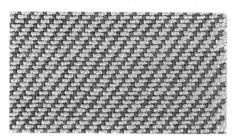

2: Warp-faced twill

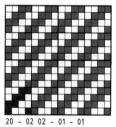

20 – 01 03 – 01 – 01

3: Pattern draft

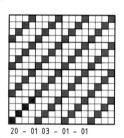

4: Weft-faced twill

The **twill order** of interlacing causes diagonal lines to appear in the fabric. The lines may run to the right (Z direction) or to the left (S direction). On the back of the fabric the twill line runs in the opposite direction and may be less distinct.

The smallest repeat size for twill weave is three warp and three weft threads. The twill line is created by floats between interlacing points which move one cell upwards (or downwards) on adjacent threads.

Warp-faced twills show a predominance of warp yarns on the face.

Weft-faced twills (twillette) have more weft than warp showing on the face.

Twill fabrics can be made soft and loose or smooth, dense, and durable depending on the fabric construction and thread density.

Typical twill fabrics are cavalry, denim, diagonal, drill, gaberdine, serge, tweed, tricotine, whipcord.

Elaborations of Twill Weave

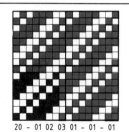

20 – 02 02 – 01 – 01

5: Pattern draft

6: Balanced twill

Balanced Twills

In balanced twills, the warp and weft floats are of equal sizes and the face and back of the cloth look the same, apart from the direction of the twill line.

Commercial styles: twill, sheeting.

20 – 01 02 03 01 – 01 – 01

7: Pattern draft

8: Diagonal

Diagonals

Diagonals are larger twills with two or more twill lines of differing widths. Can be warp-faced, weft-faced, or balanced.

Commercial styles: diagonal, cavalry.

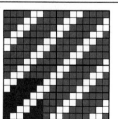

20 – 04 02 – 01 – 01

9: Pattern draft

10: Broad twill

Broad Twills

Broad twills show a very broad twill line. Warp floats usually cover more than two cells and weft floats at least two. Can be balanced or unbalanced.

Developments of Twill Weave

The basic twill weave is capable of far broader and richer development than plain weave. The form of the twill line can be extensively modified not only by variations in construction but also by colour and material effects.

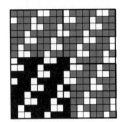

20 – 05 01 01 02 – 01 – 02

1: Pattern draft

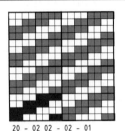

2: Steep twill

Steep Twill

With equal densities of warp and weft, the simple twills display a twill line of about 45°. A steeper twill line can be obtained either by increasing the relative density of the warp or by using a move number of two in the pattern, or by special constructions.

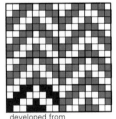

20 – 02 02 – 02 – 01

3: Pattern draft

4: Flattened twill

Flattened Twill

Flattened twills are usually weft-faced, which means that the twill line is formed by the weft yarn and the warp is mainly on the back of the fabric. Usually, the weft floats are longer than the move number which, in turn, is greater than one.

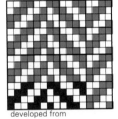

developed from
20 – 02 02 – 01 – 01

5: Pattern draft

6: Herringbone

Herringbone

This is made by reversing the direction of the twill at regular intervals. At the reversal, the pattern is displaced by one or more cells, so that the twill lines do not meet in a point. The pattern can be emphasised by using different colours for warp and weft.

developed from
20 – 02 02 – 01 – 01

7: Pattern draft

8: Waved twill

Waved Twill

By changing the direction of the twill line at regular intervals a wave, or zigzag effect can be created either across the fabric or along its length. Diamond checks can also be made. The twill lines come to a point at the reversals.

developed from
20 – 02 02 – 01 – 01

9: Pattern draft

10: Broken twill

Broken Twill

Broken twills are formed by reversing the pattern part way through the repeat. Usually the break will be at the centre of the repeat, with only one reversal, but more complicated breaks can be made. The pattern can be broken either in the warp (**Figures 9 and 10**) or in the weft direction, and no twill line will be generated.

3.2.3   Basic Weaves and Variations

Satin and Sateen

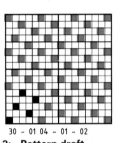

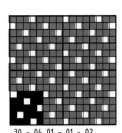

30 – 04 01 – 01 – 02
1:   Pattern draft

2:   Satin

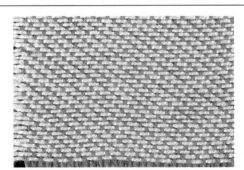

30 01 04 – 01 – 02
3:   Pattern draft

4:   Sateen

The feature of the **satin** and **sateen** weaves is a uniform distribution of the interlacings, which are never adjacent to one another. Satin and sateen repeat over at least 5 ends and 5 picks but the warp ends interlace only once per repeat. This results in the long floats which determine the appearance and the properties of these fabrics. The face and back of the fabric look quite different.

Warp satins have a predominance of warp on the face side.

The less popular **weft sateens** have the weft on the face.

Satins and sateens are smooth, uniform, and lustrous due to the scarcity of interlacings and the density of threads. A soft and supple handle and drape can be obtained with relatively loose constructions.

Commercial styles: atlas, duchesse, doeskin, satin, sateen, venetian.

Developments of Satin Weave

Variations on the satin weave are few because the interlacings must not be allowed to come close together. Patterning can be achieved by arranging for interchanging areas of satin and sateen, or by having areas of satin or sateen on a plain or twill background. Typical examples are faconné, damask, satin stripe, and many figured jacquard fabrics.

5:   Satin stripe

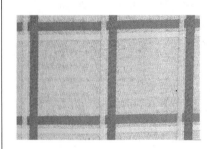

6:   Coloured satin stripe

7:   Damask

8:   Figured jacquard

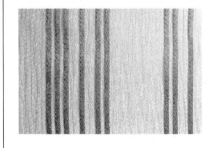

9:   Chiffon with satin stripes

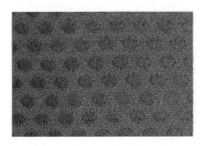

10: Satin façonné

3.2.4 Colour Woven Fabrics

Colour woven fabrics achieve their patterning effects by using dyed warp and weft yarns in various combinations. Stripes across the width are obtained by using two or more colours in the weft; length-way stripes by using multi-coloured warps. Checks and small figures use colours in both directions.

1: Chambray

2: Fil-á-fil (end-on-end)

Chambray

The whole warp is a different colour from the weft. A shimmering effect can be obtained by using filament yarns (changeant, shot silk).

Fil-á-fil (end-on-end)

Dark and light yarns alternate in both warp and weft. With a 2/2 twill construction a miniature staircase effect results.

3: Pin stripe

4: Oxford

Pin Stripe

Fine lines are formed by the use of individual light-coloured ends on a darker monotone background.

Oxford

A plain weave base but with two ends weaving as one and with different colours in warp and weft. Gives a tiny checkered appearance.

5: Tartan

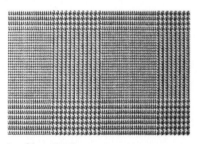

6: Glen check

Tartan

Large squares of colour overlaid by warp and weft stripes, from coloured warp and weft. The patterns and colours derive from traditional Scottish dress.

Glen Check

Glen check is made on a 2/2 twill base by having dark and white threads and a colouring order of n sets of 4:4 followed by 2n sets of 2:2 in both directions.

7: Pepita

8: Houndstooth

Shepherd's Check

Small checks in contrasting colours, usually on a 2/2 twill base with 4:4, 6:6 or 8:8 colouring. Thought to derive from the black and white checked plaids once worn by Scottish shepherds. Also made in 4/4 twill and 4/4 basket weave.

Pepita and houndstooth are particular types based on 2/2 twill. The former is said to be named after a Spanish actress and does not show the prominent jagged edges to the squares which are a feature of houndstooth.

Crêpe fabrics have a grainy, irregular surface texture which is obtained by various means, including high twist yarns, special weave constructions, and special finishing processes or combinations of these.

Crêpe Yarn

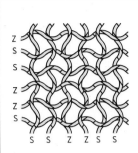

1: Yarn arrangement
   in a full crêpe

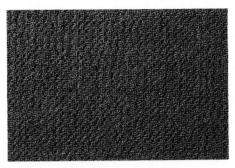

2: Crêpe georgette

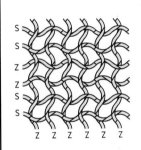

3: Yarn arrangement
   in a half-crêpe

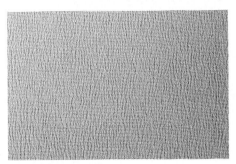

4: Crêpe marocain

Crêpe-yarn fabrics are made from highly twisted yarns (crêpe yarns). The fabric is light and soft with an irregular and finely textured surface and a sandy handle.

Full crêpe is made with crêpe yarns in both directions **(Figure 1)**. The weave is either a plain or crêpe construction. Commercial styles: crêpe georgette **(Figure 2)**, chiffon.

Half crêpe has crêpe yarns in only one direction, usually the weft.

A crêpe with a fine rib effect in the weft direction is made with a flat filament or Z twist warp and a 2:2 pattern of alternating S and Z twist crêpe yarns in the weft **(Figure 3)**. Commercial styles: crêpe de chine, crêpe marocain **(Figure 4)**.

A crêpe with a grainy texture in the warp direction is made with weft crêpe yarns all having the same twist direction. Commercial styles: crêpon, crêpe suzette, bark crêpe.

Alternating flat and crinkled stripes are made by inserting groups of crêpe yarns in the warp, woven at different tension to the normal warp yarns. A similar effect can be obtained using yarns with high shrinkage. Commercial style: seersucker.

Crêpe Weaves

5: Example of a
   crêpe weave

6: Sand crêpe

Crêpe weave fabrics have a grainy, irregular appearance. It is achieved by special weave construction techniques. Almost any weave can be rearranged, modified, or combined with another to make a crêpe weave. There should be no stripes, twill lines or long floats; the repeat is difficult to discern **(Figure 5)**.

Commercial styles: sand crêpe, moss crêpe, oatmeal crêpe.

Crêpe Finish

7: Bark crêpe

8: Plissé

Crêpe effects can also be achieved in finishing. Caustic soda solution may be printed onto cotton fabrics in a stripe or other pattern. The printed portions shrink and cause the fabric to cockle.

Commercial styles: plissé, blister, bark crêpe, seersucker.

Crêpe effects can also be obtained using an embossing calender (cf page 94).

Commercial styles: honeycomb, embossed seersucker.

By providing a third set of yarns, fabrics can be produced with higher strength and durability, greater weight and substance, additional patterning, or a special surface texture.

1: **Reversible, face and back**

2: **Lancé, face and back**

3: **Broché, face and back**

4: **Terry cloth**

Backed Cloths

Warp-backed fabrics have an additional set of warp threads which do not appear on the face. The two sides of the fabric can have a different appearance.

Commercial styles: reversible, backed fabric.

Weft-backed fabrics have an additional set of weft yarns. The binding points for the backing weft are invisible on the face. For raised fabrics, soft, low-twist, voluminous yarns are used for the backing.

Commercial styles: molleton, charmante.

Extra Warp and Extra Weft

Extra warp or **extra weft** yarns can be used on a plain, twill, or satin ground to produce small figured designs, somewhat like embroidery. The extra yarn stands out from the ground due to its figured pattern of interlacing and it usually has a distinctive colour, fibre type, or lustre.

Extra weft yields figures across the width. Extra warp gives figures along the length. Both effects can be combined.

The extra yarn produces the figure on the face side but it may float unbound on the back, depending on the yarn and fabric properties and the end-use requirements. If there are large spaces between the figures, then the extra yarn can be bound in at intervals or, if the long extra yarn floats would show through, they can be cut away from the back.

Commercial styles: lancé, clip spot.

Broché (swivel) Fabrics

Broché is an extra weft figured fabric made on a swivel loom. The figuring yarn is supplied from a series of small shuttles mounted over the weaving surface. The effect is like small embroidery patterns. This is a very expensive technique and is seldom used; usually fabrics are actually embroidered.

Commercial styles: broché.

Terry Fabrics

Terry, or loop-pile fabrics are made from two warps. The ground warp is normally or tightly tensioned, the pile warp is looser. Two or three weft yarns are introduced but are not fully beaten up into the cloth. With the next weft yarn all three or four threads are beaten up together. They slide over the tensioned ground warp but the pile warp is simultaneously slackened off so that it is bent up into a loop whose size corresponds to the final beating-up distance. Loops can be formed on one or both sides of the fabric. Pattern effects are achieved by introducing colour into the pile warp, and by having loops of different sizes.

The pile yarns can be singles or two-fold. The fabrics can be made more dense and durable by a fulling process.

Terry velour is produced by cropping and brushing the loops to give a velvet-like appearance.

Loop yarn fabric has the appearance of terry but is made from only two sets of yarns, with a loop yarn in the weft.

Cut Pile Fabrics

Cut pile fabrics are made by using the third yarn system to form a cut fibre pile on the face of the fabric. Fabrics with a short pile are called **velvet** or **velveteen**, long-pile fabrics are called **plush**.

Cut pile fabrics can be made either with an additional warp or with an additional weft. The former are velvets, the latter are velveteens.

The quality is determined by the density of the ground weave and by the height and density of the pile. There are different ways of binding the pile into the ground fabric, according to end-use requirements.

Mock velvets, such as duvetine, have a surface pile which is created by raising and brushing.

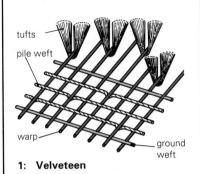

1: **Velveteen**

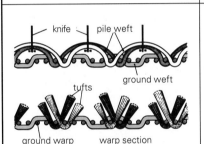

2: **Plain velveteen**

Velveteens are constructed so that the pile weft floats largely on the surface of the fabric. After cutting, the tufts are held by the warp yarns.

The density of the fabric and the pile height are determined by the interlacing pattern of ground and pile. The pile is cut in a special separate operation. It is then brushed open and cropped to a uniform height.

If the binding points for the pile yarn are uniformly distributed, then a **plain velveteen** results.

Commercial styles: velveteen.

If the pile yarns always float between the same warp yarns, then **corded velveteens** are produced after cutting.

The cords may be fine, medium or broad. Cord widths can be mixed in the same fabric.

Commercial styles: needlecord (very fine cords), corduroy.

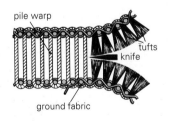

3: **Corded velveteen**

4: **Corded velveteen;
grey fabric partially cut**

Velvets are made with an additional warp and the cut fibre tufts are bound into the ground fabric by the weft.

The two main production techniques are **wire weaving** and **double plush** weaving. The latter is more economical but less uniform. Two fabrics are woven together on a special loom. The ground fabrics are independent but they share a single pile warp. The pile yarns are subsequently cut through the middle by a reciprocating knife. Thus five sets of yarns make two fabrics, each with three yarn sets.

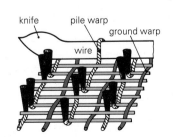

5: **Double plush**

6: **Velvet**

In **wire weaving**, the pile warp is led over either looping wires or cutting wires. When the wires are withdrawn the pile either forms loops or is cut. The pile may be cropped, to make it level then brushed and steamed.

Burned out velvets are made by printing a pattern onto the pile using a chemical which dissolves or destroys it.

7: **Wire velvet**

8: **Burned-out velvet**

Commercial styles: velvet, crushed velvet (embossed patterns), chiffon velvet (very light), panne velvet (flattened pile).

3.2.7 Fabrics with Four or More Yarn Systems

Four or more yarn systems are used to make **double cloths**. These are effectively two fabrics woven one on top of the other which are linked to each other at intervals by various techniques. Double cloths are used for greater strength, weight, and volume or to have different appearances on face and back, or for surface relief effects.

1: Double cloth, face

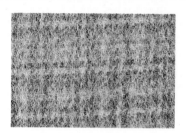

2: Double cloth, back

Self-stitched Double Cloths

Four yarn systems are used. **Warp stitching**, or tying is when the backing warp interlaces with the face weft. **Weft stitching** is when the backing weft interlaces with the face warp. The stitching is so close that the two fabrics can not be separated. The technique is often used to produce jacket and coat fabrics with an integral lining. Usually the two sides look quite different.

3: Centre warp-stitched
   double cloth

4: Centre weft-stitched
   double cloth

Centre-stitched Double Cloths

In this case, the two fabrics are stitched together by a fifth yarn system. They are softer and fuller but are less firmly united and can be pulled apart. The fabrics are suitable for making reversible garments.

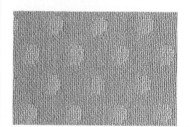

5: Double plain, face

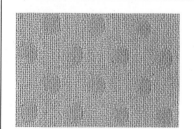

6: Double plain, back

Interchanging Double Cloths

These are double cloths in which the face and back fabrics interchange according to a specified design. The fabrics may be unstitched between the interchanges, leaving holes between the two. The pattern is the same on both sides, though they may be oppositely coloured. The fabrics may be used reversibly. They can be used for cloaks, shawls, and table cloths.

7: Cloqué, face

8: Cloqué, back

Cloqué

These are double cloths with a figured blister effect. The face fabric is made from fine yarns with normal twist. The back has crêpe yarns which are stitched to the face fabric according to a certain pattern. During wet processing, the crêpe backing fabric shrinks and causes the face fabric to crinkle. The same effect can be obtained by using high-shrink fibres in the backing fabric.

9: Matelassé, face

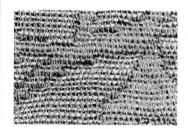

10: Matelassé, back

Matelassé

Double fabrics with a figured relief effect on the face side are called matelassé. The back cloth may be coarse. The designs are formed by floating threads or by areas of different weaves and by the stitching pattern of back to face cloth. The pattern can be emphasised by the use of additional wadding picks.

Piqué fabrics have a textured quilt-like surface.

1: Piqué, face

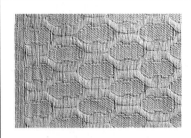

2: Piqué, back

Piqué

Nowadays, the term piqué is frequently applied to a wide range of fabrics, woven or knitted, which display a regular, prominent textured surface. The texture may be in the form of straight or wavy welts (widthways ribs), cords (lengthways ribs), or honeycomb structures.

A true piqué is a double cloth with a fine face fabric and a coarser back. The pattern of stitching is arranged to produce waved welts, welts, or small figures which can look like quilting. Extra weft, laying unbound between the two fabrics, can be used to provide a relief effect on the face. The fine stitching warp is highly tensioned to outline the pattern and press the wadding picks against the face fabric (**Figures 1 and 2**).

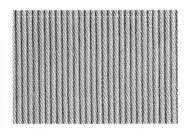

3: Piqué cord; double cloth, face

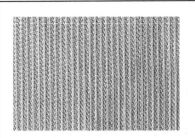

4: Piqué cord; double cloth, back

Piqué Cord

These fabrics have fine cords on the face in the length direction.

They can be made either as double cloths or single fabrics. The double cloths have a fine face fabric with a coarse wadding warp and a stitching weft on the back (**Figures 3 and 4**).

The cords in the single fabric are made by regular weft floats on the back of the fabric (**Figures 5 and 6**). They are developments of the basic bedford cord.

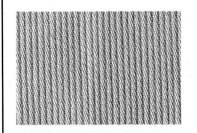

5: Piqué cord; single cloth, face

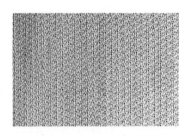

6: Piqué cord; single cloth, back

Honeycomb

Usually single cloths made by progressively lengthening and shortening both warp and weft floats to form ridges and hollows on a square pattern, to give a cellular appearance (**Figures 7 and 8**). Both sides of the fabric look the same. Sometimes called waffle or waffle piqué.

7: Honeycomb, face

8: Honeycomb, back

Bedford Cord

The basic cord weave allows a raised warp rib effect without using an extra thread system. The warp is more dense and firm so that it predominates on the face. A proportion of the weft floats on the back in a regular formation which causes the face to buckle slightly into ribs (**Figures 9 and 10**). Can also be made with wadding ends laying freely between the face cords and the back weft floats.

9: Bedford cord, face

10: Bedford cord, back

Definition after ISO 7839: 1984

Knitted fabrics are made from interlocking loops, formed from a single yarn or from many.

They are classified into weft knitted and warp knitted fabrics.

KNITTED FABRICS

WEFT KNITTED

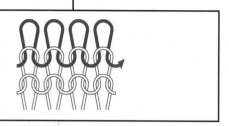

WARP KNITTED

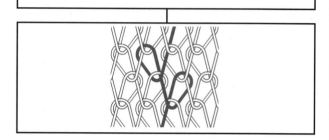

Characteristics

- May be made from a single yarn.
- The yarn is fed crosswise to the length of the fabric.
- Can be unravelled; may ladder.
- Knitting needles can work sequentially or all together.

Characteristics

- Requires a full warp sheet.
- The loop-forming yarns are fed in the direction of the length of the fabric.
- Can not be unravelled, usually does not ladder.
- Knitting needles always work together as a unit.

Production

WEFT KNITTED FABRICS		WARP KNITTED FABRICS
Sequential needles: Loops are formed in sequence across the width of the fabric. Machines can be flat or circular. Needles are usually of the latch type.	**Simultaneous needles:** All of the needles are moved together or the needles are stationary and the fabric is moved. Machines can be flat or circular. Needles are usually of the bearded type.	**Warp knitting:** Warp knitting uses one or more warp sheets. Each yarn is looped around a needle and the needles are all moved together. The needles may be of the bearded, latch, or compound type. Warp knitting machines with latch needles or compound needles are called raschel machines and the material they make is called raschel fabric.

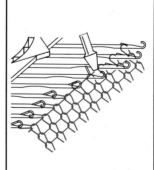

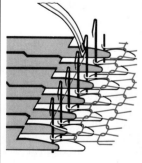

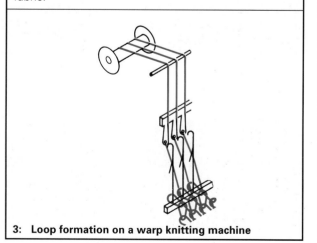

1: Sequential loop formation on a flat machine

2: Simultaneous loop formation

3: Loop formation on a warp knitting machine

Loop Formation

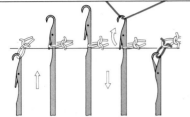

1: Latch needles

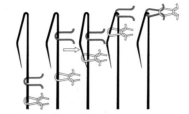

2: Bearded needles

3: Compound needles

Terminology in Weft Knitting

  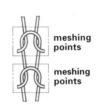

loop — head — leg — foot — meshing points — meshing points

4: Loop characteristics

The Intermeshing of Loops

The loop is the basic structural element. It comprises a **head** (the **needle loop**), **two legs**, and **two feet**. The feet joining two adjacent loops form the **sinker loop**.

Fabric is formed by intermeshing loops. Each loop has four **intermeshing points** in two pairs. The legs within a pair must always intermesh in the same sense; both legs lying either under or over the head of the preceding loop. The upper pair may intermesh in the opposite sense to the lower pair, depending on the construction.

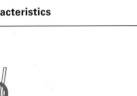

5: Back loop   **6: Face loop**

Face and Back of Knitted Loops

The lower pair of meshing points determine whether the loop is a face loop or a back loop.

A **back loop**, is formed when the loop is drawn through the previous loop in a direction away from the viewer: the legs of the loop lie under the head of the preceding loop.

A **face loop**, is formed when the loop is drawn through the previous loop in a direction towards the viewer: the legs of the loop lie over the head of the preceding loop.

Courses and Wales

A **course** is a row of loops produced by adjacent needles during the same knitting cycle.

A **wale** is a column of loops produced by the same needle on successive knitting cycles.

The size of the loop and the fineness of the yarn determine the density of courses and wales. The number of wales determines the width of the fabric, the number of courses determines it's length; their product determines the weight.

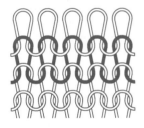 

7: A course   **8: A wale**

Tuck and Float (Miss) Loops

A **tuck stitch,** comprises a held loop and a tuck loop, both intermeshed in the same course **(Figure 9)**.

Held loop; a loop pulled through the loop of the previous course and retained by the needle over one or more courses **(Figures 9 and 11)**.

Tuck loop; a length of yarn received by a needle but not pulled through the loop of the previous course **(Figures 9 and 10)**.

Float (miss) loop, a length of yarn not received by a needle and connecting two loops of the same course that are not in adjacent wales **(Figure 11)**.

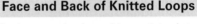

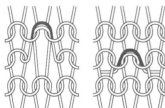 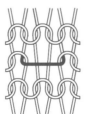

9: A tuck stitch   **10: A tuck loop**   **11: A float (or miss) loop**

Basic Weft Knitted Structures

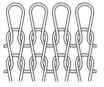
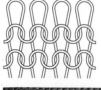
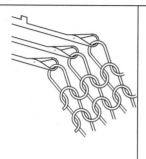

Plain, Single jersey

This structure is made with only a single set of needles. It is called single face, plain or single jersey[1].

The two sides of the fabric have a different appearance. One side shows only face loops, the other side only back loops.

It has relatively low extensibility in the width and tends to curl at the edges.

Plain jersey is used in different weights for shirts, sweaters, blouses, dresses, T-shirts, and underwear.

1: Plain, face   back   production

unravelling edge

Rib fabric

Rib fabrics are made on two needle beds with the needles in a staggered formation. The loops are drawn in opposite directions so that face and back loops alternate in each course. Both sides of the fabric show only the face loops. The back loops are exposed only when the fabric is extended in the width direction. Rib fabrics are very extensible in the width.

Applications include pullovers, waistcoats, underwear, socks.

2: Rib fabric   production

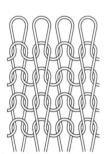

Purl fabric

Purl is usually made with double-ended latch needles, though other techniques can be used. In 1x1 purl, single courses of face and back loops alternate. Both sides of the fabric look the same with prominent course-way ribs. These are formed by the juxtaposition of the needle loops of the face course and the sinker loops of the back course.

Purl fabric has high extensibility in the length.

Applications include romper suits, pullovers and cardigans.

3: Purl fabric   production

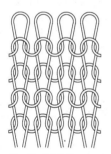
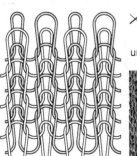

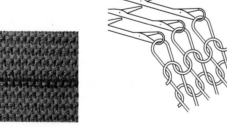

unravelling edge

Interlock

Interlock is made on two needle beds in which the needles are directly opposed and work alternately. In the fabric, the loops on one side are directly opposite those on the other. It takes two courses to make one row of loops on the face and back. Neighbouring loops in a row are displaced by half a course.

Interlock has a close surface structure. Both sides show only face loops and look identical. The fabric is extensible, but not very elastic. It is used for T-shirts, blouses, underwear, sports and leisure wear.

4: Interlock   production

[1] Jersey is a general name for knitted fabrics. It is not restricted to any particular structure.

Developments of the Single Jersey Structure

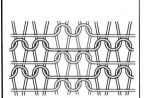

1: Jacquard, schematic

Jacquard, face

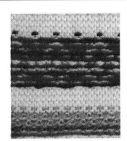

back

Jacquard

Patterns are created by selecting needles to knit with coloured yarns. Colours and needle selections are changed on each course to build up the pattern. When a colour is not required on the face, the yarn floats on the back of the fabric. A wide range of designs can be created. The fabric is not very extensible, because of the large number of floats.

Applications include fashion pullovers and waistcoats.

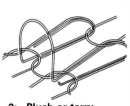

2: Plush or terry, schematic

Plush or terry

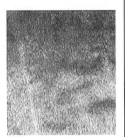

Cut plush (velour)

Plush or Terry

Plush or knitted terry fabric is made by including (plating) an extra yarn which is made to form extended sinker loops. The plated yarn can be knitted at every needle or on selected needles to form a pattern.

Cut plush, or knitted velour is made by cutting the plated yarn loops. The fabric surface then resembles velvet (velour). Applications include leisure and children's wear and socks.

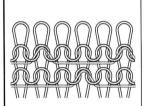

3: Inlay or loopback, schematic

Inlay or loopback, face

back (not raised)

Inlay (loopback)

An extra (inlay) yarn is floated on the technical back, tucking at regular intervals. Usually the inlay yarn is much coarser than the ground yarn. These fabrics have a fine face and a bulky looped back which is often brushed or raised, when it is known as two-thread fleece. Either side of the fabric can be used as the face side for garment making.

Applications include leisure and children's wear, track suits and sweatshirts.

4: Sliver knit, schematic

Sliver knit (fake fur), face

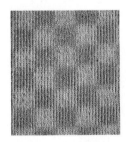

back

Sliver Knit, (fake fur)

A sliver is fed to the needles and bound in by the intermeshing. A pile or fleecy effect is formed on the technical back.

If the fabric is printed with an animal hide pattern, then it is called fake fur.

Applications include fur coats and winter wear (fleece lining) for coats and shoes.

5: Cross-tuck (piqué), face

back

Cross-tuck (piqué)

Piqué-style relief patterning can be made on single or double jersey base structures. The single jersey base is more common because it is lighter weight. The pattern is formed by alternating plain and tuck loops within one course and between one course and another. A complete course of knitted loops can be interspaced between the courses containing knit and tuck loops.

Applications include sports and leisure shirts.

Developments of the Rib Structure

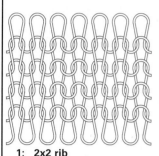

unravelling edge

1: 2x2 rib

2x2 Rib, broad ribs

A wide range of rib fabrics can be produced, depending on the set-out of the needles. The most popular is 2x2 rib which is made by taking every third needle out of action in each needle bed.

The two sides of the 2x2 rib fabric look the same. If the fabric is stretched in the width, the two rib loops are exposed between the two face loops. It is very elastic in the width direction.

Applications include cuffs and welts, pullovers and dresses.

2: Half milano, face   back

Half Milano, ripple

In half milano a course of 1x1 rib is followed by a course in which only the back needle bed knits plain. The loops on the front bed are held over and are extended. The extensibility in the width is reduced by the plain course.

If more than one course of plain loops is knitted, either on the front or back needle beds, the result is a ripple fabric. The plain courses are thrown into relief (without special patterning).

These fabrics are used for pullovers and waistcoats.

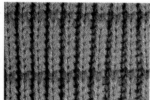

3: Cardigan   Half-cardigan

Cardigan Stitch

In cardigan stitch, the first course knits tuck loops on the front bed and plain loops on the back. The next course is the opposite. The tuck stitches emphasise the plain loops. Cardigan is heavier and wider than 1x1 rib. In half-cardigan (Royal rib) a course of 1x1 rib is followed by one with plain loops on the front bed and tuck loops on the back. The face side shows prominent wale ribs whilst the back looks like cardigan. The voluminous cardigan and half-cardigan structures are used mainly for thick winter pullovers, scarfs, and berets.

4: Double piqué, face   back

Double Piqué

Double piqué is made on rib machines by a selection of knitted loops and floats. The floats greatly reduce the width extensibility. This allows the fabric to be processed like a woven material without losing the comfortable wearing characteristics of a knit. Unlined fabrics have a tendency to bulge.

Also known as wevenit, rodier, and overknit.

Applications include women's coats, trousers, skirts, costumes.

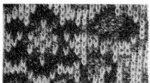

5: Jacquard, face   back

Rib Jacquard

In double jersey jacquard machines, the needles in the two needle beds (cylinder and dial) can be selected either to knit or miss. The pattern is created by selecting cylinder needles to knit or miss each coloured yarn in sequence. When the yarn is not knitting on the cylinder needles it is knitted by the dial needles to form the back of the fabric. The number of feeders required to complete one course depends on the number of colours in the design.

These fabrics are used for pullovers, dresses and jackets.

3.3.2 Weft Knitted Fabrics (5)

1: Figured purl

Developments of Purl Stitch

Purl fabrics are characterised by mixtures of face and back loops in the wale direction. Patterns are realised by controlled selection of double-headed needles to knit either face or back loops at a given point. On each course, the needles are divided over the front and back needle beds, according to the required pattern. A wide variety of patterns can be produced, mainly for women's pullovers and cardigans.

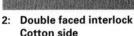

2: Double faced interlock
Cotton side   **Polypropylene side**

Developments of Interlock Stitch

Interlock fabrics are usually very fine. Patterning is often applied by printing. Nevertheless the interlock structure is capable of development. An example is the production of double faced interlock for sportswear. In these fabrics, the outer side is predominantly of cotton whereas the inner side is a synthetic fibre such as polypropylene. The cotton absorbs sweat whilst the synthetic fibre stays dry. This avoids the "wet cling" effect during intense physical exertion, (see page 129).

Manufacture of Weft Knits into Clothing

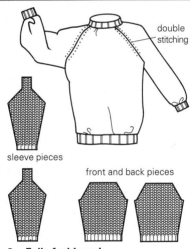

double stitching

sleeve pieces

front and back pieces

3: Fully fashioned

sleeve piece

4: Part fashioned

Fully fashioned fabrics
Fashioning is the knitting of garment parts which are shaped so that they can be sewn directly into the garment, without cutting. This results in a saving in materials. Fully fashioned garments can be distinguished by the special double stitches (loop transfers) which are used to finish off the top edges and reduce the width of the garment parts.

Partly fashioned
Parts are shaped at only one end.

Garment lengths
Fabric is knitted in successive individual panels, of defined length and width, and having a secure edge at the start.

Piece-goods
Fabric is made in long lengths in the form of a tube on a circular machine. The fabric may be processed in tubular form or cut open (usually after dyeing) and processed as a single thickness, similar to woven fabrics.

Linking, looping
Two pieces of fabric can be linked together very precisely, loop for loop, on a special linking machine using a single or double chain stitch.

Stitching damage
During sewing, it is possible to damage the fabrics causing holes or ladders at the garment seams. There are four main causes: inappropriate fabric finishing, worn or damaged needle point, needle too large, and inappropriate needle point (see page 171).

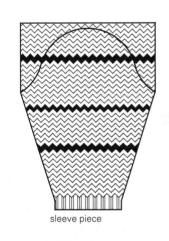

5: Garment-length (panel) knitting

6: Piece-goods, yard-goods

Production and Terminology

1: Principle of warp knitting

- warp beam
- warp sheet
- guide bar
- guides
- needles
- needle bar

Warp knitted fabrics are made with at least one sheet of warp yarns. Usually there are at least two warps, each on its own beam.

Each individual warp yarn is drawn through a guide which is mounted on a guide bar. Movements of the guide bar (lapping) cause the thread to be lapped around the needle, which may be a bearded, latch, or compound needle. After the yarns are lapped, the needle bar is moved so as to cause loops to be formed simultaneously at all needles, resulting in a whole knitted course.

Finally, the guide bar is displaced sideways (shogged) by one or more needles before the next cycle produces another course. The shogging of the guide bar determines the structure of the fabric.

Open lap: the feet of the loop do not cross.

Course: a row of loops across the fabric width.

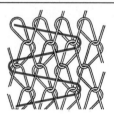

Inlay: a yarn laid between the loops and the underlaps across the width.

Closed lap: the feet of the loop are crossed.

Wale: a column of loops in the length direction.

Vertical inlay: a yarn laid between the loops and the underlaps in the length direction.

Selected Single Guide Bar Structures

Pillar (chain) Stitch	Plain (tricot) Stitch	2x1 Plain	Atlas
Chains of loops in un-connected wales are produced. They must be connected together by yarns supplied from a second guide bar.	Each yarn works in a zigzag fashion lapping between two neighbouring wales. All laps are closed.	This stitch is the same as tricot except that each yarn laps over to the next but one wale.	The guide bar laps progressively in the same direction for at least two courses, followed by an identical lapping sequence in the opposite direction. Laps at the turning points are closed; intermediate laps are open.

3.3.3 Warp Knitted Fabrics (2)

Multiple Guide Bar Fabrics

For most warp knitted fabrics, the basic lapping structures are used in combination. This means that more than one warp sheet and guide bar must be used.

Warp knitted fabrics have only a limited range of applications in apparel fabrics. The most important are: leisure and swimwear, foundation and lingerie, extensible linings, laces, ribbons and trimmings.

In household textiles, warp knits are used for curtains, bed clothing and furnishings. The widest use of warp knits is in industrial fabrics.

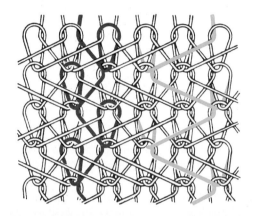

1: Locknit,
    schematic

2: Locknit, face

3: Locknit, back

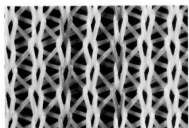

4: Warp knitted terry

5: Warp knitted plush, velour

6: Raschel net

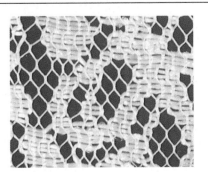

7: Raschel lace

Locknit

Locknit (charmeuse) is a combination of tricot and 2x1 plain stitches. On one side the fabric displays distinct wales of small face loops; the other side shows the zigzag formation of the underlaps. It is made from filament yarns which give the characteristic lustre. Applications: linings, lingerie (**Figures 1, 2 and 3**).

Warp knitted terry

This is made with an extra warp sheet of pile yarns which are caused to form loops, bound into a ground fabric. Applications include furnishings and bed sheets (**Figure 4**).

Warp knitted plush, velour

In this case, the pile loops are cut to give a fleecy or velvet-like surface. Applications include beach, leisure and sportswear (**Figure 5**).

Raschel net

Nowadays, net fabrics are almost always made on raschel machines. It is a combination of pillar and tricot stitches. Raschel net is most popular in bridal wear (**Figure 6**).

Raschel lace

Raschel lace fabrics are often made on a base of net fabric with a pattern formed from inlay yarns. They are used for foundation and lingerie, bridal and formal wear, and as trimmings (**Figure 7**).

3.4.1 Nonwoven Fabrics (1)

As the name implies, nonwoven fabrics are made directly from fibres, without the intermediate step of yarn formation. Two groups may be distinguished according to the method of formation.

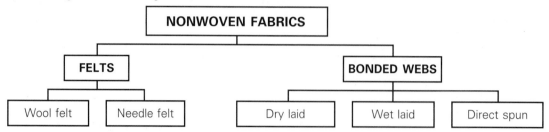

The prerequisite for a nonwoven fabric is the production of a fibre web or batt (see page 48). The web then has to be given strength. Felts are strengthened by mechanical entanglement of the fibres. Bonded webs are strengthened by the application of adhesives, by melting or dissolving individual fibres or small areas of fibres, or by stitching. In particular cases, a combination of methods may be used. A relatively recent development is fibre entanglement using high pressure water jets.

Wool Felts

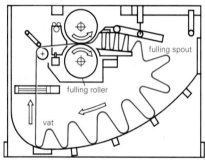

1: Principle of fulling

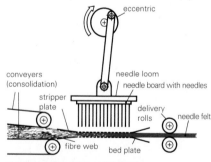

2: Wool felt

Production

Wool and some other animal fibres will become progressively entangled, eventually into a felt when a web is subjected to alkaline liquors, heat, pressure, and repeated mechanical action.

A fibre web is first consolidated on a felting machine between reciprocating boards and then treated on the fulling machine by alternate and repeated compression, beating, and squeezing until the required density of felt is achieved.

Woven felts, such as loden, are made by treating woven fabrics on the fulling (milling) machine.

Properties and Applications

The properties of a felt depend on the type of animal hair which is used, such as camel, goat, rabbit, and also on whether a proportion of non-felting fibres is mixed in.

Felts are good insulators and therefore can be made into warm garments but nowadays they are rather seldom used as such.

Main applications include: hats, collar backs for jackets and coats, furnishings, roller coverings, insulation materials, billiard cloths, conveyer bands in papermaking.

Needle Felts

3: Principle of needle felting

Production

Almost any type of fibre can be utilised for the production of needle felts. In practice synthetic fibres are usually used.

A bulky fibre web is repeatedly penetrated by a bank of barbed needles fixed in a single needle board. At each stroke, every needle drags a certain number of fibres to the lower side of the web, forming loops in the fibres. Needle felts are normally given additional strength by supplementary fibre-bonding techniques.

Properties and Applications

Needle felts are elastic and lightweight compared to most nonwovens. They are used mainly for floor coverings but also for interlinings, waddings, upholstery materials, mattress covers, coverings and filters.

5: Felting needle

4: Needle felt

1: Random-laid (air laid) web

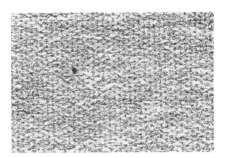

2: Oriented web

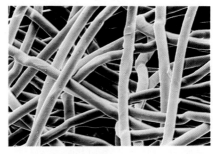

3: Adhesive bonded web

4: Web bonded by low-melting fibres

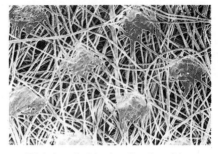

5: Web bonded by localised melting

Bonded Webs

Bonded webs are flexible materials, made directly from fibres, which have been given their strength by chemical, thermal, or mechanical treatments.

Production

First a fibre web or batt has to be made. A web can be made as described on pages 48 and 49, or the fibres can be drawn onto a suction drum. These two methods produce the so-called dry-laid webs. Wet-laid webs are made by a process similar to paper making in which fibres suspended in a liquid are filtered onto a sieve. Direct-spun, or spun-blown webs are made by spinning synthetic fibres directly onto a conveyer band.

Webs are either **random-laid (Figure 1)** or **oriented (Figure 2)**. In any of the web-forming processes, the fibres in the web may be laid in random fashion or they may be oriented in some way. The degree and direction of orientation of the fibres affects the strength and extensibility of the final product.

Bonded webs for clothing are most often prepared on the carding machine. The card webs are layered to build up a batt of the required thickness. Cross-layering is the most common but the layers can be built in either the cross or the length direction, or both. Strength and extensibility in the length and width directions will depend on the method of layering.

The card web has no strength; it can easily be pulled apart. The layers of web have to be strengthened by some form of bonding between the fibres. This can be done in several ways. Often the batt will be pre-needled or hydo-entangled using water jets to give sufficient strength for further processing. Fibre bonding may then be carried out by one of the following methods:

- Adhesive may be applied by spraying, dipping, or foam spreading, followed by pressing **(Figure 3)**.
- The fibre surfaces can be softened by a solvent, so that the fibres stick together at their touching points.
- Thermoplastic fibres can be softened by heating so that, under pressure, they fuse at the touching points.
- A small proportion of the fibres may be of a special type which can be melted or dissolved so that they bond the other fibres **(Figure 4)**.
- Bicomponent fibres can be spun from two different polymer types extruded at the same spinneret. When they are heated, one component melts and bonds the fibres.
- Thermoplastic fibres can be fused in small areas at regular intervals **(Figure 5)**.

Properties and Applications

In clothing, bonded fibre webs are used mainly as interlinings. For this, they need the following properties:

- air permeability
- form stability
- crease resistance
- stability to washing and dry cleaning
- dimensional stability and easy to work

With oriented webs, the fabric must be laid up appropriately before cutting.

Interlining fabrics are often provided with a fusible adhesive on one side, distributed in dots, diamonds, or stripes. The adhesive melts at temperatures between 120 and 180 °C so that the interlining can be fused to the outer fabric on a special heated press.

3.4.2 Stitch-bonded and Tufted Fabrics

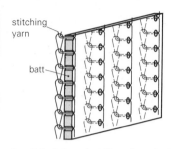

1: Stitch-bonded fibre batt (schematic)

2: Stitch-bonded fibre batt (sample)

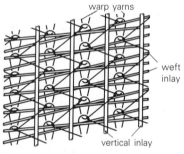

3: Stitch-bonded yarns (schematic)

4: Stitch-bonded yarns (sample)

5: Tufted fabric

6: Tufted fabric with backcoating
    (cross-section)

Stitch-bonded Fabrics

In these fabrics a **fibre batt** or a series of **laid yarns** is bonded together by sewing or stitching along the length direction. The stitching resembles the formation of loops on a warp knitting machine using chain stitch or plain tricot stitch.

Stitch-bonded batts (Arachne, Maliwatt) are warm and voluminous. They can be used as filling materials for winter clothing **(Figures 1 and 2)**.

Stitch-bonded yarns (Malimo) can be made with only cross-laid inlay yarns, or both cross-laid and vertical inlays. The inlay yarns are laid under tension side-by-side; there is no interlacing or intermeshing. It is the stitching which binds the structure together **(Figures 3 and 4)**.

In a further development, either the stitching yarns or vertical inlay yarns are taken over sinkers to form a loop pile fabric similar to terry (Araloop, Malipol).

The great advantage of stitch-bonded fabrics is that they can be manufactured at a high production rate with low capital investment. Applications are mainly in low-cost furnishings and cleaning cloths.

Tufting

In the tufting technique, a set of pile yarns is sewn into a woven fabric base in such a way that loops, or tufts are formed on one side **(Figure 7)**. The loops can be cut to form a plush or velour type surface. The tufts are not securely stitched into the fabric so that they can easily be pulled out from the back. To fix the tufts securely a backcoating has to be applied **(Figures 5 and 6)**.

Tufted fabrics are used primarily for carpets and rugs. They can also be used in clothing, with raised or cut surfaces, as warm lining materials.

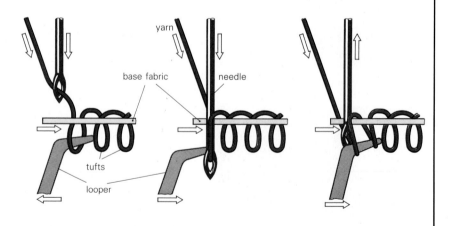

7: Tufted fabric production, schematic

3.4.3 Open-work Fabrics

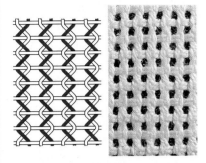

1: Gauze (leno) weave

2: Plain net (bobbinet)

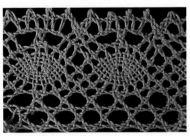

3: Bobbin lace

4: Embroidery lace (burnt out)

5: Raschel lace

Open-work fabrics have greater or lesser amounts of open space in them, created by various means such as crochet, lace, stitching, embroidery, weaving or knitting either on a machine or by hand. Nowadays most of the traditional hand techniques, such as lace-making can be imitated on a machine.

Open-work fabrics can also be created during finishing. A pattern is printed onto a fabric using etching paste, containing a destructive chemical which partly or wholly removes the printed areas. If the fabric contains two different fibre types, then the etching paste can be chosen to remove only one of the fibres, leaving a pattern of transparent areas. Such fabrics are called **burnt-out** style or **devoré** (see page 99).

Gauze (leno) Weave

In gauze and leno weaving **(Figure 1)** certain of the warp threads (crossing ends) are passed from side to side of one or more neighbouring warp threads (standard ends) and are bound into these positions by the weft. Open areas are created either all over the fabric or in a pattern. In spite of their low yarn density, the fabrics have good abrasion resistance.

Applications: dresses, drapes, filter cloths, base fabrics for embroidery and rug making.

Plain Net (bobbinet)

On the plain net or bobbinet machine a series of pairs of thread carriers (bobbins) swing backwards and forwards through the warp sheet whilst progressing from one side of the machine to the other, and back again. The bobbin yarns are thus looped around the warp yarns in a spiral formation leaving a regular series of holes in the fabric, in a honeycomb effect **(Figure 2)**. The machines can be provided with jacquard mechanisms for figuring and pattern threads can be provided in the warp. Patterning can also be applied to plain net fabrics by subsequent embroidery.

Applications: drapes, veils, laces

Laces

Lace has been used for a long time as a decorative element in clothing. Early examples of Open-work are known from the 3rd and 4th centuries BC. True lace materials for borders and trimmings, or as wide fabrics developed rapidly in the 15th and 16th centuries AD.

Lace trimmings are used in blouses, dresses, lingerie, bed clothes, napkins, pillow covers, handkerchiefs etc. Lace fabrics are made up into blouses, dresses, table cloths, curtains, etc.

Bobbin lace (Figure 3) is a kind of plaited structure made from 4 to 400 bobbin yarns. The yarns are worked into a pattern by twisting and crossing the threads. The pattern is outlined by pins stuck in a pillow. The lace may be formed directly on the pins or may be pinned to the pattern on the pillow as it is formed. Also known as **pillow lace**.

Well known examples are the laces of Brussels, Chantilly, Antwerp, and Valenciennes.

Embroidery lace (Figure 4) is made by hand or machine application of embroidered patterns to a base fabric. After the pattern has been embroidered, the base fabric may be wholly or partly removed, either by cutting or by using the burnt-out technique.

Raschel lace (Figure 5) is made on a warp knitting machine with latch needles (see pages 74 and 81). Most hand-made laces can be pretty well imitated on a warp knitting machine. Machine-made laces are now much more common than hand-made because of the volume and cost advantages over the bobbin laces.

3.5 Comparison of Textile Fabrics[1]

Type	Production	Basic Characteristics	Applications
Woven	Two sets of yarns, warp and weft (length and width), interlaced at right angles.	firm, stable, dense, low extensibility and elasticity, cut edges will fray.	jackets and coats, suits, costumes, dresses, shirts and blouses, linings and interlinings, bed clothes, table cloths, household textiles, drapes and coverings.
Weft knits	At least one yarn running cross-wise and forming rows of loops (courses). The loops on each row are intermeshed with loops on the previous row.	soft, supple, voluminous, very extensible and elastic, crease resistant, may ladder.	underwear, nightwear, babywear, socks and stockings, pullovers, cardigans, caps and scarfs, sports and leisure wear.
Warp knits	At least one warp sheet is formed into lengthwise columns of loops, with columns connected laterally in a zigzag fashion.	firm, stable, smooth, moderate extensibility and elasticity, crease resistant, will not ladder.	lingerie, lace, net, trimmings, elastic linings, swimwear, sportswear, foundation garments, curtains, bed clothes, industrial textiles.
Braids	Zigzag, diagonal interlacing of at least two sets of warp yarns.	extensible, supple, formable, cut edges fray strongly.	trimmings (braids, cords) ribbons, laces, hats.
Wool felt	A random assembly of wool or other animal fibres closely interlocked as a result of the felting action of heat, moisture, and mechanical action.	stable, formable by heat plus moisture, good insulator, hygroscopic, cut edge will not fray.	hats, collar backs, decoration, slippers, insulation material.
Bonded-fibre	A random or more or less oriented batt of fibres entangled by needling and/or bonded by adhesives, solvent fusing or thermal fusing.	moderately stable, light weight, porous, cut edges will not fray.	interlinings, disposables (table cloths, serviettes, briefs, wipes), cleaning cloths.

[1] Only basic aspects are compared because, for any given fabric type, the properties are strongly dependent on the fibre type, the structure, the density, and finishing.

4 Textile Finishing 4.1 Fundamentals

Definition

Textile finishing comprises all fabric processes which are not included in fibre production, yarn production, and fabric formation. Finishing effectively means to improve or to beautify the material.

Objective

Normally a raw fabric direct from the weaver or knitter can not be used as such to make consumer products; various processes are required before it is suitable. For example, various substances, such as sizes[1] or lubricants may have been added to the yarns as part of the manufacturing process. These, together with any soiling must be removed and faults may have to be rectified. An important function of the finishing is to **enhance the appearance** of fabrics by colouration, pressing, embossing, etc. Another aspect is to impart to the textile properties which it would not normally possess; its **handle** and **drape** can be modified and it can be given better **easy-care performance**. The question of **environmental conservation** has a large impact on the finishing sector. Liquors used for colouration and finishing can not be discharged to waste without some purification. The same is true of discharge gasses, such as solvent vapours.

[1] sizes: film-forming polymers applied to strengthen and smooth warp yarns.

Finishing Processes

Finishing is always a combination of various chemical or mechanical processing stages. A process may be independent of the type of raw material but, more often, processes are tailored for the particular chemical constitution and surface characteristics of particular fibre types.

The many and various finishing processes, whether fibre-dependent or not, can be generally classified as follows:

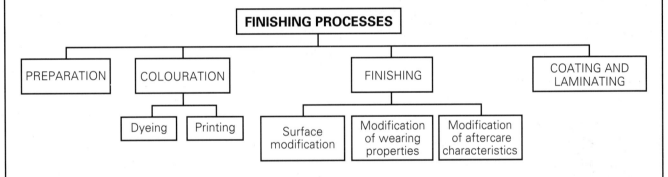

Finishing at Different Stages in Textile Production

Finishing is most efficiently carried out on fabrics. However, there are times when a finishing process must be performed at some other stage. For example, in order to make colour-woven fabrics, either the loose fibre or the yarns must be coloured.

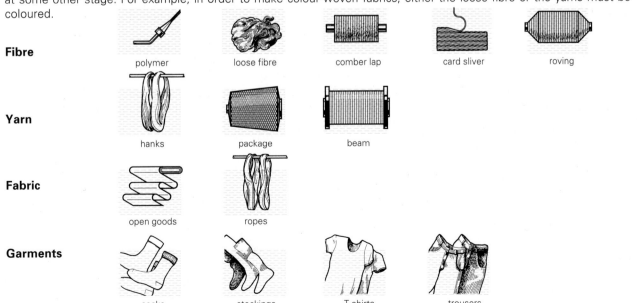

4 Textile Finishing	**4.2 Preparation**

Preparation means getting the fabric ready for dyeing, printing, or finishing. Any processing aids which may have been applied during spinning, weaving, or knitting must be removed. These might be spinning oils, waxes, sizes, etc. Any natural or adventitious contaminants must also be removed so that the fabric has the required purity for the following processes.

Thorough preparation is a prerequisite for good results at the finishing.

Process	Objective
Desizing	Removal of sizes and other substances applied as weaving aids.
Singeing	Removal of the short fibre ends from the fabric surface, by burning (see below).
Scouring	Removal of natural or adventitious impurities.
Bleaching	Destruction of natural colouring and improving the whiteness (see below).
Kier-boiling	Removal of impurities from cotton by alkaline boiling under pressure (uncommon nowadays).
Mercerizing	Treatment of cotton with strong alkali under tension (see below).
Carbonising	Destruction of cellulosic impurities in wool by acid treatment.

Singeing

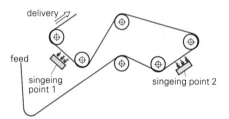

1: Gas singeing, schematic

Singeing is used mainly, but not exclusively for cotton fabrics.

During this process, projecting fibre ends are burned away using one or more banks of gas flames or other heat sources. The fabric surface is made smoother and the weave is revealed more clearly. Development of hairiness and pilling during processing is reduced.

Bleaching

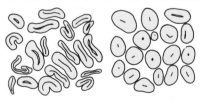

2: Cotton fabric, raw and bleached

If a pure white is required in the finished textile, or if it is to be dyed to a clear pastel shade, then bleaching will undoubtedly be necessary. In natural fibres the natural colouring is destroyed; in man-made fibres the whiteness can be enhanced.

Cotton fabrics are almost always bleached. The exception is when a good white fibre is to be dyed to a deep shade with a dark colour. Bleaching is an oxidation process and hydrogen peroxide is the most common bleaching agent. Sodium hypochlorite (once very common) and sodium chlorite are also used. Oxidation converts the naturally coloured substances into colourless, water soluble compounds which can then be rinsed away.

Bleaching can be carried out either as a batch or a continuous process. In a batch process, a defined weight of material is loaded into a relatively small machine and the whole process is carried out, step by step in that machine. In a continuous process, the fabric travels through a long machinery range made up of a series of units. Each separate unit is specialised for one step of the process.

Mercerizing

3: Cotton, raw and mercerized

Mercerizing is the treatment of cotton yarn or fabric, under tension, in a concentrated solution of caustic soda.

Mercerizing causes the fibre cross-section to become swollen and more rounded. Yarns and fabrics are made stronger, more lustrous, and capable of being dyed or printed to a much deeper shade for a given amount of colour.

Textile materials are dyed in aqueous solutions or dispersions[1] of dyestuffs, together with dyebath[2] additives such as salt, alkali, acids and other auxiliary chemicals. The dissolved or dispersed dyestuff must first be absorbed onto the fibre surface and then diffuse into its interior where finally it must be fixed.

Dyeing Machinery and Processes

The choice of dyeing equipment depends on the type of fabric (woven, knitted, nonwoven), and the fibres it contains. Polyester fibres often have to be dyed at temperatures over 100°C and so machines which can operate under pressure must be used.

The dyeing process may be continuous, discontinuous (batch), or semi-continuous.

Batch Dyeing Processes

In a batch process, a defined weight of fabric is treated in a self-contained machine, in a bath which contains a defined weight of dyestuff. Fixation of the dyestuff may be in the same machine or in a separate process.

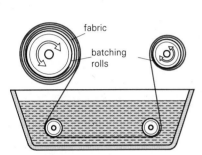

1: Jigger

The smoothly-spread fabric is led backwards and forwards through the dyebath.

Advantage: Uniform colour distribution across the width, low liquor ratio[3].

Application: Medium to heavy weight wovens.

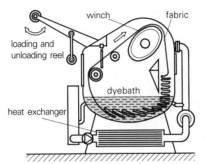

2: Winch (beck)

Fabric is circulated, either open or in rope form, by the action of the winch reel which lifts it from the front of the beck and deposits it at the back.

Advantage: relatively low tension.

Application: knits and light weight wovens.

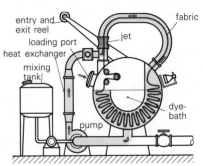

3: Jet dyeing machine

Fabric is circulated by a high pressure jet of the dyebath liquor flowing through a venturi (constriction). Machines which circulate the fabric by a combination of winch reel and low pressure jet are popular.

Advantage: low liquor ratio.

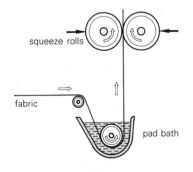

4: Padding mangle

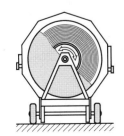

5: Docking station

Continuous Dyeing

In continuous or pad dyeing the open-width fabric is passed through a relatively small pad bath, containing the dyestuff and auxiliaries, and is then squeezed between rubber-covered rollers. The squeeze rollers ensure that a defined quantity of the liquor is uniformly penetrated and distributed within and across the fabric. After the padding station there will be some form of continuous dye fixation machinery, depending on the fibre and the dyestuff type.

The pad mangle is a component of all continuous processes, whenever there is a requirement to handle fabric in the open width and to apply a dyebath or other concentrated chemical liquor in a uniform manner.

Semi-continuous Dyeing

The dyebath is applied to the fabric on a pad mangle and the impregnated fabric is wound up onto a batching roller which can hold a very long length. Fixation of the dyestuff can be carried out on the batching roller, which may be stored in a docking station for several hours at a certain temperature, or the batch may be taken and used as the feed for a separate fixation process.

[1] dispersion: intimate mixture of a solid in a liquid
[2] bath: finite volume of liquor in which a textile is subjected to some chemical process
[3] liquor ratio: proportion by weight of liquor to fabric

Printing can be described as the controlled placing of defined areas of colour onto a substrate. The colourant must first be brought to the fibre surface usually in the form of a printing paste. If it is a soluble dyestuff, it must be diffused into the fibres. The colourant must then be fixed in place and, finally, excess unfixed colour has to be washed out.

1:   Direct print (face)

2:   Direct print (back)

3:   Discharge print (face)

4:   Discharge print (back)

5:   Resist print (face)

6:   Resist print (back)

7:   Transfer printing paper   8:   Transfer print

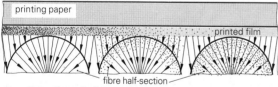

printing paper

printed film

fibre half-section

9:   Transfer printing, schematic

10: Flock print

11: Pigment print

12: Lacquer print

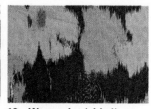

13: Warp print (chiné)

Regardless of the printing process, there are several basic **printing principles.**

Direct printing, Overprinting

The printing paste is applied directly to the prepared fabric surface. Overprinting indicates that a plain dyed fabric is printed with a pattern in a darker colour.

Discharge printing

A plain dyed fabric is overprinted with a discharge paste which destroys or decolourises or changes the colour of the dye. A white discharge is when the original white is restored to the printed area. A colour discharge is when a separate colour is applied at the same time as the discharge paste.

Resist printing

This is when a white fabric is printed with a resist paste. On subsequent dyeing the printed area is not coloured. Resist areas can also be white or coloured.

Transfer printing

The pattern is first printed onto a special type of paper with certain types of dyestuffs. These papers are prepared by specialist suppliers. The pattern is simply transferred to the fabric with the aid of a heated calender. The temperature is high enough to cause the dyestuffs to pass into the vapour phase (sublime). Since it is held in close proximity to the paper, under pressure, some of the dye vapour finds its way onto the fabric and diffuses into the fibres.

The process represents about 6% of print production and finds its most direct and simple application on synthetic fibre textiles. Special techniques, papers, and fabric preparations have been developed for natural fibres and blends.

Beside these basic principles, there are several types of **printing technologies.**

Flock printing

The fabric is printed with adhesive and cut fibre snippets are applied, which stick where the adhesive is present. A velvet-like appearance to the print can be obtained by electrostatic flocking, in which the fibre snippets are caused to stand upright in an electrostatic field as they are being applied.

Pigment printing

Pigments are colours which do not dissolve and penetrate into the fibres. They have to be applied together with a film-forming binder. More than 50% of all printing colours are pigment types.

Lacquer printing

A pattern is formed by printing the fabric with a coloured resin which forms a shiny film.

Warp printing

Before weaving, a pattern is printed onto the warp sheet. After weaving the design is subdued and shadowy, without a distinct outline. Also called chiné or shadow print.

Printing Processes

1: **Printing block**

2: **Block print**

3: **Roller print (face)**

4: **Roller print (back)**

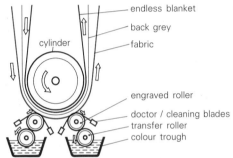

endless blanket
back grey
cylinder
fabric

engraved roller
doctor / cleaning blades
transfer roller
colour trough

5: **Principle of roller printing**

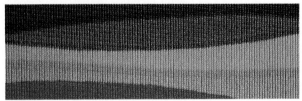

6: **Screen print**

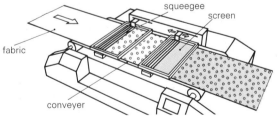

squeegee
screen
fabric
conveyer

7: **Principle of flat screen printing**

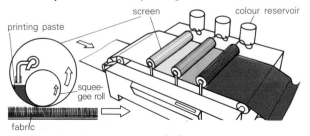

screen
colour reservoir
printing paste
squee-
gee roll
fabric

8: **Principle of rotary screen printing**

Hand printing

This is the oldest method of printing but it is seldom used nowadays in the industry. The printing paste is applied by means of a wooden block which carries the design in relief, or by a stencil.

Roller printing

The oldest mechanised method for continuous printing represents only about 16% of print production today, and is declining. Roller printing is capable of producing very sharp outlines to the printed pattern which is especially important for small figures. The maximum design repeat is the circumference of the engraved roller.

The design is engraved onto copper rollers, a separate roller for each colour. The rollers are mounted against the large main cylinder, around which the fabric travels together with a resilient blanket and a protective back grey.

The printing paste is located in a trough. A transfer roller runs partly immersed in the paste and in contact with the engraved roller. A doctor blade, scrapes away all of the paste except for that contained in the engraving. A cleaning blade on the other side scrapes away any lint picked up from the fabric. The pressure of the engraved roller against the fabric causes the design to be transferred. Any excess paste which is squeezed through the fabric, is taken up by the back grey. This protects the blanket and prevents the design from being smeared.

Screen printing

Screen printing (flat and rotary) is the most important printing method with about 78% of total production.

The design is formed by blocking off those parts of the screen where no printing iś to occur. The screen is coated with a light sensitive polymer and then selectively exposed through a stencil. Exposed areas are made insoluble; unexposed areas are washed away. A modern alternative is to coat the screen with an insoluble polymer which is then selectively etched away by a computer driven laser beam.

A separate screen is required for each colour. The maximum design repeat is the size of the screen which can be much larger than an engraved roller.

Flat screen printing

The fabric is held firm and flat on a conveyer blanket by a tacky adhesive. The conveyer moves intermittently over the printing table, one screen width at a time. When the fabric stops, the screens are lowered onto the printing table, printing paste is supplied to the screens and forced through the patterned areas by a squeegee blade or roller. The screens are lifted and the next cycle begins with the fabric moving forward one further screen width. Flat screen printing is used for about 18% of printed fabric production.

Rotary screen printing

The rotary screen system is a further development which allows continuous production. The printing paste is pumped at a defined rate from the reservoirs to the insides of the cylindrical screens, from where it is continuously squeezed through onto the moving fabric by a blade or roller squeegee. Rotary printing has almost 60% of the market and is growing.

4.3.3   Dyestuffs, Colour Fastness

The desire to colour textiles is as old as spinning and weaving. Natural colouring materials have been used for thousands of years; mineral pigments such as yellow and red ochre, cinnabar; vegetable dyes such as indigo, litmus, logwood, madder, saffron; animal dyes such as cochineal, Tyrian purple. Synthetic dyes were first produced in the 19th century and have now almost completely replaced the natural colours. **Environmental and product safety** aspects are currently very important.

With the exception of pigment/binder systems the type of dyestuff has to be chosen to suit the fibre substrate, because the formation of a physical or chemical bond between dye and fibre depends on the chemical and physical structures of both dye and fibre. A broad spectrum of colours is available in countless shades and a wide range of fastness for the different fibre types and blends.

Colour fastness means the resistance of the colour to various insults which textiles may suffer during manufacture and use. Fastness depends on the type of dyestuff and the fibre substrate; there is no universal colour with the same fastness on all substrates. Moreover, different end uses have different fastness requirements; underwear has different requirements from furnishings.

There are standardised methods (ISO 105) of evaluating the different types of fastness. The most important are:

Rubbing	Resistance of the colour to rubbing, either wet or dry. Even the best dyeings, in a very deep shade, may lose some colour in wet rubbing.
Washing	The fastness to washing determines the wash program which must be used by the consumer. Nowadays, fastness to a strong wash at 60 °C is expected.
Perspiration	Resistance to the effects of perspiration is important for underwear, outerwear, and sportswear.

Colours may also be required to be fast to light, weather, sea water, solvents, ironing, etc.

Dyestuffs in Relation to the Fibre Substrate[1]

Dyestuff	Substrate	Method	Fastness
Direct	cotton, linen, viscose, silk	Simple diffusion into the fibre, from aqueous solution.	Relatively poor fastness to light, washing and perspiration. Can be improved by aftertreatment.
Reactive	cotton, linen, viscose, wool, silk	The dyestuff forms a chemical link with the fibre.	Very good fastness properties.
Vat	cotton, linen, viscose	The insoluble dyestuff is made soluble in a reducing vat[2] so that it can diffuse into the fibre. After diffusion is complete, it is then re-oxidised into its insoluble form.	High fastness to washing, chlorine, boiling, light, weather, rubbing and perspiration.
Sulphur	cotton, linen, viscose	Insoluble dyestuffs, similar to vat dyes.	Fast to washing but not to light or chlorine. Dull colours.
Azoic	cotton, linen, viscose	After diffusion into the fibre, two different chemicals are made to react together to form the insoluble colour.	Good fastness properties.
Metal complex	wool, silk, nylon	Combinations of chromium or cobalt with chromophores[3]; applied from an acidic dyebath.	Good fastness properties due to large size and low solubility of the complex dye molecule.
Acid	wool, silk, nylon	Applied from an acidic dyebath.	Depends on the dye and fibre type.
Disperse	acetate, polyester, nylon	Water insoluble; applied from dispersions; diffuse into the fibre at high temperature.	Good fastness properties.
Basic	acrylics (other fibres by mordanting)	Reaction with acidic groups, or mordants[4] in the fibre.	Good fastness properties on acrylics.
Chrome	wool, silk, nylon	The same as metal complex dyes, except that the metal complex is not pre-formed; it is formed inside the fibre during the dyeing process (mordanting).	Good fastness except for rubbing.

[1] refers to dyeing; for printing, pigment systems are the most important   [2] vat: dyeing vessel, dyebath   [3] chromophore: coloured molecule
[4] mordant: a chemical which can react or complex with a chromophore to form an insoluble colour

After dyeing, printing, or other preparatory processes, the fabric may need to undergo various other treatments in order to make it suitable for the final finishing stages.

Fixation

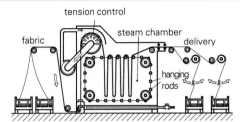

1: Festoon (loop) steamer

The dyed or printed colour may need to be fixed (durably bound) within the fibre and this often is accomplished with the aid of steam, for example in a festoon steamer (**Figure 1**). Condensation of steam onto the fabric provides rapid heating and accelerates the diffusion of the dyestuff into the fibres.

Polyester is dyed with disperse colours which require dry heat for diffusion. This is done on a stenter frame at 180 to 200 °C together with heat setting (see below).

Pigment/binder systems are fixed by curing in dry air at about 150 °C.

Washing

Washing treatments are used at all stages in finishing for the removal of impurities, oils, sizes, etc. In addition, any unfixed dyestuff, or printing auxiliaries must be washed out. Various types of washing machine are available, depending on the type of material to be washed (**Figures 2 and 3**). Total water consumption is minimised by the use of counter-flow and recycling systems.

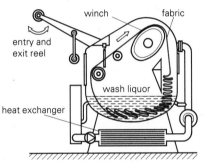

2: Rope washing machine

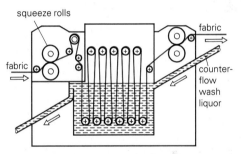

3: Open-width continuous washer unit

Dewatering and Drying

The evaporation of water using heat is expensive. Therefore, after any wet process an attempt will be made to reduce the fabric's water content to a minimum by mechanical means. These include centrifuging, suction, and squeezing. Drying machinery varies, depending on the fabric type. For woven fabrics, the most common is the stenter frame (**Figure 4**).

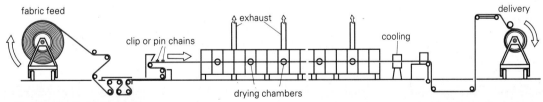

4: Stenter drying frame

During previous processes, the fabric will have been extended in length and reduced in width, due to processing tensions. The dimensions have to be corrected on the stenter frame. The fabric is overfed into the machine where its edges are gripped by clips, or pinned plates on a pair of endless chains. At the machine entry, the distance between the chains is that of the wet fabric but before it enters the drying chambers the fabric is stretched to just over its proper width and the length is reduced. To reduce energy costs and protect the environment, exhaust heat is recycled.

Heat Setting

Heat setting is one of the most important processes for synthetic fibres. During all of the processes from fibre manufacture through to dyed fabric, the material has been subjected to various tensions which have resulted in stresses being stored within the fibres. If these stresses are not relieved, they will result in an irregular fabric appearance and dimensional instability. With synthetic fibres, especially polyester, they can be relieved only by heat treatment, followed by controlled cooling at the required fabric dimensions.

4.5.1 Mechanical Finishing (1)

The term **finishing** covers a wide range of processes. In general it means making the fabric suitable for its intended end use. Therefore, it is usually the last stage of fabric processing and a fabric is often said to have a certain "finish". Originally, finishing was simply the starching of cotton fabrics.

There are generally three basic objectives in finishing:

- Modification of the surface (raising, smoothing, embossing, etc.)
- Modification of the wearing properties (staining, creasing, draping, etc.)
- Modification of aftercare characteristics (ironing, shrinking, etc.)

In dry (mechanical) finishing, a desired effect is achieved by a mechanical process. In wet (chemical) finishing, a desired effect is achieved by a chemical reaction.

Final finishing can sometimes require a combination of processes which are not very compatible. For example a stiffening finish and a crease resistant finish have mutually contradictory effects. The requirements of the market, in terms of end uses and consumer requirements, are constantly changing and this places great demands on the ingenuity of the finisher.

Mechanical Finishing

Process	Effect
Framing	Correct and uniform width and smoothness (stenter frame).
Raising	Fluffy surface, soft handle and warm fabric (see page 95).
Shearing	Removal of short hairs from smooth fabrics. Level and uniform pile on raised, velvet, and plush fabrics (spiral bladed shearing machine).
Rateening	Ratiné (curled) and similar effects produced on raised fabrics by special brushing or rubbing devices (**Figure 1**).
Calendering	Smoothing and compacting with hard, heavy rollers (see page 95).
Embossing	Relief effects by means of an engraved roller. Fixation by resins (cotton) or by heat setting (synthetics) for a permanent effect (**Figure 2**).
Sanding, Emerising	Light raising of the surface by emery rollers.
Pleating	Introduction of permanent creases. Fixation by resins (cotton) or by heat setting (synthetics) (**Figure 3**).
Shrinking	Allowing or forcing the fabrics to shrink in the length direction (see page 95).
Pressing	Smoothing by means of pressing platens; mainly for wool.
Decatizing	Steam pressing treatment for wool fabrics to improve uniformity of appearance, dimensional stability and handle.

1: **Ratiné fabric**

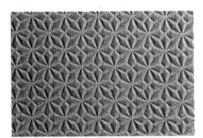

2: **Embossed fabric**

3: **Pleated fabric**

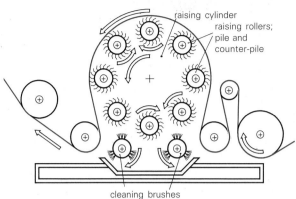

1: **Principle of raising**

2: **Fleece fabric, unraised**

3: **Fleece fabric, raised**

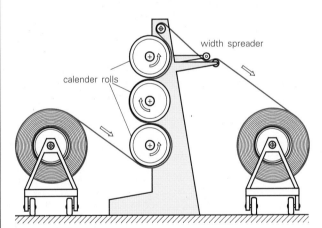

4: **Principle of calendering**

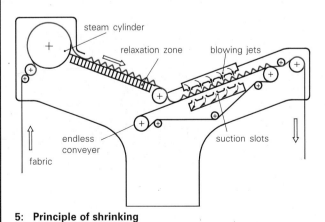

5: **Principle of shrinking**

Raising

On the raising machine (**Figure 1**), fibre ends are teased from the fabric to form a fibre pile which can more or less obscure the fabric weave. This is accomplished by the action of fine wire-clad rollers which hook into the fabric surface as they rotate. The raising action must not be too strong or the fabric can be weakened.

Raised fabrics have a soft and fluffy handle. They are also very warm, due to the increased volume of enclosed air (**Figures 2 and 3**).

Calendering

The calender (**Figure 4**) is an important final finishing process, with the following effects:

- smoothing the surface,
- compacting the fabric, by pressure,
- improving lustre,
- embossing patterns.

The fabric is passed between pressure rollers. Various effects can be achieved depending on the nature of the roller surfaces, the roller temperature, the roller clothing and relative speeds of the rollers (slippage gives polishing). The effects of calendering are usually not permanent.

Particular forms of calender are:

Chintz   The fabric, impregnated with a synthetic resin, is made firm and very lustrous.

Moiré   The typical watermark pattern is produced when two ribbed fabrics are calendered together, or one fabric is calendered with a specially engraved roller (see page 109).

Emboss   Engraved calender rolls are used to produce a relief pattern on the fabric. With synthetic fabrics the effect can be made durable by using heated rolls.

Shrinking

The fabric is made to shrink so that it will not shrink later, in use. During all previous processes, the fabric has suffered greater or lesser stretching forces. Tensions are built into the material which tend to be relieved during subsequent (tensionless) washing. The resulting shrinkage is facilitated (in cellulosic fabrics) by swelling in water or (in synthetic fabrics) by heat. This potential dimensional instability must be anticipated in the finishing by a controlled induced shrinking of the fabric. There are several methods to achieve this shrinkage. In the method shown in **Figure 5**, the fabric is steamed and allowed to relax on a vibrating table without tension. The fibres swell and induce the fabric to shrink in length and width, aided by the vibration.

Trade marks such as "Krumpex®" and "Sanforised®" guarantee a certain level of dimensional stability.

4.5.2 Chemical Finishing

Whereas mechanical finishing is concerned mainly with modifying the surface of the fabric, chemical finishing aims to effect a radical change in the basic fibre or fabric properties, in order to improve some aspect of its behaviour.

Process	Trade Mark Examples	Applications	Procedure and Objective
Water repellent	*Hydrophobol*	all apparel fabrics, especially all-weather clothing, tents and awnings	Impregnation or spraying with water repellent chemicals (e.g. silicones). Can be temporary or durable depending on the chemical and process.
Stain resistant	**Scotchgard** FLECKSCHUTZ IM STOFF	all apparel fabrics and table cloths	Application of stain-repellent substances. Silicones are used mainly for water-borne stains; synthetic resins for oil-borne stains. Usually a degree of water repellence is also imparted.
Antistatic		synthetic fibres for apparel and floor coverings	Enhancement of the surface conductivity of the fibres, to prevent the build-up of static charge at low humidity.
Flame resistant		all fabrics, but especially furnishings made from cellulosic fibres intended for public buildings	Application and fixation of substances which render the textiles non-flammable or difficult to ignite.
Hygienic (bactericidal, fungicidal)	*Sanitized*	all apparel fabrics; fabrics for hospitals and floor coverings	Application of chemicals which hinder the growth of micro-organisms on the textile and on the human skin.
Rot proofing	antimikrobiell EULAN ASEPT Bayer Leverkusen	natural fibres, especially in technical textiles	Protection of the textile from organisms that promote decomposition.
Anti-pilling		synthetic fibres, wool	Reduction of the tendency for pilling (formation of tiny fibre pills on the fabric surface) using film-forming polymers, or solvents.
Easy-care		cotton, viscose	Application and fixation of chemicals which reduce the sensitivity of the fibre to moisture and to creasing. Fabrics become more resistant to wrinkling, do not shrink, and will dry faster.
Felting		wool, animal hairs	Controlled felting in a fulling machine. The natural felting properties of the fibres are encouraged by repeated compressions under the influence of moisture, heat, and chemicals to form a felt-like appearance in the fabric. The fabric shrinks in length and width, and becomes much denser with improved strength and durability. The intensity and time of treatment determines the degree of felting.
Anti-felting	Reine Schur-Wolle Pure New Wool Pure Laine Vierge mit Spezialausrüstung filzt nicht	wool	Felting of wool fibres can be reduced by two methods: • softening the scale tips by oxidative treatment, • encapsulating the scale surfaces with a synthetic polymer film.
Moth proofing	MOTTENECHT DURCH EULAN BAYER LEVERKUSEN / MITIN	wool	Impregnation of the fabric with chemicals which make the fibres inedible and to which the moths are averse.
Parchmentizing		cotton	A range of processes giving a variety of effects from transparency to opalescence, together with more or less stiffening. Often there is a high degree of lustre. Use is made of chemicals which have a very severe swelling or partial degrading effect to render the fibres almost gelatinous. The fabric is calendered and the chemicals removed before the fibres can be degraded.

Coating

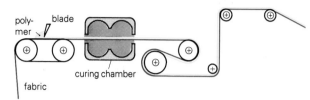

1: Principle of direct coating

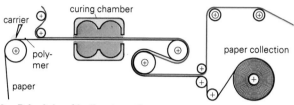

2: Principle of indirect coating

3: Coated fabric

4: Protective clothing

Coating is the application of a layer of natural or synthetic polymer to one side of the fabric, followed by fixation in a curing oven.

The polymer film can be applied directly to the fabric (**Figure 1**). However, if the fabric is an open one, or the material to be applied has a low viscosity, the liquid will first be applied to a carrier paper and then transferred from there to the target fabric (**Figure 2**).

The coating imparts new properties to the fabric which are a combination of the original material (woven, knitted, nonwoven) and the coating (polyurethane, polyvinylchloride).

Coated textiles (**Figures 3 and 4**) have a wide range of uses from clothing to industrial fabrics. In clothing uses, it is important that the coating should be permeable to air and moisture vapour.

Applications

- sporting, protective, working clothing;
- highly visible (fluorescent) clothing;
- shoe uppers, leather cloth;
- handbags and luggage;
- furniture and automobile seat coverings;
- bookbinding, maps, albums;
- window blinds, shower curtains, fabrics for lamination;
- floor and wall coverings;
- fabrics for conveyor belts, tarpaulins, awnings, air-supported structures, inflatable dinghies, textile roofing, etc.

Lamination

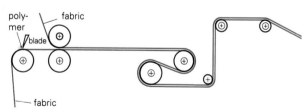

5: Adhesive lamination

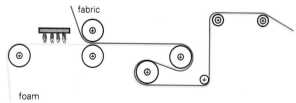

6: Foam lamination

Lamination is the superimposition and bonding of two or more fabrics, or a fabric with paper, film, or foam.

The bonding can be achieved with an adhesive (**Figure 5**) or by heat (**Figure 6**), whereby a polymer film or foam is melted onto the surface of one fabric and then the other fabric is pressed onto it (**Figure 7**).

7:   Foam laminated fabric

5 Fabric Descriptions   5.1 Fabric Inspection

Inspection and testing are carried out in order to ensure consistent product quality. The range of tests, the methods, and the instruments used depend on the individual company and the application.

Inspection of the fabric at the earliest possible stage serves not only for **quality control** but also to ensure **customer satisfaction** and **cost savings**.

Inspection of Incoming Goods

Inspection of incoming goods is to check for conformance to the specification, so that a claim for compensation from the supplier can be made if deficiencies are found.

Checks may be made on the fabric type, design, piece lengths and widths, repeat, weight per unit area, thread density, permeability and frequency of faults.

Fabric faults may result from a variety of circumstances at any stage from the raw fibre through to the final finished fabric. Examples are variation in yarn count, neps, knots, thick places, floating threads, broken threads, faulty weave, stripes, colour variations, stains, holes, tears, missed picks.

Quality Data for Garment Manufacture

Collection of technical quality data allows the various production departments to be informed about potential disruptions to production which can then be planned for.

Raw material (fibre analysis)	Test methods may include handle, fibre identification, burning, tearing, solubility, wetting, absorption, microscopy (see page 43).
Face side of the fabric	The face is generally smoother, cleaner and more regular. Printed patterns are bolder, any pile is properly laid.
Cutting direction	Most garment parts are aligned in the length direction for cutting. In woven fabrics, the length direction is easily identified by the selvedges. The warp will usually be smoother and more highly twisted, often with a higher thread density. Raised piles and directional designs are usually laid in the length direction.
Seam properties and seam strength	The various types of seam puckering (transport, structural, tension pucker; see page 170) can be evaluated at an early stage. The integrity of the seam during wear and aftercare can also be tested.
Pressing and fusing behaviour, bond strength	Different materials react differently to heat, pressure and moisture. They may shrink, become shiny, melt, or burn. The bonding between face fabric and interlining must not be weakened by aftercare treatments.

End-use Performance

For apparel fabrics the quality is largely determined by their performance in garments; comfort, drape, protection, etc. Therefore, in addition to the technical features, tests may be carried out to indicate the performance in wearing, in use, and in aftercare regimes.

Water permeability	A measurement of the pressure required to force water through the fabric.
Vapour permeability	The amount of water vapour transmitted through the fabric in a given time.
Air permeability	The rate of flow of air through the fabric at a given pressure.
Durability (slipping resistance)	Measurement of tensile and tearing strengths and resistance to abrasion. Resistance to slippage of warp and weft yarns in the fabric or in a seam.
Form stability	Resistance to changes in shape (elasticity); bagging, stretching, wrinkling, wrinkle recovery.
Pilling resistance	Measurement of the number of pills that form during a defined period of surface rubbing.
Colour fastness	Fastness of dyes and prints to rubbing, washing, cross staining, light, weather, sea water, ironing, dry cleaning solvents.
Dimensional stability	Dimensional changes (shrinking or stretching) during aftercare laundering and cleaning procedures.

Commercial descriptions imply information about the general appearance, properties and applications of fabrics. These names have not been standardised and therefore do not always give unambiguous information. Nevertheless, certain names have become accepted in the trade for certain types of fabrics.

A given fabric is defined by its fibre type, yarn type, structure, and finishing. The two main sets of characteristics are its surface appearance, e.g. patterning, lustre, surface texture, and its bulk properties, e.g. drape, wrinkle resistance, thermal insulation.

Commercial names may be pure invention or they may be derived from particular characteristics of the fabric, e.g.

- the raw material (cheviot, pima)
- the yarn type (bouclé, loop)
- the structure (satin, gaberdine)
- the production system (jacquard, velvet)
- the application (lining, sheeting)
- the town or country of origin (shetland, denim, honan)
- the fabric appearance (changeant, moiré)

In the following set of photographs, it is not possible to indicate all of the distinctive features of particular descriptions. It is necessary to handle an actual sample.

Afghalaine

Plain weave, medium weight, all wool woven fabric for dressgoods. A lightly pearled appearance due to the use of pairs of S and Z yarns alternately in both warp and weft.

Ajour
à jour (Fr.)
= open-work

Ajour is a collective term for open-work fabrics, woven or knitted. The open-work areas are produced by the structure e.g. leno, basket weave, missing warp or weft threads.

Leather cloth

Nonwoven imitation suede made from a microfibre batt impregnated with polyurethane. It handles like fine leather but is light weight and easy-care.

Burnt out
devoré

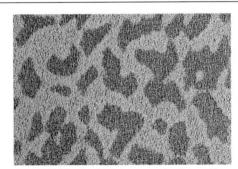

General term for fabrics of all types, made from fibre blends, in which one of the fibres has been selectively removed according to a pattern. The design appears opaque on a transparent ground.

Embroidery lace

Heavy relief lace fabric made by machine embroidering on a base fabric which is subsequently dissolved out or cut away.

Batiste

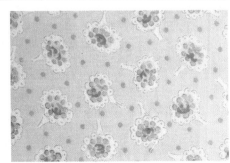

Fine plain weave fabric in cotton, linen, wool, or cotton/polyester. Used for dresses, blouses, lingerie, and interlinings. Swiss batiste has an embroidery pattern, usually as edging.

Flannelette

Medium to heavy weight plain weave; cotton warp and soft-spun cotton weft raised on both sides. Soft and voluminous, often used for bed sheets.

Bark crêpe

The bark-like surface texture may be achieved by alkali treatment, by embossing, or by the use of crêpe yarns in the weft. Applications include blouses, dresses and shirts.

Bouclé

Fabrics with a knoppy, knotty surface texture made with loop or bouclé yarns. Used in dresses, costumes and coats.

Buckram

Stiffly finished, loosely woven, plain cotton or linen fabric. Used as a stiff interlining e.g. for collars and cuffs, as support padding.

Bourette

Dull neppy fabric made from noil silk in plain or twill weave. Used for women's outerwear and furnishings.

Broché

Fabrics in which the design is made by extra weft on a swivel weaving loom. The figuring threads are present only at the figured motif. Used in traditional costume, ribbons and trimmings.

Brocade

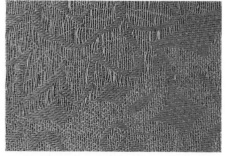

Heavily figured jacquard fabric, often with lustre yarn effects. Used in formal wear and furnishings.

Changeant
changeable,
shot

An iridescent effect produced by different colours in warp and weft. Usually made from filament yarns (shot silk) and employed in dresses, blouses, and linings.

Charmelaine

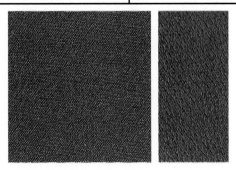

A soft worsted fabric in twill or satin weave with a lustrous face and matt reverse. The lustre is developed by shearing and pressing. Used in women's outerwear.

Locknit
charmeuse

Light weight, smooth, non-laddering warp knitted fabric made from filament yarns. Used for linings, lingerie, and blouses.

Cheviot

Heavy, durable, smooth-finished worsted or woollen tweed fabrics in twill weaves. May or may not be made from cheviot wool. Used for jackets, suits, costumes and coats.

Chiffon

Delicate, sheer, open fabrics. originally of silk in plain weave using crêpe yarns; may be embossed. Used for blouses, dresses, squares, and evening wear.

Chiné

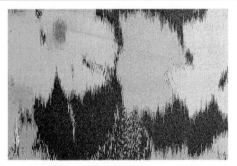

Fabric woven from a printed warp. After weaving the design appears shadowy and indistinct. Often made from filament yarns for dresses and furnishings.

Chintz

Strongly lustrous cotton fabrics; surface appears almost as if waxed. Finished for stain and water repellence by impregnation and calendering. Used in sportswear and furnishings.

Cloqué
blister

Double fabric with a figured blister effect on the face and a crêpe back. Used in women's outerwear.

Corduroy

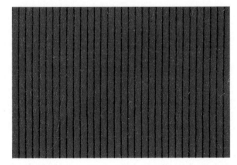

A cut pile cord, usually in cotton. The cords may be of various widths. Used mainly in leisure and business wear.

Bedford cord

Hollow or wadded, length-wise cords. Light weight qualities for women's outerwear, heavier weights for trousers and furnishings.

Crash

Originally unbleached, rough, coarse, plain weave linen fabrics made with irregular yarns. Nowadays often deliberately creased by pressing and fixing creases during finishing. Fashionable outerwear.

Crêpe de chine

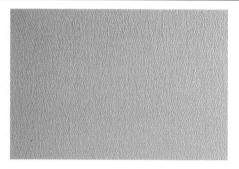

Light weight, supple, plain weave silk fabric with S and Z crêpe yarns in the weft and lightly twisted warp. Used for dresses and blouses.

Crêpe georgette

Plain weave in silk, polyester, wool, cotton, or viscose with S and Z crêpe yarns in both warp and weft; has a grainy, sandy handle. Women's outerwear.

Crêpe lavable
warp crêpe

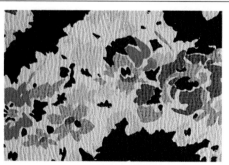

Plain woven, filament crêpe fabrics with crêpe yarns in the warp and normal yarns in the weft. Dresses and blouses.

Crêpe marocain

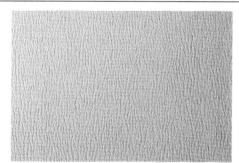

Plain woven, filament yarn fabric with crêpe yarns in the weft, all having the same twist direction. The rib effect can be strengthened by embossing. Used for dresses and blouses.

Satin crêpe

Softly draping, supple satin weave filament yarn fabrics with crêpe yarns in the weft and normal yarns in the warp. The face is lustrous; the back is matt. Used for dresses and blouses.

Croisé
twill

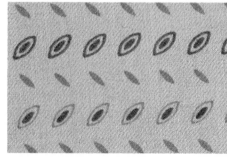

Regular, two-sided twill weave fabrics with a soft handle and drape. Twills from cotton and blends are used for shirts and nightwear. Lining twills are used in menswear for waistcoats and sleeve linings.

Damask

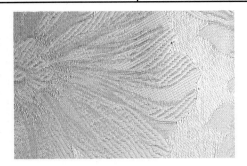

Woven fabrics made from expensive mercerized cotton for bed clothing and table cloths. The figured design often is made by interchanging satin and sateen weaves.

Clip spot

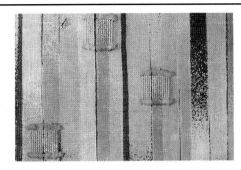

Woven fabric figured with extra weft in a small motif. The long floats of extra weft are cut away from the back of the fabric. Used for dresses and blouses.

Denim

Durable woven cotton twill, originally with an indigo dyed warp and white weft (blue denim). For jeans, leisure wear and workwear.

Donegal

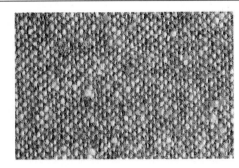

Coarse, woollen, plain woven tweed fabrics with differently coloured warp and weft yarns having random flecks of other colours. For sports jackets, suits, costumes and coats.

Rib 2x2

Weft knitted rib fabric with high width extensibility. Used for welts and cuffs, cardigans and tops.

Double face

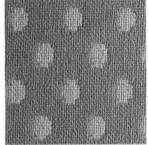

General term for reversible double cloths, usually with contrasting colours; either side may be used as the face. Used for jackets, coats, dresses, furnishings.

Doupion
dupion

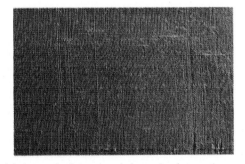

Plain woven fabric made from rough irregular (sometimes wild) silk yarns. Doupion means a double cocoon. Silk strands reeled from such cocoons are very irregular. Used for women's outerwear and furnishings.

Duchesse

Densely woven, highly lustrous, filament yarn satin cloth. Used for ornamental and formal wear, satin linings for jackets and coats.

Duvetine
duvetyn

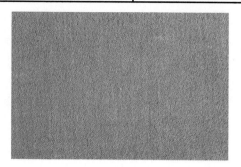

Cotton sateen with a dull, velour type surface made by raising or emerising and brushing. Used for jackets and trousers.

Amazon,
venetian

Very fine, satin weave for business suitings with fine worsted warp yarns and woollen weft. A light milling or raising finish may be given.

Drill

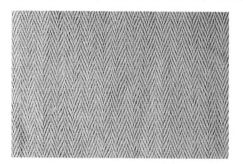

Strong, dense, durable woven 2/1 or 3/1 twill fabrics. Other twills, including herringbone may be used. High quality types may have a twofold warp. Used for work clothing.

Etamine

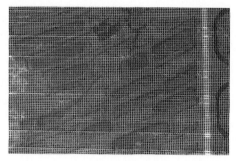

Light weight, open weave, gauze fabric used in dresses, blouses and shirts.

Faconné

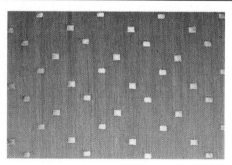

General term for small figured jacquard effects. The pattern is made by local changes in weave structure. Used for dresses, blouses and linings.

Fine Rib
1x1 rib

Fine to medium weight, extensible and elastic weft knitted cotton fabrics used for underwear and ladies tops.

Fil-à-fil

2/2 twill weave fabrics in which light and dark colours alternate in both warp and weft, making a miniature staircase pattern. Used for suits and costumes.

Brushed twill

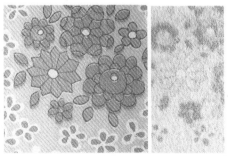

Cotton 2/2 twill weave fabrics, often printed, raised and brushed on the back. Used for shirts and nightwear.

Herringbone

General term for fabrics woven in a reversing twill, often with contrasting colours in warp and weft. Used for suits, costumes and coats.

Flannel

Light or medium weight plain or twill weave fabrics, originally in wool, often in mixture yarns, raised on one or both sides by varying degrees. Cotton flannel is used for shirts, nightwear and bed clothing; wool flannel is for outerwear.

Fleece

Voluminous, woollen yarn, woven fabric with a long raised pile, made with three to five yarn systems. Used for jackets and coats.

Flock print

The velvet-like relief pattern is obtained by printing the design with adhesive and then flocking with small snippets of fibres. Used for dresses and blouses.

Fresco suiting

Firm, durable, worsted, plain woven fabric with hard twisted unicolour or marl yarns. Used for men's suitings.

Frisé,
loop fabric

Fabrics woven from fine loop (bouclé) yarns, having a grainy surface texture. Used for dresses.

Frotté,
imitation
terry

A woven fabric with loop yarns in the weft, made to imitate terry cloth

Terry

A soft, voluminous, loop pile fabric. The loops are formed in a second warp sheet by a special weaving technique. Used for bath robes, towels, sports and leisure wear.

Gaberdine

Densely woven fabric with a distinct steep twill line. The face is made smooth and clear by shearing and pressing. Used for suits, costumes, and coats.

Glacé batiste

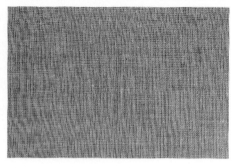

Fine, plain woven cotton made lustrous, transparent, and stiff by parchmentizing. Used for blouses, trimmings, and evening wear.

Glen check

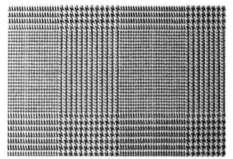

Colour woven with overlaid checks of different sizes, in tone on tone or contrasting colours. Used for suits and costumes.

Hounds-tooth

Particular form of shepherd's check, having short diagonal extensions at the corners (see page 68). The pattern may also be printed. Used in suits and costumes.

Henkel plush, knitted terry

Weft knitted loop pile fabric with an extra plated yarn which is caused to form a uniform surface of loops on one side of the fabric. Used for babywear, bed sheets, beachwear and leisure wear.

Honan silk

Fine to medium weight, plain woven fabric, with a scroopy handle made from wild silk. Usually somewhat irregular in warp and weft, plain dyed or printed. For dresses, blouses and furnishings.

Inlet, downproof

Sturdy, densely woven fine cotton twill for pillow and duvet cases. Usually plain dyed but may also be made in stripes with dyed warp yarns. Also known as bedstout in heavier qualities.

Interlock

Fine, extensible, double sided weft knitted fabric in interlock structure. Used for dresses, blouses, T-shirts, underwear.

Jacquard, woven

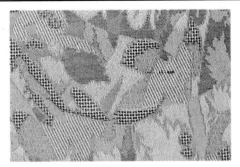

Fabric with a complicated figured design. Figuring is commonly by interchanging satin, sateen, plain, and twill weaves. Colour and yarn effects may be used to accentuate the design. Mainly for furnishing fabrics and formal wear.

Jacquard, knitted

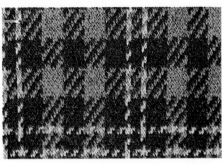

Numerous designs made by selecting coloured yarns to knit on the face in the required pattern. Used in knitted outerwear such as jackets, skirts, pullovers and cardigans.

Bavarian linen

Plain woven, green-brown fabrics from linen, half linen, or cotton. Used for suits and costumes.

Calico

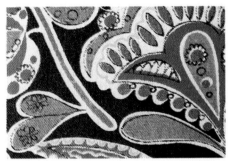

Basic, medium weight, plain woven cotton fabric for bedsheets, aprons, light Summer clothing.

Cheese cloth

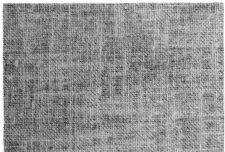

Soft, light weight, plain woven cotton fabric with low thread density. Used for dresses, blouses, squares.

Interlining, woven

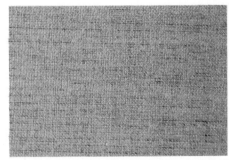

Firm, plain woven linen or cotton fabric. May be supplied with or without stiffening or fusible adhesive dressing. Used in men's outerwear.

Plissé

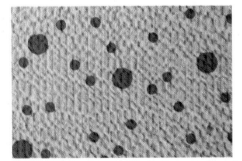

Cotton fabrics with a puckered or crinkled effect produced by the action of caustic soda. Used for dresses and blouses. Also known as crinkle or blister.

Cretonne

Medium to heavy weight cotton plain woven printed fabric. Used for aprons and Summer clothing.

Chalk stripe

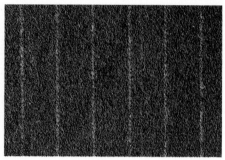

White stripes, broader than pin stripes on a dark background. Usually woven wool fabrics for suits and costumes. Stripes may be partially obscured by raising. Can also be printed.

Lamé

General term for woven fabrics in which metal threads are featured, usually in the weft, providing a glitter effect. The warp is usually silk or cotton. Used for women's formal evening wear.

Lancé,
clip-spot

Woven fabrics in which the design is provided by an extra warp or extra weft, which is interlaced only in the pattern area. Used for dresses, blouses and furnishings. With clip-spot the surplus patterning yarn is cut away.

Lawn

High quality, light weight, plain woven cotton fabrics made with fine or very fine yarns. Usually printed and lightly stiffened for dresses and blouses.

Linon

General term for cotton fabrics with a glazed, linen-like finish obtained by heavy calendering. Also known as French lawn. Used for house-coats, aprons, bed sheets.

Loden

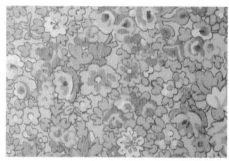

Medium to heavy wool fabric, often made from mixture yarns. Heavily milled to make it dense and durable; may also be raised. Used for suits, costumes and overcoats.

Loop

Loose, plain woven fabric with large loops on the surface, made by weaving with loop yarns in the weft. Used for jackets and costumes.

Lustre

Light weight, wrinkle-resistant, plain woven worsted fabric, including e.g. mohair or alpaca fibres for lustre. Used for Summer suits and nun's habits.

Madras

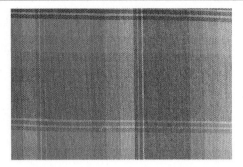

Light weight, fine, plain woven cotton fabric with a large colour-woven check pattern in darkish tones with bright accents. Used for shirts, blouses and dresses.

Marengo

Dark wool fabric with 2 to 5% of white fibres mixed in, so that fluff will not show up. Used for overcoats, suits and costumes.

Matelassé

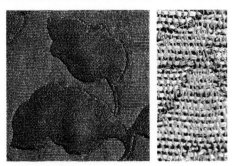

Double cloth with large figured designs which are given a quilted effect by wadding. Used for women's coats, evening wear and furnishings.

Moiré

The veined watermark effect is obtained by calendering or pressing together two superimposed warp ribbed fabrics, or by embossing. Used for dresses, blouses and linings.

Moleskin

Thick, heavily wefted cotton fabric in sateen weave. Usually raised and sheared to give a suede finish for trousers, leisure wear and workwear.

Silence cloth

Heavy, thick cotton flannel, strongly raised on both sides and used as underlays for table cloths, ironing boards and beds.

Mull

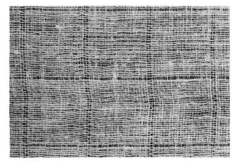

Soft, fine, open, plain weave cotton fabric with a very low thread density in both warp and weft. Used for blouses and squares.

Mousseline

General name for a broad range of soft, sheer, light weight plain woven fabrics made from cotton, silk, or man-made fibres, finer than muslin. Mousseline de laine (illustrated) is somewhat heavier and made from worsted yarns.

Mock Leno

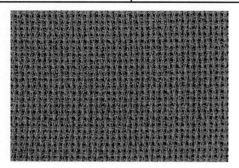

Loose, open fabric with the appearance of leno created by the weave and the thread spacing. Used for shirts, blouses and dresses.

Pin stripe

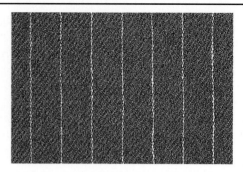

Worsted woven fabric with fine light-coloured lines in the warp direction. Used for suits and costumes.

Opal,
opaline

Fine, white, semi-transparent cotton lawn with a soft finish for blouses and nightwear.

Organdie,
organdy

Fine semi-transparent lawn or batiste with a permanently stiff finish, plain dyed or printed for dresses, blouses and trimmings.

Organza

Thin, transparent, filament yarn, plain woven fabric with a stiff finish used for formal wear and blouses or as light weight interlinings.

Ottoman

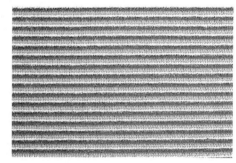

Warp-faced rib fabric with 3 to 10 ribs per cm for coats, jackets, and furnishings.

Oxford

Good quality cotton shirting and blouse fabric made in plain weave but with two ends weaving as one. Contrasting colours in warp and weft give a miniature diced pattern.

Panama

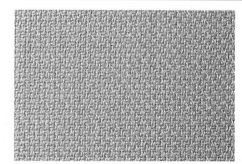

General term for a plain-based weave where two or more warp and weft yarns interlace as one, giving a chequered appearance. Made from cotton for shirts, tropical suits and leisure wear, or wool for suits and costumes.

Panne velvet

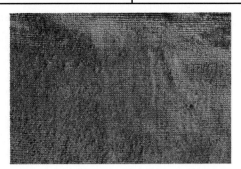

A light weight, highly lustrous velvet fabric made from filament yarns. The pile is flattened and laid in one direction during finishing, by means of heavy rollers. Used for sophisticated womenswear.

Pepita

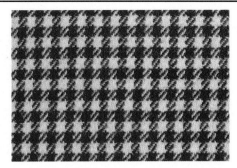

Particular form of shepherd's check which, in contrast to houndstooth, does not show the jagged edges to the squares (see page 68). Used for suits and costumes.

Piqué

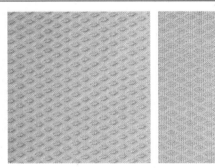

Cotton double cloth showing rounded, wavy welts in the weft direction, with pronounced sunken areas between. The face fabric is in plain weave with fine yarns. Used for women's Summer clothing.

Plush

Woven or knitted fabric with a long pile, more than 3 mm. The pile is usually acrylic and may be printed to imitate an animal skin. Used as fleecy linings and imitation furs.

Plaid

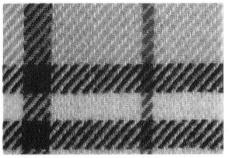

Large, colour woven checks in cotton, viscose, acrylic, wool, or blends. Often raised and brushed for warm linings in jackets and coats.

Pocketing

Cotton plain woven fabric made smooth and dense by calendering, for pocket linings.

Poplin

Plain woven fabric with fine weft-way ribs made by using a fine, densely sett warp over a coarser weft. Used in different weights for shirts and blouses, jackets and trousers, or coats.

Pongé

Very fine, plain woven fabric in pure, degummed, unweighted silk or synthetic filament yarns. Used for linings, blouses, squares.

Renforcé

Originally a strong, heavy sailcloth; nowadays also a medium weight plain dyed or printed plain cotton fabric of the percale type for blouses, dresses and bed sheets.

Reversible

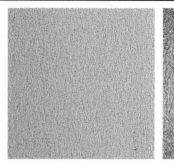

A fabric with different appearance on the two sides, either of which can be used as the face. Usually has either a very dense warp or a very dense weft. Used for dresses and costumes.

Rib

Woven fabric with pronounced ridges in either the warp (weft rib) or the weft (warp rib) direction. Warp ribs are more common. Made in any fibre but often in cotton, wool and silk for dresses, costumes, coats, and furnishings.

Haircloth

Stiff and springy fabric made with a cotton warp and horsehair fibre weft. Used for interlinings in coats and suits.

Sand crêpe

Apparel weight fabrics in the crêpe weave. Short yarn floats in no discernible pattern give an irregular surface texture. Used for dresses and blouses.

Satin

General term for fabrics woven in the satin (or sateen) structure, with a smooth surface and supple drape. Used for dresses and blouses, linings and sheetings.

Velour, knitted

Velvet-like knitted fabric made from a plated loop-pile fabric by cutting and shearing the loops. Used for leisure wear and children's wear.

Velvet

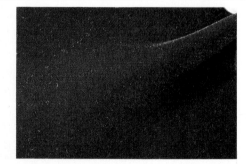

General term for woven cut pile fabrics with a pile height up to 3 mm. The pile is formed from an extra yarn system. Used for sophisticated clothing and furnishings.

Henrietta

Very soft and supple fabric woven in 2/1 twill with a silk or other filament warp and fine wool weft. Used for blouses, dresses, skirts.

Seersucker

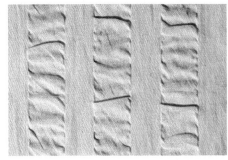

Cotton fabric with crinkled length-way stripes caused by differential shrinkage. True seersucker is generated by differential warp tensions but finishing treatments can produce a similar effect. Used for blouses, shirts, dresses.

Serge

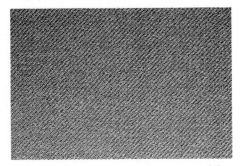

Densely woven twill fabric. Wool serge is lightly milled and raised for suits and costumes. High lustre viscose filament serge is used for linings in lounge suits and coats.

Shantung

Plain weave fabric originally made with raw tussah silk. The yarn irregularities and occasional thicker threads in the weft give a rough texture. Used for dresses, blouses and furnishings.

Shetland

Soft, shaggy, woollen fabrics usually in regular twill weaves. Often made from mottled yarns containing a proportion of stiffer hairs. Used for suits, costumes and coats.

Surah

Soft, lustrous, silk fabric with distinct, fine twill lines for blouses, ties, dresses and furnishings.

Plain jersey

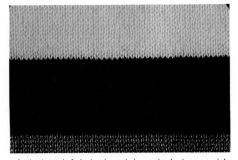

Single-sided weft knitted fabric in plain stitch in a wide range of weights. Usually in cotton for shirts, blouses, nightwear and T-shirts.

Taffeta

A general term for smooth, closely woven plain weave made from filament yarns and showing a faint weft-way rib due to a higher density of warp than weft. Handle is firm to stiff. Used for linings and evening wear.

Toile de soie

toile (Fr.) = fabric,
soie (Fr.) = silk

Softly, flowing, fairly open plain weave fabric in soft twist filament silk yarns for blouses, dresses, fine nightwear, lingerie, and bed clothing.

Tricotine

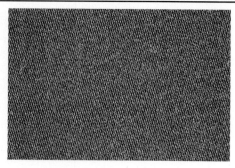

Firm, durable, clean-finished, warp faced fabric with a fine, steep twill line. Also known as cavalry twill. Used for trousers, uniforms and coats.

Tropical

Light weight Summer suiting made in a wide range of weaves and fibres. Fine, hard-twisted worsted fabrics in plain weave are wrinkle-resistant and breathable and have been termed "Cool Wool".

Woollen

Heavily milled, raised, brushed and cropped woven woollen fabric with a dull lustre for suits, costumes and coats.

Tulle

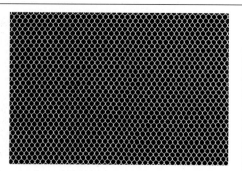

Plain net fabrics made on a bobbinet machine or simulated by warp knitting. The honeycomb-type structure may be used as such or as a base for embroidery, for sophisticated blouses and dresses, trimmings, layering or veils.

Tweed

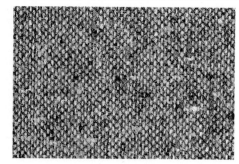

Homespun-type woven woollen fabrics made from coarse, irregular, mottled yarns. Often warp and weft have contrasting colours. Used for jackets, suits, costumes and coats.

Twill

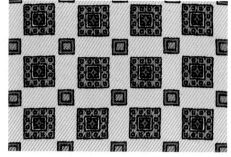

Soft, light twill weaves, usually printed, often in filament yarns for dresses, blouses, ties, scarfs.

Velour, woven

Soft, closely woven fabric with a short thick pile formed by raising, brushing and sometimes cropping. Used for jackets and coats.

Gingham

Plain woven cotton fabrics with block checks in contrasting colours for shirts, blouses and table linen. Also known as vichy.

Interlining, nonwoven

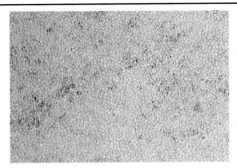

Fibre-bonded, or stitch-bonded nonwovens of various weights. Fusible interlinings are supplied with a full surface coating for stiff reinforcement or dot coated for flexible products.

Voile

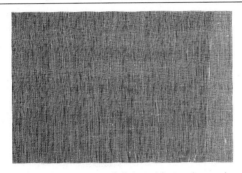

Light weight, sheer, plain woven fabric with a crisp, wiry handle made from hard-twisted yarns, for dresses and blouses.

Honeycomb

Woven cotton fabric in which warp and weft threads form ridges and hollows, giving a cellular appearance. Also known as waffle. Fine qualities for blouses and trimmings; heavier types for towels and bathrobes.

Watteline

Very loose and open warp knitted fabric in tricot stitch, raised on the back. Used for waddings and interlinings.

Weveknit

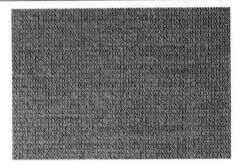

Weft knitted double piqué fabric which has a firm construction and can be handled like a woven fabric. Used for dresses, costumes, trousers, jackets.

Whipcord

General term for densely woven warp-faced fabrics with a steep twill line. In worsted yarns with a clean finish for trousers, suits and coats.

Zephyr

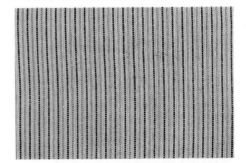

General term for light weight, sheer, soft fabrics used for shirts and blouses. Usually made in plain weave; often colour woven with stripes on a white ground.

Interlinings

The primary purpose of interlining is to ensure that the garment maintains its shape. Stabilisation is achieved by careful attention to edge stitching, layering, and fusing. Shape can be imparted by forming and steaming.

A large number of interlining materials is available to satisfy the widest range of performance requirements, such as elasticity, padding, stiffening, formability, and tolerance to different manufacturing, end use, and aftercare regimes. They may be constructed as woven, knitted, or nonwoven materials and they may be supplied either as fusibles or for sewing.

1:   Stitch bonded nonwoven interlining

**2:   Knitted interlining
(chain stitch with inlay)**

Woven interlinings include haircloth. These are very resilient in the weft direction and cling to the outer cloth because of their rough surface texture. Together with lighter wool interlinings, they are used for the front parts of suits, jackets and coats made from medium to heavy weight fabrics.

Cotton interlinings are suited for the lighter qualities of top cloth. They are often lightly raised which makes them soft and supple and suited for particularly soft applications.

Stiffening fabrics are more or less strongly finished. Cotton stiffeners, such as buckram are used mainly for collars and cuffs in shirts. Linen interlinings are used mainly in men's tailoring. Organza is used as a light stiffener in women's outerwear.

Nonwoven interlinings are available in various strengths. Examples with fluffy surfaces are particularly soft; stitch bonded types are more stable (**Figure 1**).

Warp knitted interlinings are smooth and elastic, like locknit, or soft and open, like watteline. Other stitch variations, such as chain stitch with inlay, can be both flexible and stable (**Figure 2**).

Linings

The purpose of lining is to upgrade the quality and value of a garment by improving both its appearance and its performance. It helps the outer cloth to hang well and protects it from perspiration, rubbing, and staining. Lined garments keep their shape better, are easier to put on and remove, and are warmer. Seams and stitchings are neatly covered and thin fabrics are made less transparent.

Linings also allow the construction of invisible details such as outer pockets and inside pockets, covering of lapels and small parts, finishing of waistbands, and back panels for waistcoats.

The main **requirements** for linings are comfortable wearing properties and tolerance to use, dry cleaning and washing conditions. These are secured by appropriate choice of fibre type, fabric structure and density, and finishing. Linings are often constructed from filament yarns of viscose, polyester, acetate, nylon, cupro, or silk.

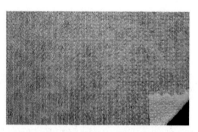

3:   Serge lining

Body linings are used to line jackets and coats, dresses and skirts, trousers etc. Examples are taffeta, serge, satin, duchesse, croisé, pongé, changeant.

Sleeve linings are often striped designs on a light ground.

Waistcoat linings are in colour and weave effects such as faconné.

Warp knitted linings made from nylon or viscose are extensible and easy to fit.

Pocket linings have to be dense and have good abrasion resistance. Cotton materials such as moleskin and pocketing are heavily finished. Brushed fabrics are warm; synthetic fibre fabrics are very durable.

Warm linings are used for the insides of jackets and coats. Examples are quilted fabrics, brushed plaid, and plush.

A garment is made not only from the apparel fabric but also various accessory items. These have to be chosen in such a way that they complement the outer fabric, both aesthetically, in terms of decoration, and practically, in terms of ensuring that the garment performs as expected in its intended end use.

The manufacture of ribbons, tapes, and decorations is similar to that of textile fabrics; weaving, knitting, braiding, or nonwoven techniques. In many cases, different patterning elements are combined such as fibre and colour effects, structure and finishing.

The commercial names for ribbons often follow from the application or the structure, for example piping ribbon, velvet ribbon. Decorative ribbons (trimmings) are also used for ornamentation.

Ribbons and Tapes

1: Ribbons and tapes

Name	Features, Properties, Applications
Trimmings	General name for a patterned, woven or knitted ribbon in cotton, silk, wool, or man-made fibre.
Scalloping, Rick-rack	Narrow bowed, zigzag, or scalloped ribbon, plain or multi-coloured in cotton or man-made fibres for edge trimming of traditional costumes and children's wear.
Elastic tape	Highly elastic, flat, braided band containing rubber or elastomer fibres.
Button hole tape	Broad elastic tape with button holes located in the centre.
Piping	Cotton or linen plain woven ribbon about 1 cm wide, used as a tailoring aid for edges, reveres, and collars.
Moiré ribbon	Cotton, silk, or man-made fibre ribbon with a moiré pattern for hat bands and bows.
Seaming tape	Cotton or viscose twill woven tape for stabilising seams.
Welted tape	Cotton or viscose tape with a narrow welt at the edge.
Ribbed tape	Cotton, silk, or viscose tape with pronounced ribs for decoration or for waistbands.
Bias binding	Tape cut on the bias (diagonally) in various widths and materials, plain or patterned, either flat or folded for use as binding.
Velvet ribbon	Cotton, silk or viscose narrow-woven velvet; sensitive to handling.
Stamped tape	Interlining tape with pre-stamped marks to show sewing width and seam allowance. Allows more efficient working.
Taffeta ribbon	Filament yarn ribbon, plain or check patterned, for ribbon bows.
Galloon	A particularly supple, plain or patterned braided ribbon for piping or binding in outerwear.

Decorations

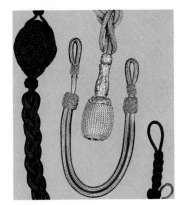

2: Decorations

Fringes	A narrow edging of projecting yarns which are not woven into the fabric, in viscose, wool, or silk.
Cords	Circular braided materials of various thickness in viscose, cotton or synthetics. Used as decoration for clothing, in household textiles, and in sporting goods.
Tassels	Expensive, hand-made articles in silk or viscose. A combination of fringes, cords, and braids.
Rosettes	Decorative items used either alone or in combination with ornamental textiles.
Soutache	A mouldable flat braid with two ribs in silk or viscose, used for formal clothes.
Pompons	Bunches of wool, silk, or synthetics used as trimmings, hanging alone or in groups.

Fastenings include buttons, hooks, press studs, zips, etc. They can also be used for decoration.

Buttons

The size of a button is given in millimetres. The shape may be round, elongated, oval, crenellated, rhomboid, globular, flat, etc. Buttons are secured to the fabric by means of attached or machined rings, by elongated loops of yarn, or by stitching through a set of two, three, or four bored holes.

Polyester buttons are resistant to heat and dry cleaning. They are produced in imitation horn and mother of pearl for all sectors of the clothing industry, especially for shirts, blouses, and lingerie.

Nylon buttons are made in a wide range of colours and shapes. They can imitate all kinds of natural materials and are used in women's and men's outerwear, sports and leisure wear.

Metal buttons are made in brass, nickel or aluminium with an engraved or stamped face and used for blazers, jeans, knitted waistcoats, and traditional costume.

Leather, or **imitation leather** buttons are sensitive to moisture and not very resistant to abrasion. They are used in leather and sports jackets as well as knitted jackets.

Wood buttons, made from many different woods, are light and sensitive to heat and moisture. They are suitable for knitted goods and sporty outerwear.

Mother of pearl buttons, from the mussel shell, with their uneven scintillating surface, are very expensive decorative buttons. They are resistant to heat, maintain their lustre and are used for women's outerwear and lingerie.

Ivory, **horn**, **amber**, **porcelain**, **plexiglass**, **jet**, **tortoise shell**, and **buffalo horn** are now of reduced importance, being replaced by synthetic materials.

1: **Buttons**

Other Fastenings

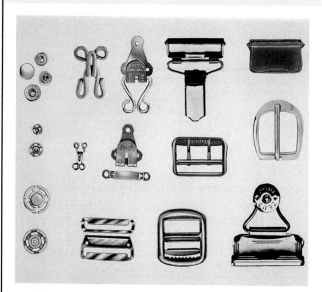

Next to the button, the **zip fastener** is the most important fastening accessory. For light weight and fine fabrics plastic zippers should be used. For trousers, the tab of the slider has a locking tooth. Metal zippers for sporting goods are broad and firm. Single and double sided zippers are used in leisure and sportswear.

Velcro fastenings have one surface covered with small nylon hooks and an opposite surface covered with loops.

Hooks and eyes in a wide range of sizes and types are used for trousers, skirts, dresses and foundation garments.

Press studs in various sizes are made from metal or plastic. The type which require no stitching are practical and economic.

Buckles and **clasps** are made from metal, leather or plastic. They are used to fasten narrow articles such as belts and suspenders.

2: **Other fastenings**

6 Leather and Fur

6.1 Leather Manufacture (1)

The conversion of hides and pelts to leather is one of the oldest of human activities. Hides and pelts can not be utilised in their raw state because they decompose quickly and become hard and brittle when dried. Therefore, it was necessary to develop tanning materials and processes to preserve the hides. Different regions developed different tanning and preservation techniques, including smoking, mastication (Eskimos), use of fats or various bark extracts (tannins) dissolved in water.

Traditional tanning techniques were not refined and improved until the 19th century with the development of technology for extraction, manipulation, and storage of tanning materials. The first synthetic tannins were introduced at the beginning of the 20th century.

The Raw Hide

Raw hides are produced in and exported from many different parts of the world.

The hides of cattle, lambs, sheep, pigs, deer, and reindeer are all used for leather clothing.
There are two basic types

- **domesticated hides**, from farmed animals, and
- **wild hides**, from wild animals.

Structure of the Hide

outer skin (epidermis)	—— keratin layer	ca 1% of the skin
grain layer	⌐ papillary layer └ reticular layer	
corium	—— main part of the structure made into leather	
under side (subcutaneous material)	—— removed before tanning	

The following terms are also used

- **Grain side**, the outer side with respect to the animal; also called the skin side, and
- **Flesh side**, to which the subcutaneous connection tissue adheres; also called the suede side.

Skin Quality

The hides of large animals (cow, horse, buffalo) are called hides; those of the smaller animals (sheep, goat, pig) are called skins. When the skin or hide is laid out, different areas can be recognised which are given specific names **(Figure 1)**.

1: **Parts of the hide**

The highest quality is found in the butt area. Large hides are sometimes cut into segments (segmented). The segments will usually correspond to the butt (first grade) shoulder (second grade) and belly and flanks (third grade), and will be processed separately. Smaller skins are almost always processed whole, without segmenting. Most clothing leather comes from skins rather than hides.

The Tannery

There are three stages in leather production:

- preparation or beamhouse
- tanning
- finishing

Preparation (Beamhouse)

2: **Soaking in vats**

The skins have almost always been cured or preserved so they can be stored until needed. Skins which have not been preserved ("green skins") must be put into work immediately. There are three main stages in preparation.

Soaking: the dried or salted skins are softened in water containing additives such as detergents, salts, enzymes etc. This removes dirt and restores the moisture to the skin which has been removed by curing or preservation.

Liming: the skin is treated with a chemical (originally lime) to loosen and remove the hairs. Very thick hides, intended for shoe leather may be split at this stage.

Fleshing: a machine is used to strip away any material which can not be made into leather, leaving the hide or skin in a clean state, ready to absorb the tanning chemicals.

As a final preparation, the skin may be shaved, smoothed and trimmed.

The Tanning Process

The skin is placed in the tanning drum (**Figure 1**) from which it takes up the tanning liquor. The liquor penetrates into the protein fibres and converts them into leather fibres. Thus a new substance is created with new properties, especially resistance to water and decomposition.

There are several tanning systems:

Vegetable tanning	The tannins are natural extracts of certain barks, woods, fruits, leaves, or vegetables.
	The tanned skins are light brown to dark reddish brown and can not be dyed to light shades. They are also rather heavy.
Mineral tanning	This is the most popular. About 80% of all apparel leathers are tanned with chromium salts. Other mineral salts, such as aluminium salts, can also be used. Chrome leather is grey-green in colour. It is easy to dye, is strong, light, and with good resistance to sunlight.
Oil tanning (chamois)	Oil tanning is an organic, though not vegetable-based process. The skin is impregnated with the type of fatty acid ester which absorbs oxygen. Typically cod oil is used.
	The chamois process is used predominantly for hides such as deer and elk, and for sheep skin which is made into cleaning leathers.
Combination tanning	It is possible to tan by a combination of methods, e.g. semi-chrome for clothing which is a vegetable tannage followed by a chrome retannage.

Finishing

The tanned skins are finished in the sequence described briefly below to obtain apparel leathers.

Dewatering	Excess water is removed by pressing and by passing the tanned skins through thick felt-covered rollers.
Drying	A warm air drying tunnel reduces the moisture content further.
Shaving	The leather is scraped on the flesh side to produce a uniform thickness.
Dyeing	There are several ways to dye leather. Drum dyeing (**Figure 2**) with a wide range of dyestuff types, but predominantly acid dyes. Brush dyeing, in which the colour is applied only on the leather side, is uncommon. Spray dyeing is also used for blotch effects and to colour crust leather (flattened, dried skins).
Oiling (fat liquoring)	Oil is applied, usually as an emulsion, to render the leather supple.
Drying	The leathers are brought into a chamber with a controlled temperature and humidity to dry.
Staking	Repeated stretching and bending to soften the leather.
Sueding	For nubuk leather, the grain side is buffed. For suede, the flesh side is buffed using emery paper to abrade the surface.
Finishing	A lustrous and protective coating may be applied usually to the grain side to improve the appearance and handle.
Glazing	The lustre can be enhanced on a glazing machine (**Figure 3**).
Waxing (brushing)	The waxing machine imparts a subdued lustre to the grain side (important for blotch dyed materials).

1:   **Tanning drum**

2:   **Leather dyeing**

3:   **Glazing**

Every animal has its own individual skin character. The pore structure depends on the animal's coat - fleece, hair, or bristle - yielding a range of grain patterns from very fine (as in lamb) to deeply-marked (as in pig).

Every hide has two distinct surfaces; the outer face is the hair side or the grain side. This side is used to make smooth leather. The grain side may be buffed with a very fine emery to make a fine suede (nubuk). The flesh side of the hide is rough. It is buffed to give a short, silky suede finish.

Thick hides can be split into two or more layers. Split leathers are rough on both sides; they are heavy and have a strong handle. Splits are used mainly for upholstery and shoe suedes, but sometimes for garments where very large panels are needed.

1: Leather section

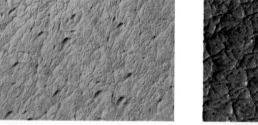

2: Split Cowhide

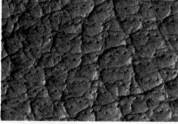

3: Calfskin leather

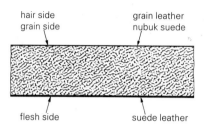

4: Calfskin[1]

Calfskin is a very expensive leather with a fine and uniform grain.

Calfskin suede is a top quality leather because of its elegant, silky surface.

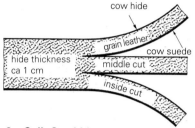

5: Cowhide[1]

Cowhide is a strong and durable leather which keeps its shape. It has a fine, regular grain.

Cow suede may be used for clothing.

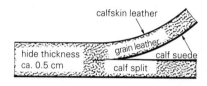

6: Goatskin[1]

Goatskin has a coarse grain and is used for expensive clothing.

Goat suede has a silky surface and a soft handle; it is elegant and keeps its shape.

7: Lambskin[1]

Lambskin has the finest grain, light weight and a soft handle; a fine and sophisticated clothing leather. Lower quality skins may exhibit ribbiness or show double hiding (folds).

Lamb suede has a short nap. In early wear, some loose fibres may be shed.

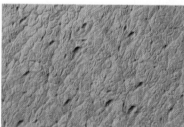

8: Pigskin[1]

Pigskin is a high value, durable leather. The strong pig's bristle leaves a pronounced pock-marked, sporty appearance on the grain side and typical perforations on the suede side.

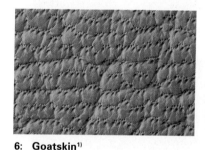

9: Deerskin[1]

Deerskin is a true wild leather with a rustic, heavily grained pore structure.

[1] enlarged photograph

1: Leather skin

2: Cutting templates in place

3: Cutting tools

4: Producing a seam

5: Leather clothing

Because of their limited size, it may take from 6 (for a jacket) to 15 (for a coat) skins to make a garment.

The area of each skin is measured with a pinwheel or with a computerised electronic instrument. It is given in square feet. 1 square foot = 30.48 x 30.48 = 929 cm^2.

The construction of a quality garment from several skins, with their natural variations, requires a great deal of know-how. Economic garment manufacture can be achieved only with properly rationalised production technology.

Following are the separate stages of garment manufacture.

Sorting

The skins are sorted according to colour, thickness and structure. In spite of the fact that 3000 to 4000 skins may have been dyed in the same drum, there will be natural variations in the way that the colour is taken up. The different shades have to be identified and grouped. The sorter has to have a very good eye for colour and texture because it is important that different skins in the same garment must look the same.

Cutting

Leather can not be cut using automated equipment, as is used for textiles. Leather cutting is an expensive, manual process using knives.

Since every skin is different, the following points have to be watched carefully during cutting.

- different sizes
- irregular areas such as scars, bellies
- variations in colour and sueding
- holes, tears

The cutter places his cutting templates on the skin in such a way that he makes the best use of the material whilst avoiding the faults and irregularities. The parts are cut out using a razor sharp knife.

Interlining

A tape made of woven or nonwoven material, carrying a dot-coated adhesive, is used to strengthen the edges, collars, reveres, etc. Application may be done with an iron or a press.

Sewing

All leather qualities, from fine skins to suede splits can easily be converted into clothing, using high speed sewing machines, special equipment, and robots. During all seaming operations, the leather is guided and moved manually through the sewing head by the operator, because this is where the highest demands on quality are felt. A seam which has to be unpicked will leave a trail of holes. Visible seam lines must be right first time. Conditions for a clean and strong leather seam are as follows.

Needle size (metric)	80 to 130
Feed type	alternating: top and needle feed
Presser foot	roller or teflon
Yarn size (metric)	50 to 70

Glueing

After sewing, seams, hems, and linings may be dressed with a special adhesive and pressed. This lays the seams flat and gives the required stability to the garment. In modern clothing production, glueing is increasingly being replaced by the improved design and effective use of interlinings.

6.4 Fur Types

Furs are nearly always used as cold weather garments. They are designated as long or short, rough or smooth, according to their length and density.

Furs are produced from the pelts of a wide range of animals. Currently about 8 to 10% of furs come from wild animals and 90% from specially bred and farmed animals. Trade in wild animals is governed by the Washington Agreement on protected species (CITES), to which more than 90 countries are voluntary signatories. It is reviewed every two years by participating states. Appendix 1 of the agreement lists those animals in which trade is completely forbidden; appendix 2 lists those animals which may be traded only by express permission of the country from which they are to be exported.

For several years the breeding and trading of fur animals has been surrounded by controversy over conservation. Therefore the highest standards are laid down by the agreement on conservation of species concerning the breeding of fur animals.

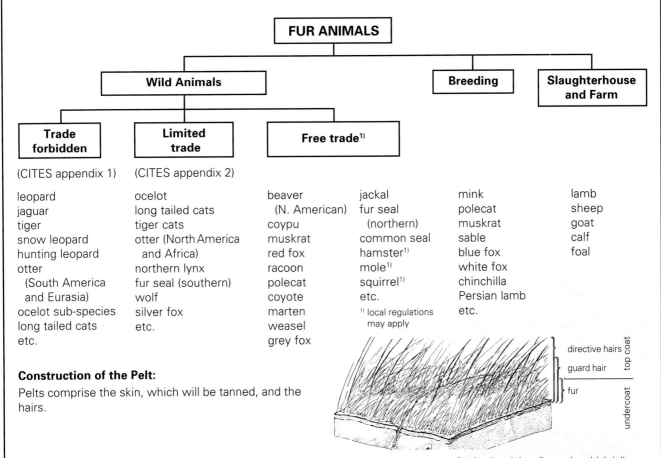

```
                          FUR ANIMALS
            ┌──────────────┴──────────┬──────────────────┐
       Wild Animals                Breeding      Slaughterhouse
   ┌────────┼────────┐                            and Farm
Trade    Limited    Free trade[1]
forbidden  trade
```

(CITES appendix 1) (CITES appendix 2)

leopard	ocelot	beaver	jackal	mink	lamb
jaguar	long tailed cats	(N. American)	fur seal	polecat	sheep
tiger	tiger cats	coypu	(northern)	muskrat	goat
snow leopard	otter (North America	muskrat	common seal	sable	calf
hunting leopard	and Africa)	red fox	hamster[1]	blue fox	foal
otter	northern lynx	racoon	mole[1]	white fox	
(South America	fur seal (southern)	polecat	squirrel[1]	chinchilla	
and Eurasia)	wolf	coyote	etc.	Persian lamb	
ocelot sub-species	silver fox	marten	[1] local regulations	etc.	
long tailed cats	etc.	weasel	may apply		
etc.		grey fox			

Construction of the Pelt:

Pelts comprise the skin, which will be tanned, and the hairs.

directive hairs — top coat
guard hair
fur
undercoat

The different layers of hair may be more or less prominent, or absent, according to the type of animal and the climate in which it lives.

1: Protected species: tiger

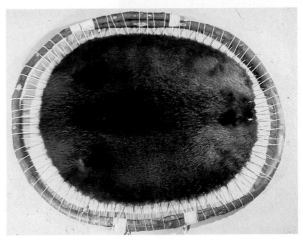

2: Canadian beaver (stretched)

123

6.5 Pelt Preparation

In leather production, the hair is separated from the skin before tanning. However, in fur production the pelts have to be processed in such a way that the hair remains firmly attached. This is accomplished by up to 140 separate mechanical or chemical processing stages. A few of the important stages are described below.

1: **Red fox: Western (left), Eastern (right)**

2: **Soaking**

Soaking   (Figure 2)

The raw pelts are preserved by drying so they are hard and brittle. The pelt is brought back to its original condition by immersion in water, either stationary or agitated. Fine furs can not withstand mechanical action.

Washing

Heavily stained pelts, such as lamb and sheep, or pelts with a high grease content which can withstand mechanical action, are washed in a neutral liquor.

Fleshing   (Figure 3)

The flesh is stripped from the underside of the pelt either manually or by machine. Removal of the subcutaneous tissues allows better penetration by chemicals in subsequent processes.

Pickling, Dressing

A solution of acid and salt causes the hair to be firmly locked into the skin, as a preparation for tanning.

Tanning

The skin is converted into leather using mineral salts or synthetic tannins. The degree of tanning has to be very precisely controlled in order to maintain a good bond between skin and hair.

Oiling

The tanned leather is treated on the flesh side with animal, or vegetable, or synthetic oils in order to impart a durable softness.

Dewatering and Drying

Loose water is removed by centrifuging and pressing. The remaining liquid water is dried off in special drying rooms or machines.

Sawdust Drumming, Conditioning

Excess oil, dirt, salts etc. are removed, the hairs are polished, the leather is softened, and the correct moisture content is obtained by tumbling in warm air in a drum containing beech wood sawdust with a particle size of about 1mm. The sawdust particles are later shaken out in a separate cage drum.

Shaving   (Figure 4)

The leather side is shaved to achieve the required thickness and uniformity of thickness.

Stretching   (Figure 5)

The pelts are stretched in length and width to recover their original shape.

Mending

A final process in which faults or blemishes are ameliorated.

3: **Stripping the flesh**

4: **Shaving**

5: **Stretching**

Pelt Finishing

Pelt finishing is the modification and enhancement of the appearance of the fur.

Colour Adjustment

The natural colour of the fur may be enhanced, or made more uniform.

Dyeing

In principle, a wide range of colours is possible but the actual range is restricted by quality considerations. Pale shades require a pre-bleaching which can lead to weakening of the hairs. Pelt leathers are also sensitive to water temperatures above about 60°C. The so called fur bases (oxidation colours) with good light-fastness are generally preferred. The fur can be given the pattern of exotic animals, by hand painting or using spray guns or stencils.

Shearing and Deburring

The fur may be shorn, either all over or selectively, or the guard hairs may be removed by plucking.

Sueding   (Figure 1)

In order to have a two-sided pelt, the leather side may be retanned and given a polished or a suede finish.

Ironing

Special rotating ironing machines with combs and heated rollers are used to remove distortions and irregularities, to enhance the gloss of the fur.

1: Sueding Persian lamb

From Pelt to Fur Clothing

Depending on the type of fur, there may be from 25 to more than 45 different stages in creating a garment from a prepared pelt. This can not be done in the same way as with a textile fabric. It is first necessary to create a larger, harmonious assembly from a collection of relatively small pelts.

Pelt Selection and Cutting Pattern   (Figure 2)

First the material requirements for each cutting pattern must be calculated, according to the type of fur and the manufacturing style. Then the pelts must be selected. If the calculation is not correctly made, there may be too few pelts, so the garment can not be completed, or too many, so the garment is too expensive.

Stretching and Cutting

If the pelt does not lie flat, it is cut and stretched over the edge of a table. This flattens it and gives it the proper shape. Where appropriate, the pelts are cut into shapes which are specific to particular animals. Portions which are cut away, such as the hoof and tail areas, will be used in patchwork furs.

Mending   (Figure 3, page 126)

Upgrading the pelt and making it usable by removing or correcting faults as well as marking on the leather side to indicate nonuniformities in dyeing or hair height, brand marks, or structural peculiarities.

Sorting   (Figure 3)

This is one of the furrier's most important tasks. Sorting is the assembly, in correct placement, of all of the pelts that will go to make a garment. This determines the appearance of the finished product. Successful sorting is heavily dependent on skill and experience; there are no fixed rules but the best pieces are placed where they will be most apparent in the garment, such as the back, collar, front edge, and top of the arms. Sorting is according to colour, lustre, hair structure, and pelt size.

After these processes, the pelts have to be assembled into a larger piece. There are several ways to do this, depending on the type of garment, the type of pelt and the required effect. The pelts will first be cut into sections and the sections will be sewn together in particular patterns.

2: Pelt selection

3: Sorting for a mink coat

6.7 From Pelt to Fur Clothing (2)

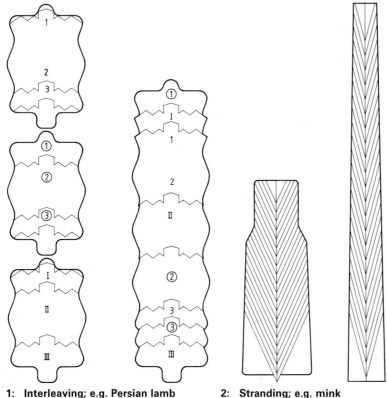

1: Interleaving; e.g. Persian lamb

2: Stranding; e.g. mink

3: Pelt repair

4: Stranding at the fur machine

5: Rearranging

6: Cut pelt (front). Sewn (stranded) pieces (behind).

Cutting Techniques

During cutting, it is important to ensure that only the leather is cut; the hair must not be damaged. Cutting is done either with a furrier's knife or on a cutting machine. There are several cutting techniques.

Assembly: This system is also known as whole-pelt sewing. The pelts are simply sewn together side by side and end to end, without significant alteration of their natural size and shape.

Interleaving (Figure 1): This technique allows pelts to be enlarged or made smaller. Two or more compatible pelts are cut across their widths into shoulder, back, and rump sections to form interlocking shapes which later can be sewn into invisible joins. When the pieces are reassembled with the appropriate sections from several pelts interleaved, the effect is of a single pelt of several times the length. The width is extended by sewing several interleaved panels together, to make an area sufficient for a whole garment.

Stranding (Figures 2, 4, 6): This technique allows short, wide pelts to be converted into much longer, narrower pieces, having a uniform fur structure from top to bottom, without cross sewings. Stranding is a very expensive procedure but it gives an elegant chevron effect e.g. in mink coats.

In **Figure 2** a pelt about 50 cm long is cut into narrow strips in a V formation. The strips are then assembled into a strand of about 120 cm on the fur sewing machine. Because the colour and structure of the fur has been changed, the strands must then be sorted again to decide exactly how to assemble them into a whole garment. Finally, the strands are sewn together to obtain an area sufficient for the garment piece.

Rearranging (Figure 5): Variations in hair structure and colour can be evened out by cutting the pelt into narrow longitudinal strips which are then systematically rearranged. The strips are numbered in order and then assembled into two or three smaller pieces, e.g. using strip numbers 1, 3, 5 and 2, 4, 6; or 1, 4, 7 and 2, 5, 8 and 3, 6, 9.

Trimming: Pelts with a pronounced undercoat can be cut into strips and assembled together with leather strips to achieve a uniform effect.

1: Shaping

2: Garment assembly

3: Stranded mink coat

Shaping

The assembled pieces destined for individual garment parts are moistened on the leather side and are stapled to a cutting pattern engraved on a wooden platen (**Figure 1**). Moistening makes the leather more or less plastic so that it can be shaped to the required form. After a twelve hour drying period, and after removal from the platen, the shaping is retained. The seams are smoothed out using wooden shapers with rounded edges or with seam rollers, especially when the stranding technique has been used.

Conditioning

After removal from the wood platens the pieces are again conditioned in sawdust (see page 124) and then cut exactly to the required pattern.

Finishing

Since the fur may have been more or less compressed by the heavy forces it has endured during some of the previous procedures, a range of final finishing processes is carried out to restore the fur to its original condition. These may include ironing, beating, conditioning, glazing and combing.

Garment Assembly   (Figure 2)

The individual pieces are strengthened with interlining, then assembled on the fur sewing machine into the finished garment, and finally lined.

Construction of Furs Compared to Textile Clothing

Different construction techniques have to be used for furs, as compared to textiles, because of the basic differences in properties and behaviour.

- Sewing techniques have to be quite different. Textile seams are made with excess fabric at the seams; furs are joined edge to edge in a butt seam. Therefore the garment pieces in a fur article have to be measured and cut exactly right, since corrections can not be made by letting out or bringing in the seams.

- Furs can not be allowed to suffer stretching in use, since they will not recover from extension. Therefore stretching is prevented by the application of interlinings. Every garment must be assembled from its parts in such a way that possible distortions, caused by stretching when damp, are avoided. The designer must always take heed of the shape, the size, and the placing of individual pelts in a garment.

- The supple and uniform draping qualities of textiles can not be obtained in furs, because of the natural variations in thickness, weight, and roughness which will be found within a given garment. A large size fur garment can be uncomfortably heavy for women, and also will be very expensive.

- Novel fashionable effects can be obtained through printing, shearing, and patchwork techniques.

7 Functions of Clothing   7.1 Basic Functions and Requirements

Basic Functions

Together with food and shelter, clothing is one of the three basic needs of humans. It fulfils many requirements:

1: Protection

2: Decoration   3: Identification

Protection

Clothing serves as protection against the elements, heat, cold, wind, rain and snow, and against injury at work, in transport, or in sport (**Figure 1**). In addition clothing should supplement the thermal regulation system of the human body. Even in climates where clothing is not required for protection, it may still be used simply to avoid nakedness.

Decoration

Every age has its own fashions for the decorative function of clothing. Through fashion, wearers proclaim their own personality and individuality. As the old saying goes, "clothing makes the man" (**Figure 2**).

Identification

Clothing can also signal the belonging of an individual to a more or less specific group within a given society or geographical region (**Figure 3**). Examples are traditional costumes, uniforms of police, military or fire services, and the dress codes of social movements such as punk, or football fans.

These basic functions condition the various requirements which are placed upon clothing.

Requirements

General

Suitability
The basic requirements of protection, decoration, and identification must be satisfied.

Appearance
It should fit properly and present an appearance appropriate to the wishes of the wearer.

Stability
It should maintain its intended form and be durable.

Comfort
It should remain comfortable within the range of environments for which it is intended.

Aftercare
It should retain its shape and function through laundering and cleaning.

Physiological

Clothing physiology is the study of the interaction between the human body and its clothing in different environments (**Figure 4**). The comfort of a person in a given situation depends on these interactions.

A person can be subjected to many different environments and his bodily requirements can vary widely. An involuntary, internal regulation system always attempts to maintain the body temperature at about 37 °C. Under normal circumstances, heat is continuously being dispersed from the body through the skin (about 90%) and through respiration (about 10%). During vigorous activity, the body produces a great deal of excess heat (**Figure 5**).

If the generation of excess heat is greater than can normally be dispersed, then the body reacts by producing an increased flow of liquid perspiration at the surface of the skin. Evaporation of the perspiration has a strong cooling effect. If the dispersal of heat from the body is greater than that which is being generated internally, then the body begins to chill (hypothermia).

In order for the wearer to be comfortable, clothing must participate in regulating the interchange between the body and its surrounding microclimate through insulation, ventilation, moisture absorption, and moisture transport. By appropriate choice of clothing, even extreme climatic conditions can be accommodated.

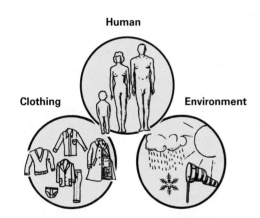

4: **Interaction between body and clothing in different environments**

Situation	Heat generation
sitting still	ca 100 Watt
walking	ca 350 Watt
vigorous sport	ca 1000 Watt

5: **Heat generation by humans**

1: Shaping

2: Garment assembly

3: Stranded mink coat

Shaping

The assembled pieces destined for individual garment parts are moistened on the leather side and are stapled to a cutting pattern engraved on a wooden platen (**Figure 1**). Moistening makes the leather more or less plastic so that it can be shaped to the required form. After a twelve hour drying period, and after removal from the platen, the shaping is retained. The seams are smoothed out using wooden shapers with rounded edges or with seam rollers, especially when the stranding technique has been used.

Conditioning

After removal from the wood platens the pieces are again conditioned in sawdust (see page 124) and then cut exactly to the required pattern.

Finishing

Since the fur may have been more or less compressed by the heavy forces it has endured during some of the previous procedures, a range of final finishing processes is carried out to restore the fur to its original condition. These may include ironing, beating, conditioning, glazing and combing.

Garment Assembly   (Figure 2)

The individual pieces are strengthened with interlining, then assembled on the fur sewing machine into the finished garment, and finally lined.

Construction of Furs Compared to Textile Clothing

Different construction techniques have to be used for furs, as compared to textiles, because of the basic differences in properties and behaviour.

- Sewing techniques have to be quite different. Textile seams are made with excess fabric at the seams; furs are joined edge to edge in a butt seam. Therefore the garment pieces in a fur article have to be measured and cut exactly right, since corrections can not be made by letting out or bringing in the seams.

- Furs can not be allowed to suffer stretching in use, since they will not recover from extension. Therefore stretching is prevented by the application of interlinings. Every garment must be assembled from its parts in such a way that possible distortions, caused by stretching when damp, are avoided. The designer must always take heed of the shape, the size, and the placing of individual pelts in a garment.

- The supple and uniform draping qualities of textiles can not be obtained in furs, because of the natural variations in thickness, weight, and roughness which will be found within a given garment. A large size fur garment can be uncomfortably heavy for women, and also will be very expensive.

- Novel fashionable effects can be obtained through printing, shearing, and patchwork techniques.

Basic Functions

Together with food and shelter, clothing is one of the three basic needs of humans. It fulfils many requirements:

1: Protection

Protection

Clothing serves as protection against the elements, heat, cold, wind, rain and snow, and against injury at work, in transport, or in sport (**Figure 1**). In addition clothing should supplement the thermal regulation system of the human body. Even in climates where clothing is not required for protection, it may still be used simply to avoid nakedness.

Decoration

Every age has its own fashions for the decorative function of clothing. Through fashion, wearers proclaim their own personality and individuality. As the old saying goes, "clothing makes the man" (**Figure 2**).

Identification

Clothing can also signal the belonging of an individual to a more or less specific group within a given society or geographical region (**Figure 3**). Examples are traditional costumes, uniforms of police, military or fire services, and the dress codes of social movements such as punk, or football fans.

These basic functions condition the various requirements which are placed upon clothing.

2: Decoration   3: Identification

Requirements

General

Suitability
The basic requirements of protection, decoration, and identification must be satisfied.

Appearance
It should fit properly and present an appearance appropriate to the wishes of the wearer.

Stability
It should maintain its intended form and be durable.

Comfort
It should remain comfortable within the range of environments for which it is intended.

Aftercare
It should retain its shape and function through laundering and cleaning.

Physiological

Clothing physiology is the study of the interaction between the human body and its clothing in different environments (**Figure 4**). The comfort of a person in a given situation depends on these interactions.

A person can be subjected to many different environments and his bodily requirements can vary widely. An involuntary, internal regulation system always attempts to maintain the body temperature at about 37 °C. Under normal circumstances, heat is continuously being dispersed from the body through the skin (about 90%) and through respiration (about 10%). During vigorous activity, the body produces a great deal of excess heat (**Figure 5**).

If the generation of excess heat is greater than can normally be dispersed, then the body reacts by producing an increased flow of liquid perspiration at the surface of the skin. Evaporation of the perspiration has a strong cooling effect. If the dispersal of heat from the body is greater than that which is being generated internally, then the body begins to chill (hypothermia).

In order for the wearer to be comfortable, clothing must participate in regulating the interchange between the body and its surrounding microclimate through insulation, ventilation, moisture absorption, and moisture transport. By appropriate choice of clothing, even extreme climatic conditions can be accommodated.

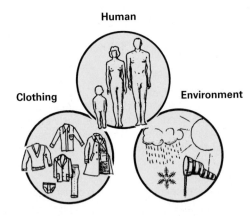

Human

Clothing   Environment

4: Interaction between body and clothing in different environments

Situation	Heat generation
sitting still	ca 100 Watt
walking	ca 350 Watt
vigorous sport	ca 1000 Watt

5: Heat generation by humans

Ecology and the Textile Pipeline (1)

Ecology is the study of the relationships between life and its physical environment.

Conservation of and responsibility for the environment is a duty of all human enterprises, since every generation must bequeath a safe and healthy environment to the next. Textiles are worn in intimate contact with the body; they form a personal environment which should be protected by appropriate systems of manufacturing and eventual disposal.

General Principles of Environmental Conservation

- **Avoidance**
  of materials which stress the environment

- **Reduction**
  in consumption of materials

- **Recycling**
  of used materials

Collaboration is required between manufacturers, retailers, consumers, and legislature. Legislation should be directed towards those areas which are most important in preserving and enhancing the quality of life. Examples are the regulations governing the handling of hazardous and poisonous substances, and controls on emissions, waste, and water purity.

The interactions between man, textiles, and the environment are demonstrated by life cycle analysis of a given product through the whole textile pipeline (**Figure 1**).

Fibre production	Yarn production	Fabric production	Finishing	Clothing manufacture	Wearing, Aftercare: laundering, dry cleaning	Recycling Incineration, Burial
Manufacturing					**Utilization**	**Disposal**

1: **The textile pipeline**

Life-cycle Analysis		
Input		**Output**
Material requirements	P R O C E S S I N G	**Products**
Raw materials Fibres, yarns, fabrics		**underwear stockings outerwear** etc.
Auxiliary materials Dyes, solvents, Oils, fats, lubricants, other chemicals		
Packaging	U T I L I Z A T I O N	**Waste**
Office supplies		**special waste useful by-products residuals**
Other materials		
Factory plant		**Use of land**
Water		**Waste water**
Air		**Exhaust air**
Energy production, Transportation Gas, oil, coal electricity	D I S P O S A L	**Emissions, Dust, Noise** energy consumption energy dissipation energy recycling
Land		**Stress on Land**

2: **In a life-cycle analysis, the resources required for production and consumption of a product (inputs) are set against the value of the products and their environmental consequences (outputs). Source: Kunert**

Life-cycle Analysis

A life-cycle analysis attempts to determine the impact upon the environment of a product throughout its whole lifetime (**Figure 2**). It considers the consumption of raw materials, energy, chemicals, water, etc. in production, utilization, and disposal. Industry is beginning to make increasing use of life-cycle analysis because there can be positive advantages in identifying potential for savings in materials and energy. Life cycle analysis is a relatively new discipline which has not yet been standardised or fully developed.

Ecology and Manufacturing

Economic production of natural fibres requires fertilisation and irrigation of the land, and protection of the plants or animals against pests and diseases. There is a risk of degrading the soil and contaminating groundwater if the proper precautions are not taken. The production of man-made fibres, either from natural polymers or from fossil fuels requires expensive chemical processes. In spinning, weaving, and knitting, chemicals are required as lubricants and protectives. Chemicals are indispensable in finishing: for colouration and to enhance the fibre and fabric properties. In many production stages there is the risk of contaminating the air or water; noise and waste are generally produced and considerable quantities of energy are consumed. The textile industry world-wide makes extensive use of road, rail, sea, and air transport. Large quantities of packaging materials are used both for transportation and for final presentation to the consumer.

Ecology and the Textile Pipeline (2)

Measures which can be taken to reduce the impact of manufacturing upon the environment include:

- **Improved agronomic practices**, such as breeding new varieties, integrated pest management, soil conservation, computer-controlled fertilisation and irrigation, use of non-persistent pest-control chemicals.
- **Improved process management**, such as minimizing the consumption of water, energy, and chemicals; substitution of persistent chemicals with biodegradable ones; introduction and observation of environmental controls; installation of more "environmentally friendly" plant and machinery. The disadvantage is the enormous cost of implementation which leads to higher product prices. Industries which have few environmental controls also have lower manufacturing costs.

Ecology and Utilization

Wearing of Clothing

Adverse reactions of the human skin to clothing are rare. They usually are connected with wearing very tightly fitting clothing, abrasive materials or nickel plated buttons or other decoration. In very rare cases, allergies have been found to certain dyestuffs (benzidine derivatives), dyeing auxiliaries (carriers), or formaldehyde derivatives (easy-care finish), natural rubber and silk gum (sericin). Various so-called "eco labels" have been devised (see below) which guarantee that the products have been tested and found to contain not more than certain permitted levels of various chemicals which (when present in highly concentrated form) may be injurious to health.

Clothing Aftercare

Laundering and dry cleaning require energy, water, and chemicals. Laundering assistants contain primarily detergents, bleaching agents (oxidants, fluorescents) and water-softening agents (phosphates). Phosphates are fertilizers; they can cause eutrophication of waste water by encouraging the growth of plant life (algae). Modern washing powders and liquids use substitutes for phosphates which are usually biodegradable. Dry cleaning uses hydrocarbons to dissolve greasy soil. Modern dry cleaning processes are closed systems, subject to strict regulation, in which the solvent is almost completely recycled.

Eco-labelling

There is a demand from some consumer groups that textile labels should give information about any potentially harmful chemicals which may be contained in the product. In various countries, either governmental or private organisations have developed sets of criteria which can be embodied in a labelling scheme to satisfy these demands. A typical example from Europe is the label for "Textiles Tested for Harmful Substances" by the "Eco-tex Standard 100" (**Figure 1**). This label guarantees that:

- no potentially carcinogenic dyestuffs have been used
- heavy metals are present in such small quantities that their concentration, when dissolved in perspiration, would be lower than the permitted levels for drinking water
- pesticides are present in concentrations lower than those permitted for foodstuffs
- formaldehyde shall not exceed a certain concentration
- the pH value is neutral or slightly acid (like human skin)
- textiles intended for babies and small children shall not release any dyestuff on contact with saliva

1: Eco-tex Standard 100 label

For a given textile product to participate in such a labelling scheme, it is necessary that, periodically, samples of the product are taken from the manufacturer or distributor, and subjected to the appropriate testing regime, in an independent laboratory, to ensure that they conform to the requirements of the label.

The Eco-tex Standard 100 label was developed by Austrian and German research (testing) laboratories and has now been extended to several other laboratories across Europe. These laboratories carry out testing of textile products to ensure that they conform to certain criteria with respect to their concentrations of certain chemicals.

Ecology and Disposal

The useful life of clothing can be extended by various second-hand clothing collection and redistribution schemes. Used clothing can also be recycled to some extent by tearing them apart to regenerate a fibrous raw material for use in making textiles, insulation, and soundproofing. The suitability of a textile for recycling depends on the basic fibre composition. Cellulose and protein fibres are biodegradable so they can be put to landfill. Synthetic fibres are not decomposed. Under some circumstances it is possible to regenerate the original fibre-forming polymer, or they can be incinerated. Recycling is difficult (expensive) when a textile is made from different raw materials. In principle, for example, polyester/cotton blends can be recycled by dissolving out the polyester component with an appropriate solvent.

7.2 Clothing Physiology

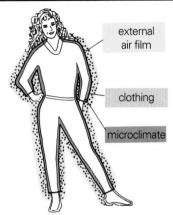

1: Insulation from clothing

2: Air movements affect the microclimate

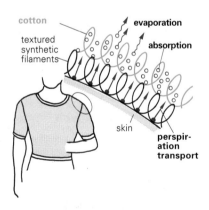

3: Functional aspects of double-layer sportswear

Heat Insulation and Air Exchange

To prevent excessive heat losses in cooler climates, the body's natural thermal regulation mechanisms have to be supplemented by **insulation**. For a stationary person, about 50% of the insulation is provided by air trapped inside the clothing, about 30% by the external air film, and about 20% by the fibres. Thus, the enclosed air is the most important insulator (**Figure 1**). Bulky constructions, having a large volume of enclosed air have good insulation properties and are especially suitable for Winter clothing; thin, smooth fabrics are better for warm environments.

To maintain an equable balance of heat and moisture in the **microclimate**, between skin and clothing, some **ventilation** is required. Air exchange is regulated mainly by three factors.

Firstly it depends on the **surface texture**, mediated by fibre type, yarn and fabric construction, and finishing.

Secondly it depends on the **garment construction**. Tight-fitting garments will restrict ventilation and may lead to discomfort due to a build-up of heat and moisture. Loose garments can promote ventilation like a chimney.

The third influence is **motion** which can be provided externally by wind or by transportation (such as a bicycle), or internally by the pumping action of body movements such as working (**Figure 2**) or running. Motion disturbs one or more of the various air layers and thus reduces heat insulation considerably.

The so-called "functional clothing", i.e. work- sports- and protective clothing, may regulate ventilation by various enclosures. A very effective supplement to the human thermoregulation system is obtained by providing more or fewer layers of clothing (the onion effect).

Moisture Absorption and Moisture Transport

The human thermoregulation system dispenses dry heat and, according to the heat load, more or less moisture. This moisture has to be taken up and dispersed by the clothing. This is accomplished by **absorption** into the fibres and by **capillary transport** between the fibres. At normal levels of heat stress and low to medium levels of perspiration, hygroscopic (absorbent) fibres are preferable (see page 45). Their absorptivity is quite sufficient to take up the released moisture and to transport it, by diffusion within the fibres, to the surface where it is evaporated into the external air layer. When perspiration rates are very high, then more liquid moisture is formed which has to be transported by capillary action (wicking). Wicking is much faster than diffusion so greater quantities of moisture can be transported to the outside. However, if the rate of evaporation at the surface is much less than the rate of generation of liquid perspiration at the skin, then the fabric may become saturated which leads to the uncomfortable "wet cling" effect. Because fabrics made from non-absorbent (synthetic) fibres dry more rapidly, the wet cling effect may persist for a shorter time and so, provided that their construction allows efficient wicking, non-absorbent fabrics may feel more comfortable under some circumstances than absorbent ones.

Special **double-layer** fabrics have been developed for sportswear in which the inner layer of the fabric comprises a non-absorbent, synthetic material in a yarn with excellent wicking properties whilst the outer layer is made of an absorbent fibre such as cotton (**Figure 3**). Liquid perspiration is transported rapidly through the inner layer to the outer where it is stored and evaporated. The inner layer remains (or quickly becomes) dry so the wet cling effect is avoided or minimised. Good results can also be obtained by using mixtures of fibres with different absorptive capacities (page 45).

Next-to-Skin Comfort

The sensation of contact of clothing with the skin can be very comfortable (softness, suppleness) or it can be unpleasant (scratching, prickling, clinging). These sensations depend mainly on the fineness of the fibres and their moisture content. Coarse fibres tend to yield scratchy and prickly sensations.

Perspiration can build a film on a smooth fabric surface, which can cling to the skin and feel uncomfortable; a similar effect can arise on dry skin through static charging of the fabric. An irregular or hairy fabric surface makes fewer contacts with the skin. This allows the air to move more freely between skin and clothing.

Requirements for Protective Clothing

Protective clothing is used to guard against potential harm in the workplace, from the weather, or during sporting activities. Protection has to be achieved without excessive hindrance to free movement, by suitable choice of materials and construction. Durability and maintenance requirements must also be appropriate for the end use. It is not always possible to fulfil all of the technical and practical requirements simultaneously.

Applications for Protective Clothing

Protection against	Groups at risk	Protective measures
Rain **Snow** **Wind**	Hikers, construction and farm workers, community, emergency, and military services	**Wind and weather** protection with impregnated and laminated fabrics, microfibre fabrics and membrane systems e.g. Gore-Tex®, Sympatex®
Extreme cold **Snow and ice**	Winter sports, cool-room workers, polar researchers, astronauts	**Low temperature** protection from multiple-layer and wadded clothing
Extreme heat **Fire** **Sparks**	Furnace, forge and foundry, glass and ceramics workers, welders, fire fighters, racing drivers, astronauts	**High temperature and flame** protection from flame retardant finished fabrics, special synthetic fibres, lamination with aluminium
Mechanical forces	Mountaineers, welders, foundry workers, motor cyclists, fencers, police, military	**Injury** protection by padded leather or fabrics made from special fibres, e.g. Kevlar®
Smoke **Toxic fumes** **Acids, Alkalis**	Chemical workers, emergency services	**Chemical** protection with waterproof and gas proof fabrics e.g. rubber coating; special nonwovens with activated carbon
Dust	Workers in micro-electronics and optics, spray painting and finishing	**Clean-room** filters from special nonwovens
Water **Hypothermia**	Surfers, divers	**Surfing and diving suits** made from elastomeric fabrics e.g. Neoprene® or rubber
Radiation	Welders, atomic energy workers	**Radiation** protection with special synthetic fibres; leather welders aprons
Bacteria	Doctors, hospital staff	**Bacterial** protection using dense fabrics with smooth surfaces for low particle retention and easy cleaning
Electrostatic charge **Electric current**	Surgeons, high-voltage line workers	**Highly conducting** fabrics including carbon or metal fibres (Faraday cage effect)

1: Fire service uniform

2: High temperature protection

3: Low temperature protection

7.3 Protection (2)

Weather-proof clothing is particularly important, both in the workplace and also in sports and leisure activities.

1: **Weather-proof clothing requirements: resistant to wind and water but permeable to vapour**

2: **Water resistant fabric**

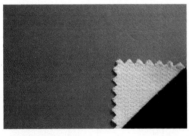

3: **Coated fabric**

4: **Fabric with membrane lining**

5: **Fabric with laminated membrane**

Function of Weather-proof Clothing

The main purpose of weather-proof clothing is to keep out wind and rain, but also cold, whilst allowing perspiration moisture to escape from the body (**Figure 1**). If these requirements are not met then, even under normal conditions of exertion, either the body becomes soaked with perspiration or the clothing becomes wet, which can lead to hypothermia.

There are various textile constructions which are more or less capable of fulfilling these requirements. Liquid water is prevented from entering by having fabrics with a dense, smooth and hydrophobic (non wetting) surface. Water vapour can diffuse outwards between the yarns and fibres, driven by the higher temperature and vapour pressure on the inside of the garment.

Traditional Weather Protection

Heavily-milled and raised wool fabrics and densely-woven fabrics of cotton, nylon, or polyester, with a hydrophobic finish will resist the penetration of water for a certain time (**Figure 2**). However, with continuous exposure to severe conditions, clothing made from such materials will eventually become wet and its protective value will diminish.

For a complete and durable barrier to wind and water, coated textiles can be used (**Figure 3**) which, however, normally do not permit the escape of water vapour.

Modern Weather Protection

Modern textile constructions are impermeable to water, or resist wetting for a longer time, whilst allowing water vapour to diffuse through. When made from synthetic fibres they are also easy-care. Four basic systems can be distinguished.

• **Microporous coatings**

The coating has very fine pores which allow the passage of water vapour but not liquid water.

• **Microporous membranes**

These are very fine films, about 0.02 mm (the thickness of domestic cling-film), containing very fine pores. They are used either by laminating onto a textile structure or by interleaving between two fabrics (**Figure 4**). In Gore-Tex® the membrane is made from polytetrafluoroethylene (PTFE).

• **Hygroscopic membranes**

Hygroscopic means water-absorbing. They take up the perspiration and transport the vapour through the continuous film to the outside. Sympatex® is a hygroscopic membrane made from polyester (**Figure 5**).

• **Microfibre fabrics with a hydrophobic finish**

This is a development of the traditional technology, in which very fine synthetic fibres are used to make tightly woven fabrics having very small pores. These are better able to resist wetting and penetration by liquid water whilst still allowing water vapour to diffuse. As with the traditional technology, a hydrophobic finish enhances the water resistance. Examples are Tactel® in nylon and Trevira-Finesse® in polyester.

8 Clothing Manufacture   8.1 Overview

Organization is a resource for company management. Its purpose is to achieve the fulfilment of certain defined tasks by creating a structure of tasks and responsibilities. The specific tasks are allocated to individual persons at identified production stages, and/or groups of individuals are allocated to specific production stages.

The following organization chart (organigram) serves as a connecting thread throughout this chapter and also provides an overview of the relationship between the individual stages of production.

Organization of a Clothing Manufacturing Company

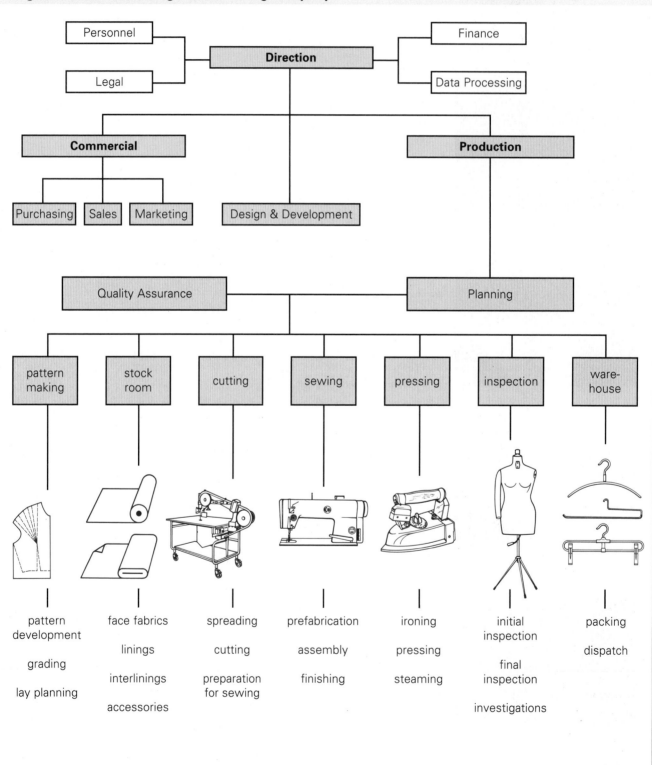

8.2.1 Design, Pattern Construction

Design

1: Design sketch   **2: Modelling**

3: CAD System[1]

Design in the clothing industry means determining the shape and the cutting pattern of a garment. The traditional method (haute couture, bespoke) is to make a concept drawing and then actually to model it on a dummy mannequin. Modern technology offers systems, which allow concept sketching to be accomplished on a computer using a colour monitor. A wide variety of shapes, colours and patterns can be selectively "painted" at will to individual areas of the figurine on the screen.

Pattern Construction

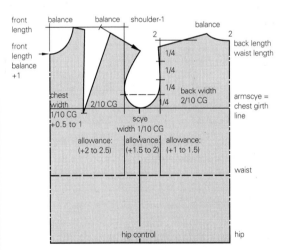

4: Manual pattern construction

A pattern draft is a diagrammatic representation of the way a garment is constructed. This forms the working plan for its manufacture.

The pattern draft is geared towards a specific cutting system; the objective is to develop a set of templates (patterns) for the cutting room to use.

The pattern draft is developed by calculation, taking account of the following measurements.

- actual **body size** measurements,
- **size charts**, related to the end use and derived from anthropometric[2] studies (see page 194),
- **grading increments** derived from body measurements and size charts.
- **ease allowances** (cf page 194)

[1] CAD: Computer aided design
[2] anthropometric: measurements made on human bodies
[3] digitise: convert into a series of numbers for the computer

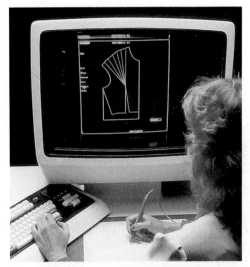

5: Computer aided pattern construction

In practice the development of a new collection is usually effected by appropriate modification of existing, stock designs (block patterns). These are basic patterns constructed from appropriate body measurements but without any styling features. This time-consuming work is made considerably easier and faster through the use of a CAD system.

The basic patterns must first be digitised[3] but, once this is done, they can then be retrieved from the computer, displayed on the screen and modified at any time. Thus the whole shape can be adjusted, lines can be deleted or extended, lines and points can be superimposed.

Darts can be altered, parts can be moved and rotated. The result can be saved, in a range of sizes, and is immediately ready for use in generating the lay plan.

This procedure is fast becoming standard practice in the industry.

Grading means the stepwise increase or decrease of a master pattern piece to create larger or smaller sizes. The starting point can be the smallest size or the middle size. Grading alters the overall size of a design but not its general shape and appearance. Computer-aided grading systems utilise internal calculation algorithms (grading rules) for pattern construction.

Manual Grading

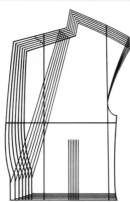

1:   Grading a front piece

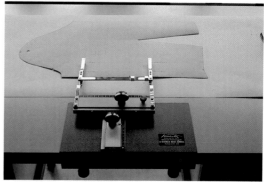

2:   Grading machine

The desired range of sizes is created, one by one, using a pattern template. Marks are made around the master pattern at the appropriate distances and the marks are later joined up to form the enlarged pattern.

In this way a full set of templates, the "pattern set", is generated.

A grading machine eases the task of creating the pattern set. The device grips the master pattern and displaces it by a precise vertical and horizontal distance, after which the appropriate edge can be traced.

Computer-aided Grading

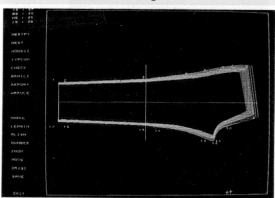

3:   Grading on the computer screen

4:   Printing the pattern at a plotter

Computer based grading systems operate in one of two ways:

1. The grading increments are fed into the computer and the different sizes are generated automatically using the same method as applied for manual grading.

2. The pattern for each individual size is calculated separately starting from the data in the size charts.

   The resulting nest of patterns can be displayed to scale on the computer monitor for visual assessment and, if necessary, adjustment.

Once the pattern set has been generated on the computer, it may be used in various ways, depending on the level of automation in the factory.

In a fully automated system, the garment parts will be sorted automatically and arranged into a lay plan which can then be transmitted in the form of a control program to the automatic laying and cutting system. Alternatively, the patterns can be sent to a large plotting device where they will be drawn at full scale to serve as paper patterns for manual cutting. The patterns can also be used in an automatic device for cutting templates from more durable material.

The cutting templates representing all of the individual components of a garment have to be laid out together in such a way that they fit within the confines of the fabric width as closely and efficiently as possible, in order to minimise waste. This is the lay plan.

Guide-lines for the Lay Plan

The templates have to be laid in a way that takes account of the directional properties of the fabric, such as thread directions, pattern direction, grain of nap or pile. It may also be necessary to allow for matching of stripes, checks, or designs.

Orientation and Direction

The orientation of the pattern templates will depend on the construction of the textile material and its pattern design features. There are three basic types of orientation.

Fabrics for which neither the orientation nor the direction is important e.g. random-laid non-woven fabrics.

Fabrics for which the orientation is important but the templates may be laid in either direction e.g. linings and laminated fabrics.

Fabrics in which orientation and direction are both important e.g. pile fabrics, fabrics with a directional pattern or pile, knitted fabrics.

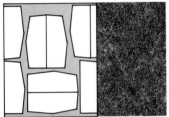

1: Nonwovens

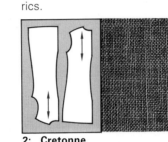

2: Cretonne

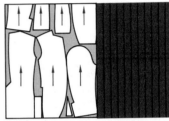

3: Corduroy

Pattern Matching

The quality of a product is affected significantly by the accuracy of pattern matching. A flawless execution, especially with checks and stripes, demands a high consumption of fabric and takes a great deal of time. The colouring, the repeat size, and the prominence of the pattern, as well as the degree of matching required between individual garment pieces are crucial in determining the cost and difficulty in making the lay plan, in spreading the cloth, and in cutting.

During **spreading**, it is necessary to match the pattern exactly at each end of the lay and in every ply.

Cutting may have to be carried out in two stages, with a preliminary rough cut being followed by more precise second cutting together with pattern matching.

In making the **lay plan**, the pattern markers can not be laid in such a way as to minimise cutting waste; they have to be disposed according to the requirements of the pattern.

4: Pattern matching with stripes

Features of accurate pattern matching

Symmetry: The pattern must be symmetrical about the central axis. Examples: left and right front panels (**Figure 4**), collars and backs.

Lengthwise continuity: The pattern must not be interrupted or displaced at horizontal seams. Example: pockets (**Figure 4**)

Horizontal continuity: The pattern must not be interrupted or displaced at vertical seams or across adjacent parts. Example: arm and front panel (**Figure 5**).

Overall continuity: The form and the repeat of the pattern must be maintained across all seams, facings, trimmings, patches etc. Examples: patch pockets, flaps, darts, facings (**Figure 5**).

5: Pattern matching with checks

8.2.3 Making a Lay Plan (2)

Procedures for Making a Lay Plan

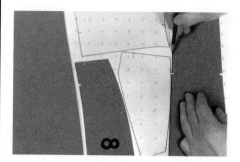

1: **Tracing the templates**

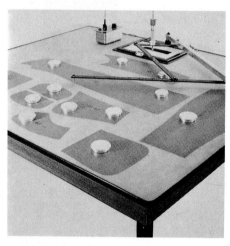

2: **Pantograph**

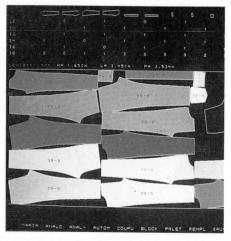

3: **Lay plan on a computer screen**

Manual Methods

The simplest method of making a lay plan is to arrange the cutting templates manually.

The outlines of the templates are then traced either directly onto the fabric or onto a special marker paper (**Figure 1**).

The detailed arrangement of the templates is decided either by experience and know-how, or by following a small-scale printed diagram.

Miniaturisation (pantograph)

Using a pantograph (**Figure 2**), the full-size cutting templates are reduced in a scale of 1:5. This simplifies the task of manual arrangement of the pieces and makes it easier to arrive at a lay which optimises material use and minimises cutting waste.

The miniature lay plan will be photographed or photocopied for archiving, and then enlarged to full scale to provide the actual cutting marker.

Computerised Systems

After grading, the computer can be used to produce the lay plan and the cutting marker. User-friendly systems allow the recall and arrangement of the patterns on the monitor screen, according to given technological requirements (**Figure 3**). Individual pieces can be moved around the screen using a light pen to produce an optimized layout. The more sophisticated programs will make the lay automatically according to predetermined criteria.

These advanced systems will calculate material utilisation and cutting waste, and make the lay accordingly.

The finished lay plan is stored in the computer. It can be recalled and drawn out as a miniature plan at any time. When required, the cutting marker can be drawn at a plotter in full scale.

With the most modern technology, it is not necessary to make a physical cutting marker. The cutting instructions are sent direct (on-line) to the fully automatic cutting machine (see page 140).

8.2.4 Types of Lay Plan

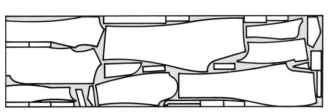

1: Half garment lay

Half Garment Lay

This includes only half of the garment pieces (for example the right side).

They are used for folded or tubular fabrics and for fabrics which are spread face to face (see page 138).

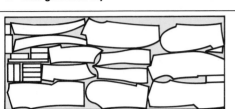

2: Full garment lay

Whole Garment Lay

All of the garment pieces, left and right sides, are included in the lay.

Used for open width fabrics.

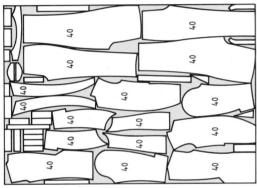

3: Single size lay

Single Size Lay

The lay includes all of the pieces for a single size.

Restricting the lay to a single size makes order planning and laying up the fabric easier, but the disadvantage is a somewhat higher material consumption, compared to multi-size lays.

Multi-size Lays

- **Sectional lay:**

  The lay is made in at least two distinct rectangular sections. Each section contains all of the parts for a single size. Adjacent sections may be the same or a different size.

- **Interlocking lay:**

  Two or more sections, one after the other, usually different sizes, but the sections are not confined to strict rectangular areas; the pieces for the different sections may merge at the borders.

- **Mixed multi-size lay:**

  In this case there are no distinct sections; the pieces for the two or more different garment sizes are intermingled. This is the arrangement which normally gives the best material utilisation.

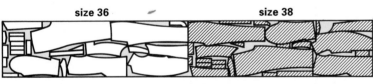

size 36   size 38

4: Sectional multi-size lay for two sizes

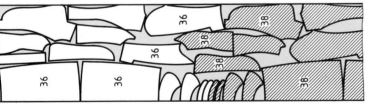

5: Interlocking multi-size lay for two sizes

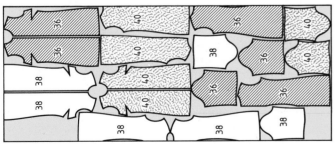

6: Mixed multi-size lay for three sizes

Spreading means the smooth laying out of the fabric in superimposed layers (plies) of specified length. The cutting marker is laid on the topmost layer. The maximum width of the cutting marker is constrained by the usable width of the fabric. The usable width is the width of the narrowest place minus the width of any unusable selvedges. Fabric utilisation is the amount of fabric actually utilised in the marker as a percentage of the total fabric area.

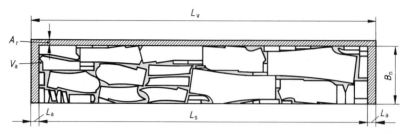

1: **Example of a cutting marker**

L_a End allowance = allowance at the beginning and end of a layer

L_v Lay length = marker length + end allowance

A_r Edge allowance = allowance at the fabric edges

V_a Cutting loss = waste from within the lay plan

B_n Usable width = cloth width - edge allowance

L_s Marker length

Types of Lay

Single ply

A single layer of fabric, e.g. for cutting a prototype garment

Multiple-ply

A number of fabric layers stacked one on the top of the other.

Stepped lay

A multiple-ply lay in which groups of layers have different lengths, e.g. for multi-size lays.

Presentation of Fabrics

Presentation of fabrics means the form in which the material has been delivered.

Presentation depends on the type of material (velvet), the application (sample length, sale in the retail trade) and the internal handling equipment (unrolling stands, platform trolley, fork-lift truck with pallets). Presentation has to be taken into account when making the lay plan and choosing the type of spreading. The following symbols are sometimes used:

open-width:

rolled:

doubled:

wound:

tubular:

plaited:

Forms of Spreading

One-way	Each layer of fabric is laid the same way up, with the grain or pattern running in the same direction. The fabric has to be cut at the end of each ply and, in machine spreading, the carriage must return, inactive, to the beginning of the lay. This method is used for fabrics with a grain or a directional pattern.
Face-to-face	The plies are laid in pairs, face to face. The grain or pattern runs in the same direction. After each ply is cut off, the fabric has to be turned and, with machine spreading, the carriage has to return, inactive, to the starting point. Used for the same types of fabrics as the one-way system.
Two-way	The plies are laid continuously from left to right and right to left, without cutting and without returning to the starting point for each ply. This is the most efficient method of spreading but it can not be used for fabrics with grain or directional patterns.

The fabric is spread out on the laying-up table according to a predetermined plan, as single-ply or multiple-ply, ready for cutting.

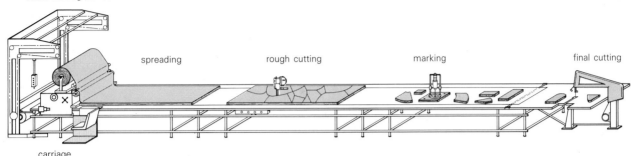

fabric loading device

spreading   rough cutting   marking   final cutting

carriage

1: Sequence of cutting operations

In the first section the fabric is spread into a **lay**.

A lay consists of multiple plies. When a cutting marker is applied, this is a **cutting lay**.

In the second section the individual pieces are cut out roughly or accurately with an electrically driven knife.

Next, various important reference points, such as pocket folds and notches are **marked**.

The final **accurate cutting** of the pieces may be done with templates and a band knife. This procedure allows a high precision to be achieved.

Spreading Methods

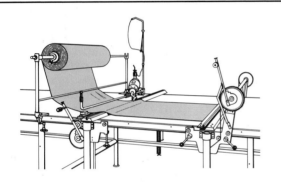

Manual Spreading

The cloth is pulled carefully from the fabric roll by hand and is cut to the appropriate length. Mechanical devices can be provided to facilitate the unrolling and cutting operations but the proper alignment of the fabric edges is the responsibility of the human operator.

This procedure is suitable for short lays and for frequent changes in fabrics and colours. It is often used in small businesses.

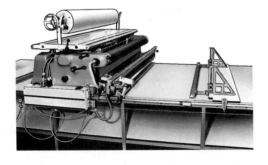

Spreading Carriage

The cloth is unwound and spread semi-automatically, using a manually-driven carriage.

The carriage is moved back and forth over the laying-up table. Built-in mechanisms take care of aligning the fabric edges and smoothing the plies. This system is favoured when the lays are long and broad and/or if the fabric is presented in large batches for relatively large orders.

The method is very efficient and is suitable for small businesses.

Automatic Spreading Machines

The moving carriage has been more or less fully automated to provide a more efficient production for large-scale enterprises.

Common attachments for such equipment include photo cells for correct alignment of the selvedges, fabric loading and threading devices, cutting devices at the end of the lay, a platform on which the operator can sit or stand while the machine is traversing.

In this context, cutting means to cut out the garment pieces from lays of fabric with the help of cutting templates (markers). Generally the marker is applied (drawn, traced, sprayed, stuck, clipped, pinned) to the top ply of a lay.

Cutting often is carried out in two stages; rough cutting (separating the individual pieces) and the final cutting (accurate cutting of the individual shapes). Different types of cutting tools have different degrees of precision.

Circular Cutters	Straight Knives	Band Knives

power shears

circular cutter

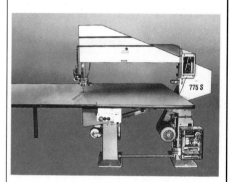

Circular cutting tools use a rotating circular blade.

The smallest devices (power shears) are used for cutting single ply lays and for cutting fabric plies to length during manual spreading. Depending on the size of the device it is possible to cut to a depth of about 10 mm.

The larger circular cutter is used mainly for dividing a lay into sections. It is suitable only for cutting in straight lines or very gradual curves, in depths of up to about 150 mm.

A straight knife cutter, has a vertical blade which reciprocates up and down. It is capable of both coarse and precise cutting to a depth of about 300 mm. Corners and curves can be cut accurately. Since all of the layers are cut at the same place (unlike a circular cutter), and provided that the knife is held vertical, then all of the pieces cut from a lay are identical.

Circular cutters and straight knives are pushed by hand through the stationary material.

The band knife cutting machine contains a narrow, sharpened, endless steel band moving vertically through the layers of fabric. The fabric layers are guided by hand against the blade. An air cushion will often be provided below the fabric layers to make it easier to guide the material. The plies may be stapled together to prevent slippage. Band knives are used for precision cutting to a depth of up to 300 mm. Corners, tight curves and pointed incisions are cut precisely.

Die Cutting	Automatic Cutter

A die cutting machine is provided with prefabricated cutting tools (cutting dies) having the exact shape of the garment pieces. The fabric pieces are stamped out on a base plate. Die cutters are used mainly for leather, coated and laminated material and in areas where the same patterns are used over a long period, e.g. production of working clothes. The dies are expensive to make.

There are also fully automatic, computer-controlled cutting machines. Apart from special vertical knives, it is possible to use laser beams, high energy plasma (ionized gas) beams, and high pressure water jets as the cutting medium.

Position Marking

Special marks or notches have to be made on the garment pieces in order to provide guides for accurate sewing and assembly in the sewing room. These cuts or marks must not be visible in the finished garment.

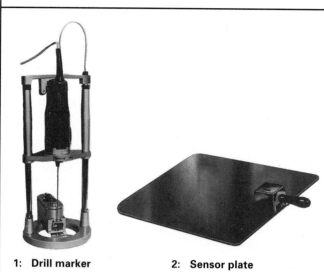

1:   Drill marker   2:   Sensor plate

Drill Marker

A small hole, which will remain visible for some time, is drilled through the fabric layers.

Hot Drill Marker

The drill needle is heated to make the holes more durable.

Dye Marker

The drilled holes are additionally marked by a colour delivered in a fluid which runs down flutes in the drill. A distinct coloured dot can be made on any kind of fabric. Alternatively, a clear fluid can be used which contains a **fluorescent**[1] marker. Thus the dot is visible only under an ultra-violet lamp. Used for marking e.g. pocket locations, dart lengths.

The drill marker may be provided with a **sensor plate** which delivers a buzzing tone when the drill has penetrated through to the bottom layer. This avoids damage to the table top.

3:   Hot notcher   4:   Thread marker

The **hot notcher** is used to make position marks at the edge of a stack of fabric plies. The temperature and the depth of the notch are adjustable.

This device is mainly used for knitted fabrics made of natural fibres. The edges of synthetic fabrics can fuse.

With the **thread marker** a tacking thread is stitched vertically through the layers and is cut off beneath the bottom ply. The thread is then cut between the single layers. If a **fluorescent**[1] thread is used then the mark will have improved visibility where ultra-violet lamps are installed at the sewing machine or other equipment. The thread marker is used when a drill would damage the cloth.

[1] fluorescent: material which emits visible light when irradiated with ultra-violet light.

Preparation

5:   Labelled cut bundle

Preparation means all of the work which has to be carried out prior to sewing, such as numbering, labelling, marking pockets, and bundling. Shade marking is to ensure that components cut from different shades of the same colour -way are not mixed within a garment. Every cut bundle is provided with a numbered ticket. Bundles of components will also be provided with a label containing a serial number, the size and other operational data. The labels have to be clearly visible but must not interfere with further processing (sewing, fusing). Modern labelling systems provide data in computer-readable form, which allow some automation in production control and progress chasing to be introduced.

Tool	Features and Uses
Set-square	Set-squares are made of crystal-clear, shatter-proof synthetic material, metal or wood. They are used in the design and pattern departments.
Pattern square	Pattern squares are generally made of light metal or synthetic material. Their special feature is the curved edge. They are used in the design and pattern department for drawing curved lines (hips, collars).
Hand ruler	The hand ruler is a measuring edge, 20 to 30 cm long, made from flexible plastic. One edge may be notched. It is especially suitable for measuring short distances and placing marks, e.g. distances between pleats or buttons.
Tape measure Waist measuring tape	Tape measures are woven bands with a durable synthetic coating. They are generally 1.5 to 2 cm wide and 1.5 to 2 m in length. They are used to take body measurements and measure curved surfaces. The waist measuring tape has a hook at the end and a series of eyes at appropriate distances.
Pattern wheel, Tracing wheel	Pattern wheels are small toothed or pinned metal wheels. They are used for transferring pattern and construction lines onto paper.
Marking chalk	Marking chalk is made from various materials. Clay chalk can be brushed out easily. Wax chalk is melted by ironing. Synthetic chalk disperses after some time. Marking chalk is applied for drawing cutting lines and positioning marks on the top cloth.
Marking pens	Marks made by marking pens may be self erasing, after 2 to 8 days, or can be removed either by water or by ironing. They are especially useful for marking on the top cloth e.g. pocket positions.
Hem marker Hem tacker	The hem marker applies chalk marks using puffs of air. The hem tacker marks the hem line with a thread. This equipment is used to ensure that hem lines are marked at a uniform height all round.

Sewing Needles and Finger Protection

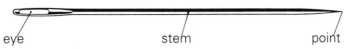

eye   stem   point

1:   The sewing needle

Name	Features and Uses
Sewing Needles	Sewing needles are classified by their length and thickness. The usual types are "standard" and "long".

standard 3 5 7 9	long 1 3 5 7 9	

The numbering system is not directly related to the length or thickness of the needles; it serves only to distinguish one needle from another.

The length and thickness of a needle will be chosen according to the fabric to be sewn, the thread to be used and the sewing technique.

Sewing needles are made of nickel-plated steel. They have to be flexible, smooth and sharp.

Embroidery Needles		**Darning Needles**
pointed 14 16 18 20 22 24	rounded 14 16 18 20 22 24	3/0 1/0 1 3 5 7 9

Embroidery and darning needles are particularly thick sewing needles. Material and yarn thickness determine the length and thickness of the needle to be used.

The numbering system is not directly related to the length or thickness of the needles; it serves only to distinguish one needle from another.

Rounded needles are used for coarse materials; pointed needles are used for finer materials.

Pins / Plastic-head Pins

Pins			Plastic-head Pins		
Length mm	Thickness ø mm		Length mm	Thickness ø mm	Head Colour
30	0.60 extra fine		30	0.60	white
34	0.60 extra fine		30	0.60	black
30	0.70 fine		30	0.60	coloured
34	0.70 fine		40	0.70	coloured
40	0.85 fine		48	0.80	white
			48	0.80	coloured

Pins are made of steel or brass and may have plastic heads.

The length, thickness and type of pins are chosen depending on the type of fabric and the application (component assembly, decoration, packaging).

Dressmakers Thimble / Tailors Thimble

Dressmakers Thimble	Tailors Thimble	
Diameter mm approx		Diameter mm approx
18.0		20
17.0		19
16.5		18
16.0		17
15.0		16
14.0		15
		14

Thimbles are made of steel or brass. The many small depressions are provided to prevent the needle from slipping off.

Protection of the middle finger allows for easier and quicker sewing.

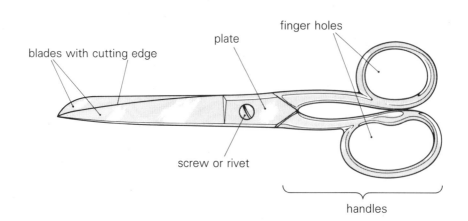

1: Scissors

Types of Scissors	Features and Uses
Paper Shears	Paper shears have long pointed blades. The blades are longer than the handles. They can be used for accurate cutting of thin paper.
Hand Scissors	Hand scissors are designed to be easy to handle, with their differently-shaped blades and finger holes. Hand scissors are used in all general-purpose cutting operations.
Tailors Shears fine serrations	Tailors shears are large and stable. The finger holes are specially contoured, shaped and positioned to make it easier to cut thick fabrics. One of the blades is provided with serrations which helps to prevent smooth fabrics from slipping. Tailors shears are suitable for cutting garment components from single layers.
Pattern Shears	The handles, which are strongly contoured, are much longer than the short, strong blades. In heavy-duty types the blades are screwed on and can be changed. They are used for cutting out pattern templates from thick cardboard, or plastic.
Pinking Shears	The shape and handling characteristics are somewhat similar to tailors shears, but the cutting edges have a zigzag profile. The zigzag edge of the cut fabric reduces the tendency for the cut edge to fray and may provide a more attractive trimming.

Types of Scissors (continued)	Features and Uses
Buttonhole Scissors	A special gap in the blades allows short cuts to be made inside the edge of the fabric. The length of cut can be adjusted by a screw.
Embroidery Scissors	The handles are longer than the narrow and pointed blades. They are suited for catching and cutting fine, short threads.
Snippers	The small, lightly spring-loaded blades open automatically. Allows very rapid and easy snipping and trimming of waste thread, or removal of tacking stitches and opening of seams. Used e.g. in fitting, final inspection, and reworking.

Other Tools	
Stitch Cutter	The stitch cutter has a hooked edge with an arrowhead. It is especially suitable for opening up machine-made button holes.
Awl bone awl steel awl	An awl is made of bone, plastic or metal. It tapers to a point and has a smooth surface. It is used for rounding off button eyes or draw-string holes, and for pulling out threads.
Hole Punch	Punches are available in diameters of 2 mm to 25 mm. The punch is generally used for making holes in card or plastic pattern templates or cutting patterns.
Revolving Hole Punch magazine	The revolving punch has a magazine of punches of different diameters. It is used to make holes close to the edge of the fabric.
Notcher notches made by different clippers	Makes notches of various shapes according to requirements. Used for placing positioning marks on cutting patterns, e.g. balance marks and seam allowances.

8.3.1   Types of Sewing Machine

The simplest form of sewing machine is the flat bed type, with the following basic components:

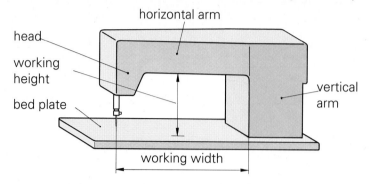

horizontal arm

head

working height

bed plate

vertical arm

working width

Modifications of the basic flat bed machine have been developed for specific operations.

Types of Sewing Machine	Stitch Type	Features and Uses
Flat bed machine (basic type)	lockstitch chain stitch	The large working area allows a wide range of applications; the material can easily be guided around the needle and the presser foot. This basic type is used for all kinds of flat sewing work.
Raised bed machine	lockstitch chain stitch	The bed plate is in the form of a plinth. It facilitates the assembly of pre-sewn parts and is especially suitable for the fitting of accessories and special attachments. This is the basic form for various specialised machines such as buttonholers
Post bed machine	lockstitch chain stitch	This type has an increased working height. Special applications are found in the working of three dimensional products, e.g. shoes and bags. The post makes it easier to work on tight curves and corners, to sew in sleeves and to complete large, half-assembled products.
Cylinder bed machine	lockstitch chain stitch	This type has an increased working height and a bed in the shape of a horizontal arm. It is especially suitable for working on tubular parts, such as cuffs, sleeves, and trouser legs, and also for button sewing and bar tacking. It is used extensively in the making of clothing from knitted fabrics.
Side bed machine	chain stitch overedge stitches	Machines which are specialised for sewing at edges need only a small working area.

Stitch types have been classified, according to ISO 4915:1991, into six basic types.

In the drawings, stitch formation proceeds from right to left. Needle threads are in yellow, underthreads and looper threads are in red, and cover threads of Class 600 are in blue. With overedge sewing, the fabric is outlined thinly.

Name	Features and Uses
Class 100: Chain stitch needle thread Type 101	Each loop is interconnected with the following loop of the same thread. Opposite sides of the seam[1] look different. This stitch type can be very easily unpicked by running back from the last stitch to the first. The seam is generally quite extensible. It is often used for temporary stitching e.g. basting.
Class 200: Hand stitch needle thread Type 209	Formed by single threads being passed completely from one side of the material to the other. The thread is held by the material. Originally made by hand, some of them can now also be formed by a machine. This stitch type is especially suitable for sewing edges.
Class 300: Lockstitch needle thread underthread Type 301	Formed by two different thread systems. A needle thread introduced from one side of the material is interlaced with an underthread supplied from a spool on the other side. The stitch is difficult to unpick and both sides have the same appearance. Generally less extensible than chain stitch seams, this type finds the widest application.
Class 400: Multi-thread chain stitch needle thread looper thread Type 401	Also formed from two thread systems. The loops of the needle thread are drawn all the way through the material and they are interconnected on the underside by thread supplied from a looper. Top and bottom sides have a different appearance. The stitch can easily be unpicked and is quite extensible. Special applications are elastic cross-over seams, seat seams, seams in knitted fabrics and seams which have to be flat e.g. side seams.
Class 500: Overedge chain stitch needle thread looper thread Type 503	Formed from one or more needle and/or looper threads. Needle thread loops are taken all the way through the material and are interconnected with themselves or with another thread. At least one thread system passes around the edge of the material. Overedge stitches of various types are used to neaten and to bind the cut edges of woven and knitted materials.
Class 600: Covering chain stitch needle threads cover thread looper thread Type 602	This stitch type is generally formed from three thread systems. The cover threads lie on the top surface and are held in place by the needle threads which in turn are interlaced on the back of the seam by the looper threads. They are used especially for making flat, extensible seams in knitted fabrics.

[1] One should always distinguish between "stitch types" and "seams", although in practice they are often wrongly used interchangeably. Seam types are defined in ISO 4916.

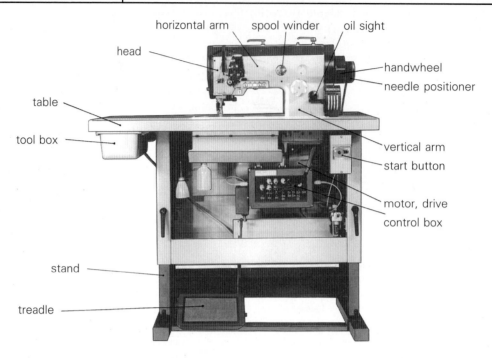

horizontal arm spool winder oil sight

head

handwheel

needle positioner

table

tool box

vertical arm

start button

motor, drive

control box

stand

treadle

1: Overall view (lockstitch machine)

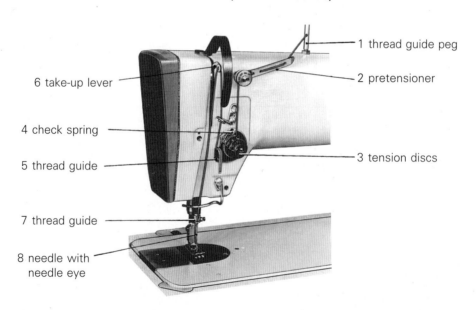

1 thread guide peg

6 take-up lever

2 pretensioner

4 check spring

5 thread guide

3 tension discs

7 thread guide

8 needle with needle eye

2: Head end with top thread guide (lockstitch machine)

Thread Guiding System - Needle Thread

Nr.	Name	Function	Nr.	Name	Function
1	**thread guide peg**	Ensures uniform draw-off (snarling).	6	**take-up lever**	Draws the needle thread from the bobbin. Releases the required length of thread for making the stitch. Tightens the stitch.
2	**pretensioner**	Ensures uniform draw-off.			
3	**tension discs**	Ensures correct tension for looping.	7	**thread guide**	Keeps the thread in its proper course.
4	**check spring**	Evens out tension fluctuations.	8	**needle with needle eye**	Pushes the thread through the material and forms the loop.
5	**thread guide**	Effects a change in direction.			

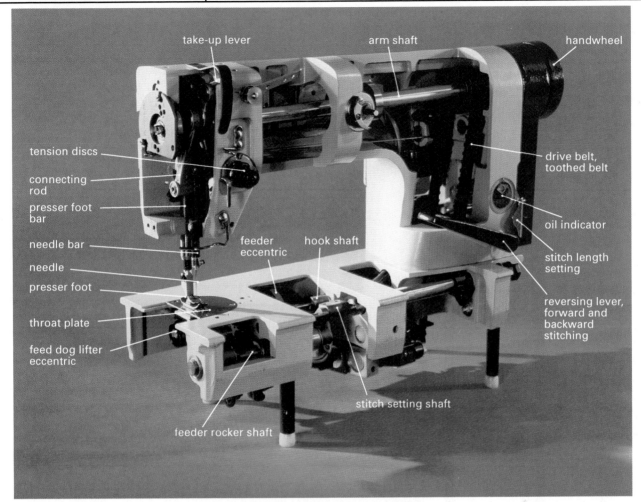

1: Cut-away model (lockstitch machine)

Stitch Formation Parts

Name	Function	Name	Function
Needle	Guides the needle thread through the material being sewn and forms a loop.	**Tension discs**	Ensures the correct tension for proper stitch formation.
Rotary hook	Catches the needle thread loop and lays it around the under-thread spool.	**Presser foot**	Presses the material being sewn against the feed dog and the throat plate. Facilitates stitch formation and feeding.
Take-up lever	Draws the needle thread from the bobbin. Releases the required length of thread for stitch formation. Tightens the stitch.	**Throat plate**	Provides openings for the needle and the feed dog.
		Feed dog	Moves the material forward, by one stitch length, after each stitch has been drawn.

Motions in a Sewing Machine

The following applies to the lockstitch machine illustrated above.

The top shaft is driven from the motor via the drive belt. The bottom shaft is driven from the top shaft via the toothed belt and gear wheels.

The rotary hook is driven by the hook shaft.

The feed dog is lifted by the feed dog eccentric and driven forward by the feeder rocker shaft. Coordination of feeder bar and needle bar is controlled by the feeder eccentric.

The incremental feed length is determined by the stitch length setting, the stitch setting shaft and the feeder rocker shaft.

The top shaft is provided with a crank and connecting rod which convert the shaft's rotation into the vertical movement of the needle bar.

Requirements

The needle has to be able to penetrate the material being sewn, without damaging it, by pushing the yarns aside. Solid materials, such as leather or plastic, will be holed. Sewing machine needles of various types are available, according to the application. Selection of the needle type will depend on the characteristics of the material, the size of the sewing thread, the type of seam and the stitch type.

circular   flattened

1:   Shank cross-sections

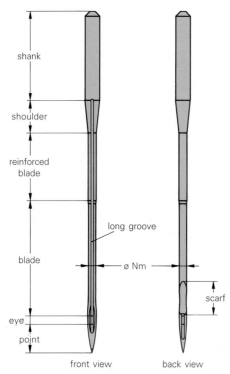

shank

shoulder

reinforced
blade

long groove

blade   ø Nm

scarf

eye

point

front view   back view

2:   Lockstitch needle

3:   Curved needle (blind stitch needle)

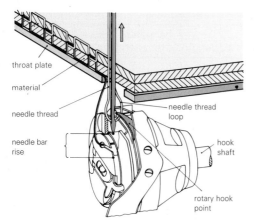

throat plate

material

needle thread

needle thread
loop

needle bar
rise

hook
shaft

rotary hook
point

4:   Forming a needle thread loop

Characteristics and Terminology

The **shank** locates the needle in the needle bar. The following types are found:

- Shanks with a circular section
- Shanks with a flat side which serves to locate the needle in a specific position in the needle bar
- Needles in which the thickness of the shank is maintained all the way down the blade. They are used in speciality machines.

The **blade** of the needle runs from the end of the shoulder to the beginning of the eye. Often the blade will increase in thickness, in stages, from the eye to the shoulder. This reinforcement of the blade increases its stiffness. Moreover, by widening the stitch hole, it tends to reduce the friction between needle and material during the upstroke which can help to avoid overheating of the needle.

There are also needles with curved blades (**Figure 3**), which are used, for example, in blind stitch machines (see page 165).

On the threading side of the needle is the **long groove**. Its function is to guide the thread while forming the stitch and to protect it against excessive friction.

Above the eye there is usually a recess or **scarf** across the whole face of the needle. This facilitates the passage of the hook into the loop and reduces the danger of missed stitches.

The shape of the **eye** is always extended in its length, because the needle thread has to pass diagonally through the needle in the length direction. The width of the eye is the same as that of the long groove.

Needle Sizes

The metric size "Nm" of a needle defines the diameter of the blade (in 1/100 mm) at a point just above the scarf (**Figure 2**).

Fine needles have a size up to about Nm 70; medium needles are about Nm 80 or Nm 90; thick needles have a size greater than about Nm 110.

Forming the Needle Thread Loop

First, the needle thread is carried all the way through the material to be sewn and beyond the underside. As the needle begins its upstroke, the thread is retarded by friction between it and the material so a loop is formed in the needle thread. The loop is caught by the point of the rotary hook, enlarged, and passed around the underthread spool. The needle thread is then withdrawn whilst the stitch is tightened by the movement of the take-up lever. These vertical movements are extremely rapid, so the efficient functioning of the long groove, in permitting smooth passage of the thread, is critically important.

Needle Points

Needles are manufactured with a wide variety of needle points appropriate for the differing properties of materials which have to be sewn. The needle point can be located either centrally –⊙- or eccentrically –◗- .

There are two basic classes of points, namely Round Points and Cutting Points.

Round Points

Round points have a circular cross-section but may have two basic shapes known as Set Points and Ball Points, which are suited for different materials.

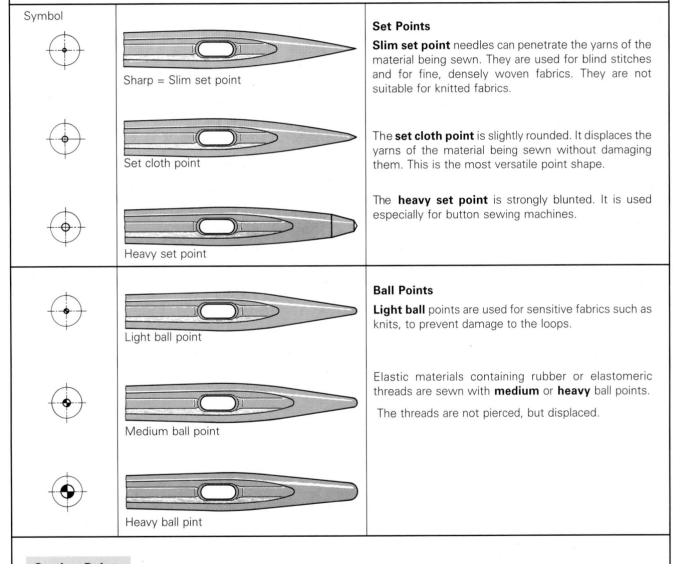

Symbol

Sharp = Slim set point

Set cloth point

Heavy set point

Light ball point

Medium ball point

Heavy ball pint

Set Points

Slim set point needles can penetrate the yarns of the material being sewn. They are used for blind stitches and for fine, densely woven fabrics. They are not suitable for knitted fabrics.

The **set cloth point** is slightly rounded. It displaces the yarns of the material being sewn without damaging them. This is the most versatile point shape.

The **heavy set point** is strongly blunted. It is used especially for button sewing machines.

Ball Points

Light ball points are used for sensitive fabrics such as knits, to prevent damage to the loops.

Elastic materials containing rubber or elastomeric threads are sewn with **medium** or **heavy** ball points.

The threads are not pierced, but displaced.

Cutting Points

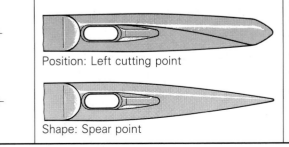

Position: Left cutting point

Shape: Spear point

Cutting points are used for sewing leather and films or coated and laminated textiles.

They are classified and named according to the position of the cutting edge and its shape.

The shapes are named with regard to the form of the cutting edge e.g. spear point, triangular point, diamond point.

Material feed means the controlled movement of the material being sewn from one stitch position to the next. Moving the material through the sewing point is what converts a series of stitches into a seam. In principle the material can be moved in any horizontal direction; in most cases it is only forwards or backwards. Usually the fabric is moved just after the needle point is raised clear of the surface and stops just as it is about to re-enter.

Principle of Material Feed

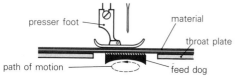

1: **Drop feed**

Material feed is achieved by the feed dog which contains several rows of serrated teeth. The feed dog is moved upwards and forwards through slits in the throat plate to engage with the under side of the material being sewn and to advance it by a distance of one stitch length. Contact between feed dog and material is controlled by the spring-loaded presser foot. The feed dog is then lowered and moved back to its starting position.

Various designs of feed dog, presser foot and throat plate are utilised according to the type of material being sewn and the particular sewing operation. Feed dogs can have different shapes and types of teeth.

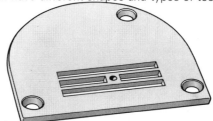

Feed dog   **Throat plate**   **Presser foot**

2: **Feeding system components**

3: **Types of feed dog**

Feed Dog Teeth

Types of teeth	saw-tooth	upright	diamond
	∿∿∿∿∿	∧∧∧∧∧	◣◢◣◢◣◢
Application	single-direction feeding	uniform two-direction feeding	feeding of fine fabrics

Types of Feed Systems

Feed systems usually work on the underside of the material but can also operate from above or from both sides at the same time, depending on requirements and on the need to avoid particular technological problems in sewing (see page 170).

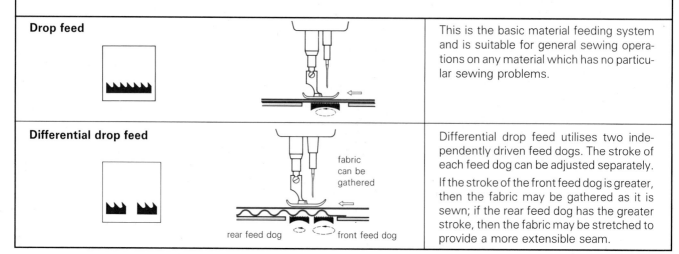

Drop feed

This is the basic material feeding system and is suitable for general sewing operations on any material which has no particular sewing problems.

Differential drop feed

fabric can be gathered

rear feed dog   front feed dog

Differential drop feed utilises two independently driven feed dogs. The stroke of each feed dog can be adjusted separately.

If the stroke of the front feed dog is greater, then the fabric may be gathered as it is sewn; if the rear feed dog has the greater stroke, then the fabric may be stretched to provide a more extensible seam.

Combined Feed Systems

Compound feed

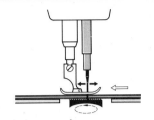

A combination of synchronised drop feed and needle feed. Feeding occurs whilst the needle is still in the material by combined motion of needle bar and feed dog.

The needle holds the fabric plies in registration during feeding to avoid slippage and seam pucker. Used mainly for edge stitching, checks and stripes.

Variable top and bottom feed ... (before the needle)

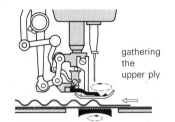

gathering the upper ply

A feeding foot, similar to the presser foot, is provided with e.g. two rows of teeth and acts alongside the presser foot.

The strokes of the feeding foot and the feed dog can be adjusted independently.

It is used, for example in gathering the top ply.

Variable top and bottom feed ... (behind the needle)

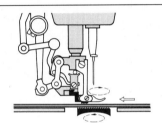

feeding foot behind the needle

In this case, the feeding foot operates behind the needle to deliver especially smooth seams.

This construction makes it easier to install machine attachments.

Alternating compound feed

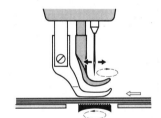

This system involves a combination of three types of feeding; feed dog, needle feed, and feeding foot. The fabric can not be gathered.

Applications:

- Sewing of multiple plies (plies are kept in registration)
- Sewing bulky seams in heavy fabrics

Puller feed, roller feed

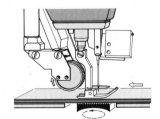

An auxiliary feed, usually a wheel or roller supplements the normal feeding system. The roller is located behind the needle and operates either continuously or intermittently.

Suitable for long straight seams such as in bed linen which can be produced without puckering.

Special Feeding Devices

Clamp feed

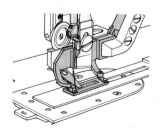

Automatic sewing stations, such as buttonholers, belt loop makers, and small part fabricators are provided with a special jig, which has openings for the stitching line, into which the fabric plies are fixed (see pages 168, 169). The jig is driven automatically and guides the material under the needle according to the required sewing pattern.

Presser Foot

1: Fixed presser foot for seams of constant thickness

2: Hinged presser foot for seams of variable thickness

The presser foot is attached to the presser foot bar. It holds the material down with an adjustable spring-loaded pressure, thus keeping it under control during sewing and assisting the operation of the feed dog. Various designs are utilised depending on the nature of the particular sewing operation and the material.

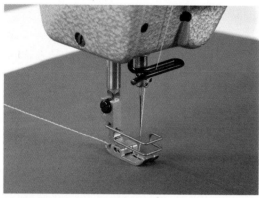

3: Hinged presser foot

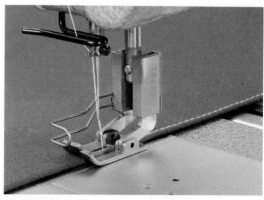

4: Double presser foot and edge guide

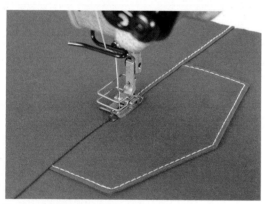

5: Double presser foot with 2 mm edge guide

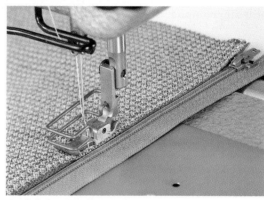

6: Left hand zipper foot

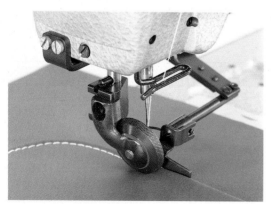

7: Presser wheel and swivelling edge guide

8: Presser foot with built-in piping guide

Fabric Guides

Fabric guides allow sewing to proceed more rapidly. Hemmers and guiders make it easier to feed the material correctly to the needle and to obtain a regular seam line.

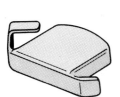

1: Magnetic edge guide

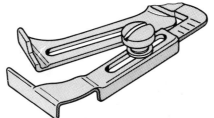

2: Adjustable edge guide

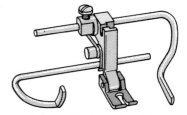

3: Edge guide for maintaining a fixed distance

4: Edge binding guide

5: Folded-in seam guide

6: Tape guide

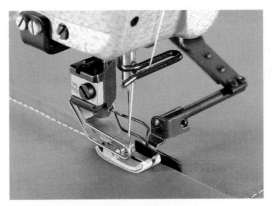

7: Teflon-coated presser foot

8: Lap seam folder

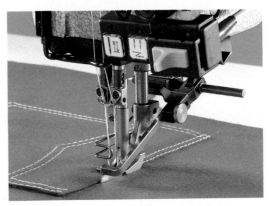

9: Lifting foot with edge guide

8.3.8 Shuttles, Hooks and Loopers

Shuttles and hooks are the means by which the underthread is taken through the loop of the needle thread in order to form a lockstitch.

Shuttles for Lockstitch

The shuttle is a carrier for the underthread. It passes completely through the enlarged needle thread loop, or guides the needle thread loop around itself.

Shuttles are used mainly for domestic sewing machines, and for working with stiff materials and thick threads, due to the lower yarn stress compared to rotary hooks. These machines work at up to 2000 stitches per minute. The oscillating shuttle is the most common type.

complete shuttle   body   spool case   spool

1: Straight shuttle   **2: Ring shuttle**   **3: Oscillating shuttle**

Rotary Hooks for Lockstitch

The hook guides the needle thread loop around a stationary spool case. The key part for forming a stitch is the underthread spool and its two-part capsule.

Horizontal Hook

complete hook   main body   gib   hook base   spool case   spool
and base

4: Rotary hook

The hook is mounted on a horizontal shaft. It has to make two rotations to form a single stitch. Depending on the design of sewing machine and hook, it is capable of working at up to 14000 rpm, making 7000 stitches per minute.

Vertical Hook

This type is mounted on a vertical shaft but works in exactly the same way as the horizontal type. They are used mainly for two needle lockstitch and post bed sewing machines.

Because of their low susceptibility to contamination, many single needle speciality sewing machines are equipped with these hooks. The maximum sewing speed of this type of hook is about 5000 stitches per minute.

Loopers for Chain Stitch

5: Oscillating looper   **6: Rotating looper**

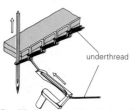

underthread

7: Oscillating double chain stitch looper

The functions of the chain stitch looper are:
- to catch the needle thread loop
- to hold the needle loop in such a way that the needle is able to stitch through it on the following cycle.

Single chain stitch loopers (see page 160) are hooked. There are two types, namely oscillating loopers and rotating loopers.

The oscillating looper has a more complicated drive mechanism. The rotating looper demands less space and is generally used for button sewing machines.

The distinguishing feature of the **double chain stitch looper** (see page 161) is the presence of a looper thread. Compared to the single chain stitch looper, it provides the additional function of making an underthread loop and guiding it through the needle thread loop.

8.3.9   Sewing Machines, Overview

Machine Types	Applications
1: **Lockstitch machine** 2: **Chain stitch machine** 3: **Double chain stitch machine**	Straight seams, zigzag seams (see page 158 to 161).
4: **Blind stitch machine** 5: **Linking machine**	Blind stitch machines for blind stitching and hemming. Linking machines for attaching trimmings and cuffs to knitted fabrics (see page 165).
6: **Overedge machine** 7: **Safety stitch machine**	Edge neatening, combined neatening and seam closing, safety stitching (see page 162 and 163).
8: **Flat seam machine** 9: **Flat seamer with cylinder bed**	Binding cut edges, flat seams on knitted fabrics (see page 164).
10: **Buttonhole machine** 11: **Button sewing machine** 12: **Bar tack machine**	Specific sewing operations (see page 168).
13: **Profile sewer** 14: **Pocket sewer**	Automatic, complex sewing operations (see page 169).

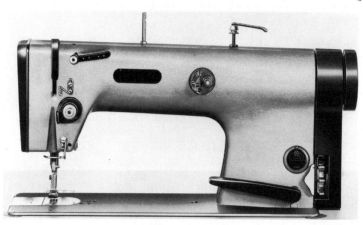

1:   Lockstitch machine

Stitch Formation (Horizontal Hook)

The needle thread loop, having been formed on the underside of the material by the needle, is interlaced with a second thread (underthread) by means of a hook.

The lockstitch machine can be distinguished by the winding device provided for the bottom thread.

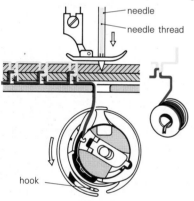

Phase 1

The needle is inserted into the material.

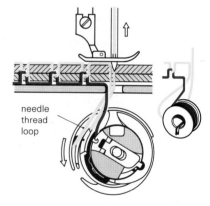

Phase 2

As the needle moves upwards from its lowest position, the needle thread forms a loop which is caught by the point of the hook.

Phase 3

The hook enlarges the needle thread loop.

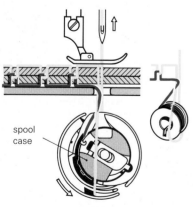

Phase 4

The needle thread loop is guided around the bottom thread spool.

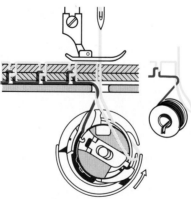

Phase 5

Interlacing begins.

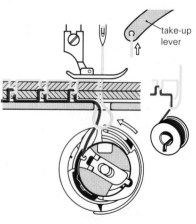

Phase 6

The take-up lever tightens the stitch into the material. The material is fed forward.

Features and Applications

Only a limited amount of sewing is possible before the supply of underthread has to be replenished. In contrast to chain stitch, it is not possible to unpick a lockstitch without destroying one of the threads. The interlacing point of the two threads is usually located in the middle of the material being sewn. However, it can be made to lie either on the top or the bottom side. In symbolic notation, the interlacing point is represented by a dot.

Both sides of the seam have the same appearance and the two threads can have different colours, if required. The consumption of thread is about 2.5 times the length of the seam, depending on the thickness of the material. Lockstitch is the most common stitch type used.

Important Members of the Lockstitch Family: Class 300 of ISO 4915

Type	Name, Stitch Diagram	Symbol	Seam Appearance
301	**Lockstitch** needle thread underthread (spool thread)	interlacing at: centre top side under side	
304	**Lockstitch (single-step zigzag)** needle thread underthread (spool thread)		
308	**Lockstitch (double-step zigzag)** needle thread underthread (spool thread)		
309	**Double thread lockstitch (piping seam)** needle thread needle thread underthread (spool thread) Top and bottom threads are interlaced on the under side of the material. When sewing piping a high tension is applied to the underthread to draw the seam tightly together.		

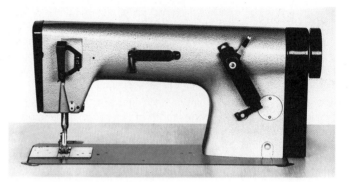

1: Chain stitch machine

Stitch Formation with an Oscillating Looper

Each loop is interlaced with the following loop of the same thread. The single thread machine is distinguished by the thread tension device situated on the arm, and the absence of a spool winder.

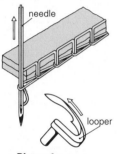

Phase 1

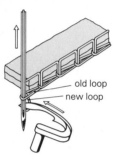

Phase 2

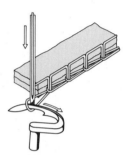

Phase 3

The needle has penetrated the material. It retains the old loop around its blade. As it moves upwards a new loop is formed, projecting sideways, beneath the material.

The new loop is caught, by the hook of the looper, above the needle eye but below the old loop. The needle continues upwards.

The old loop is cast off from the needle and slides onto the base of the new loop, which is still held by the looper, thus forming the interlacing on the under side of the material.

The looper enlarges the new loop so that, when the needle descends again it passes through the loop. The looper retreats, leaving the new loop held on the needle blade. This loop now becomes the old loop for the next cycle.

Features and Applications

This stitch type can be unpicked very easily, but only in one direction from the last stitch to the first. Therefore the simple chain stitch is used especially for tacking and basting. Because of its extensibility chain stitch is suitable for stretchy fabrics, e.g. knitted fabrics. Opposite sides of the seam have a different appearance and the thread consumption is about 3.5 times the seam length, depending on the thickness of the material being sewn.

Important Members of the Chain Stitch Family: Class 100 of ISO 4915

Type	Name, Stitch Diagram	Symbol	Seam Appearance
101	**Single thread chain stitch** — needle thread		
103	**Blind single thread chain stitch** — needle thread		

8.3.12 Multi-thread Chain Stitch

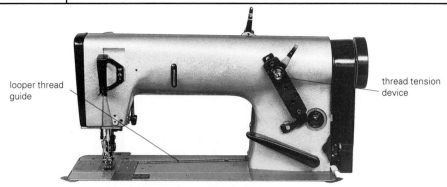

1: Multi-thread chain stitch machine

looper thread guide

thread tension device

Stitch Formation

Multi-thread chain stitch seams are made from two or more threads, one of which is an underthread or looper thread. Each needle thread loop is interlaced with the underthread.

The multi-thread chain stitch machine is distinguished by its two or more thread guides, the thread tension devices mounted on the machine arm, and the covering for the looper thread in the base plate.

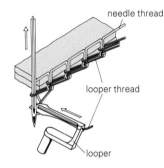
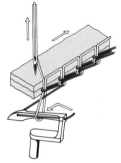
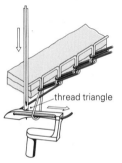

needle thread

looper thread

looper

thread triangle

Phase 1	**Phase 2**	**Phase 3**	**Phase 4**
A loop is formed in the needle thread as the needle begins to move upwards from its lowest position. The new loop is caught by the hook of the looper. At this moment the needle is in front of the looper.	The needle rises, casting off the old underthread loop onto the base of the new needle thread loop. Meanwhile the looper penetrates further into the new needle thread loop, taking the underthread with it and clearing a large triangular space for the needle to return to.	The needle descends into the triangular space formed on two sides by the underthread and on the other by the new needle thread loop. At this moment the needle is behind the looper.	The looper retreats, back through the new needle thread loop, leaving the underthread looped around the needle, ready for the next cycle. Meanwhile, the downwards movement of the needle tightens the previous stitch on the underside of the material being sewn.

Features and Applications

The two sides of the seam have a different appearance. The interlacing of needle and looper threads is always on the underside of the material. The multi-thread chain stitch produces extensible seams which usually do not show any puckering. They are especially suitable for load-bearing seams.

Depending on the seam type, thread consumption can be more than five times the seam length.

Type	Name, Stitch Diagram	Symbol	Seam Appearance
401	**Two-thread chain stitch** needle thread looper thread		

8.3.13 Overedge Chain Stitch (1)

1: Overedge chain stitch machine

Stitch Formation of a Three Thread Overedge Sewing Machine

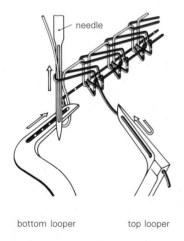

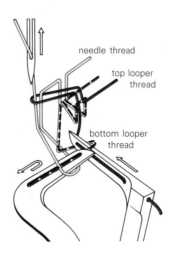

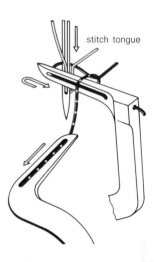

2: Type 504 stitch formation

Phase 1

A new needle thread loop is formed as the needle begins to move upwards from its lowest position.

The bottom looper catches the needle thread loop and lays its underthread into the needle thread loop.

As the needle moves upwards, the old top underthread loop is cast off from the needle and onto the new needle thread loop to form the top interlacing.

Phase 2

The top looper moves forward to catch and hold the bottom underthread loop, and to transfer its own underthread loop over a stitch tongue into the path of the needle. The stitch tongue is a small projection on the throat plate. There may also be a tongue on the presser foot.

As the bottom looper moves backwards the needle thread loop is cast off onto the bottom underthread loop to form the bottom interlacing.

Phase 3

The top looper lays its thread loop over the stitch tongue, preventing the stitch and material from over-tightening. The needle descends into the loop of the top underthread.

As the top looper moves back it casts off the bottom underthread loop to form the overedge interlacing between the two underthreads. Meanwhile, the new top underthread loop is held by the needle, ready for the cycle to begin again.

Features and Applications

Overedge sewing generally uses a variation of the chain stitch. Its distinctive feature is the one or two threads which enclose the edge of the fabric to protect it from fraying.

At the same time it can be used for joining fabric pieces (e.g. knitwear, underwear).

An **overedge seam**, formed of several threads, shows high extensibility. Very clean seams can be made using a built-in edge cutting device. The strength of the seam depends on the stitch type.

Higher strength is achieved by the **safety-stitch** (401.503) in which an additional chain stitch is made a few millimetres inside the overedge seam. The two seams are produced at the same time, but they are independent. This method of seaming is popular in modern operations because it neatens the cut edges at the same time as it joins the components.

Features and Applications

Overedge stitches have very good extensibility. The strength of the seam and coverage of the cut edges varies between the different stitch types. The stitch type number is determined by the number of threads (1 to 5) and their disposition on the material. A distinction is made between edge interlooping (503) and needle-point interlooping (504). Safety seams are a combination of two stitch types (401.503). Thread consumption can be up to 16 m thread per 1 m seam.

Important Members of the Overedge Chain Stitch Family: Class 500 of ISO 4915

Type	Name, Stitch Diagram	Symbol	Seam Appearance
501	**Single thread overedge** needle thread		
503	**Two-thread overedge (edge interlooping)** needle thread looper thread		
504	**Three-thread overedge (needle point interlooping)** needle thread looper threads		
512	**Four-thread overedge (mock safety stitch)** needle threads looper threads		
401.503	**Combination safety stitch** **Two-thread overedge and double chain stitch** needle threads 401 503 looper threads		

8.3.14 Flat Seam Stitches

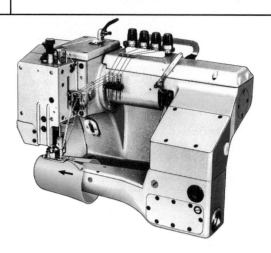

1:   Flat seaming machine

Stitch Formation

Flat seams can be made with Class 400 or Class 600 stitches. In the industry both types are known as covering stitches, although only Class 600 is classified as such by ISO 4915.

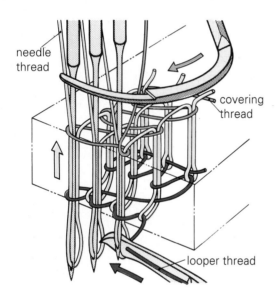

needle thread
covering thread
looper thread

Flat seams made with Class 400 stitches

Two thread systems are used. A looper thread interlaces with two needle threads on the under side, spanning and neatening the cut edge(s) on the underside of the material. This avoids having to fold in and press the cut edge.

Typical applications are hems for knitted fabrics and flat seams on straps or belt loops (402, 406).

Flat seams made with Class 600 stitches

These are made with three systems of threads. Two or more needle threads are interlaced on the under-side by a looper thread and on the needle side by a cover thread.

The Covering Chain Stitch types are used when both surfaces have to be covered and a flat seam is required.

Typical uses are butt seaming and ornamental seams e.g. knitted fabrics, tights and decorations (602).

Important Flat Seam Stitches

Type	Name, Stitch Diagram	Symbol	Seam Appearance
406	**Two-needle multi-thread chain stitch** — needle threads / looper thread		
602	**Covering chain stitch** — cover thread / needle threads / looper thread		

1: Single-thread blind stitching machine

Blind stitching means that the stitches and the needle impressions should not be visible on the outer side of the assembled article. Blind stitch seams are used for hemming and for attaching interlinings. Blind stitching machines use a curved needle (see page 150). A lifter raises the fabric just before it is penetrated by the needle and is withdrawn to allow material feeding. The lifting height is adjustable so that materials of different thickness can be accommodated. To obtain a loose seam with the minimum of needle marking, the lifter may be raised only every second or third stitch (interval setting).

no interval **1:1**

interval **2:1**

interval **3:1**

2: Interval settings

Important Blind Stitch Seams

Type	Name, Stitch Diagram	Symbol	Seam Appearance
103	**Blind single chain stitch**		
105	**Blind single chain stitch**		
320	**Blind multi-thread chain stitch**		

8.3.16 Sewing Machine Drives

Sewing machines are driven by electric motors. Various types of driving arrangements are available, the most important of which are illustrated below.

Belt Drive

This is the simplest way to drive machines which operate at relatively low speeds and low loads. The sewing speed is controlled by a foot pedal which varies the current supplied to the motor according to how far it is depressed. When the pedal is released, the motor is stopped by a brake. This type of drive is used for domestic machines (**Figure 1**).

Fixed Clutch

Once the motor has been started it runs continuously at constant speed. Depressing the foot pedal activates a clutch mechanism contained in the vertical arm and motion is supplied to the top shaft. The sewing program runs automatically to completion, after which the clutch is automatically disengaged. This type of drive is used in cam-controlled machines such as buttonholers (**Figure 2**).

Slipping Clutch

In this case the motor also runs continuously at constant speed. However, the speed of sewing can be regulated by the displacement of the foot pedal which applies increasing pressure to the clutch disk, against the motor disk. When the pedal is fully released, the clutch disk is held by a brake so the machine hand wheel is locked. To adjust the needle position, it is necessary to apply a slight pressure to the foot pedal. This system is used for simple high speed sewing machines (**Figure 3**).

Electronic Control

In the most sophisticated drive systems, a series of sensors is provided which supply information about speed and needle position to a control box. The control logic regulates the speed of the drive motor according to these inputs and a pre-selected sewing program (**Figure 4**). In general, three sets of functions can be distinguished.

Input A sensor on the hand wheel passes an electric pulse to the control box with every revolution. This allows the machine speed and the position of the needle to be deduced. Another sensor reports the position of the foot pedal so that the required machine speed can be deduced. Sewing programs can be selected from a programmer which may be placed at the top of the machine, or on the control box. Additional mechanisms such as thread cutting, presser foot operation, needle raising etc. can be operated by pedals, knee buttons, or hand buttons.

Processing The data from the sensors are analysed in the control box to decide the control actions required.

Output Signals from the control box determine the speed of the motor, the positioning of the needle and the commencement or stopping of the various sewing or additional operations. The most modern sewing machines are equipped with infinitely variable motors which operate only when the pedal is pressed.

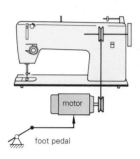

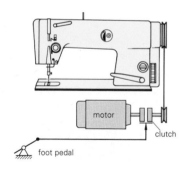

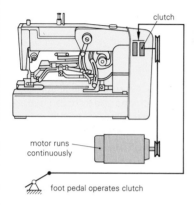

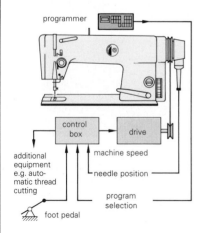

1: **Belt drive**

2: **Fixed clutch**

3: **Slipping clutch**

4: **Electronic control**

8.3.17 Ancilliary Mechanisms for High Speed Sewing Machines

Industrial sewing machines are robustly built for continuous operation at high sewing speeds (over 2000 stitches per minute). Therefore, they are called **high speed machines** and they are generally provided with several ancillary mechanisms whose function is to reduce the time needed by the operator for non-sewing activities. A prerequisite is an electronically controlled drive system (see page 166).

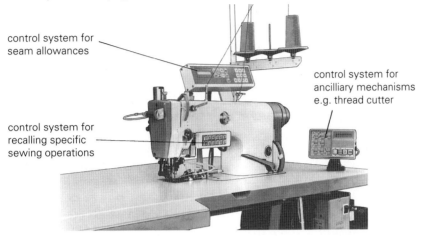

control system for seam allowances

control system for ancilliary mechanisms e.g. thread cutter

control system for recalling specific sewing operations

1: High speed sewing machine with ancillary controls

2: Thread cutter

3: Thread wiper

4: Automated presser foot

5: Needle positioning

6: Stitch compression

7: Bar tacking

8: Automatic start using an optical sensor

9: Automatic stop using an optical sensor

10: Edge trimmer

11: Edge trimmer (stepped)

Ancillary Equipment for Industrial High Speed Sewing Machines

The automatic **thread cutting device (Figure 2)** trims both needle and underthread at the material surface.

The **thread wiper (Figure 3)** lays the needle thread on top of the presser foot after the thread has been cut and the presser foot has been lifted. This avoids the needle thread becoming trapped when sewing begins again.

The **automatic presser foot** device **(Figure 4)** causes the presser foot to be lifted automatically when the sewing process is interrupted. At this time the needle is either in the lowest position (e.g. for rotating the work) or in the highest position (e.g. after cutting the thread).

The **needle positioning** device **(Figure 5)** allows the needle to stop in the low position whenever sewing is interrupted. This allows the work to be turned e.g. when sewing corners. It is also possible to raise both presser foot and needle to the higher position e.g. to adjust the fabric plies.

Stitch compression (Figure 6) ensures sufficient safety on lockstitch and chain stitch seams when it is not possible to sew backwards.

Bar tacking (Figure 7) provides back and forth stitching at the beginning and end of seams. The number of stitches to be given at the beginning and end of sewing can be predetermined.

Edge detection devices can control the start and finish of the sewing operation. Optical sensors detect the beginning **(Figure 8)** or the end **(Figure 9)** of the material and send the corresponding signals to the control box. These signals will be used by the control logic to initiate or terminate the appropriate operations such as bar tacking or needle positioning, depending on the programming. Sensors can also work inside the edges of material being sewn.

Edge trimming (Figure 10) allows the seam allowance to be trimmed away, for example when binding seam edges. It is also possible to cut in steps **(Figure 11)** or to scallop the edges.

Automatic fabric feeding and guiding devices are also used to improve the efficiency of sewing operations.

A different, and more specialised type of automation, is represented by sewing machines which are provided with special cams to control the movement of the components during an entire sewing operation. Such machines have the following features:

- An operator places the material to be sewn at the sewing station, monitors the process, and removes the completed work.
- The process is completely self-contained.
- Monitoring systems will stop the machine if a fault occurs.

These machines have a limited range of applications. They can be uneconomical, and technically limited in a situation where collections are highly diverse and fashionable, so that materials and patterns are subject to frequent change. Their big advantage lies with large quantity production using highly standardised operations. They are very easy to use; inexperienced operatives can use them effectively after only a short training period.

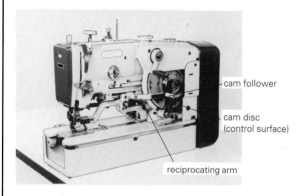

cam follower

cam disc
(control surface)

reciprocating arm

Material feed

The required pattern of movement of the material to be sewn is replicated in the shape of the cam. The motion is delivered to a reciprocating arm via two cam followers running in the cam track, and linked to the material guide system by levers.

Various zigzag stitching patterns are automatically provided in lockstitch, chain stitch or multi-thread chain stitch. The zigzag is produced by an additional, lateral needle bar movement.

Typical applications include making button holes, sewing on buttons, and sewing short seams e.g. bar tacks.

Automatic Sewing Machine with Cam Control

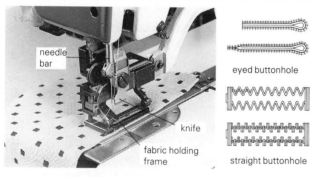

needle bar

knife

fabric holding frame

eyed buttonhole

straight buttonhole

Buttonhole sewing machine

They stitch the shape of the buttonhole. The material is cut automatically either before or after the sewing process. Adjustments to the control cam and the gear drive alter the stitch density and buttonhole length. The distance between buttonholes is fixed manually, or by transport rails.

Buttonholers use lockstitch or chain stitch.

Straight buttonholes are used mainly for shirts and blouses; eyed buttonholes are for outerwear such as jackets, coats and trousers.

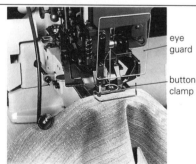

eye guard

button clamp

thread tail

types of button stitching

Button sewing machine

The buttons may be introduced either manually or by a special button magazine. The needle bar is made to oscillate between the two holes being sewn. If there are four holes, then the button clamp is also moved, at the appropriate moment, to bring the second pair of holes into work.

Buttons can be fastened using lockstitch or chain stitch. Buttons sewn with chain stitch can be unstitched easily if the last stitch is not fastened properly.

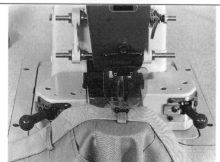

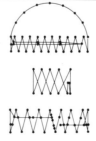

types of bar tacking

Bar tacking machines

Bar tackers sew special, short seams automatically.

The sewing program is determined by a cam.

Usually, every different seam type demands its own design of cam and fabric holder.

Bar tacks are used e.g. to secure pocket corners and openings, or for fastening belt loops and labels.

Automated sewing equipment includes additional operations such as automatic picking and laying up of the components to be sewn, ancillary functions such as binding or backstitching of sewn pieces, trimming of edges, bar tacking, etc.

Profile Sewing Systems

1: Pocket flap maker

Profile sewing systems are controlled by a template and jig. The material is fixed on the jig and the outline of the template guides the sewing operation.

By changing the design of the template, a wide range of different shapes can be produced. The template is moved by an independent drive system.

This type of equipment allows the accurate, and repeatable production of components having very consistent quality at increased production rates.

The picture shows a profile sewing system for small components. Such machines are also used for long seams, e.g. side seams.

CNC Sewing Machines[1]

programming and control console   clamp

2: Collar assembly

CNC machines are controlled by a computer. The required sequence of movements of the material is converted into X,Y coordinates in the workspace. These coordinates are used by a computer program. During the sewing operation, the program continuously delivers the X,Y coordinates to servo motors acting either on the material or on the sewing head.

Two different methods of programming are available:

- **Learning mode**: In learning mode, the machine is taken manually through each step in the sewing cycle, whilst the computer monitors the operation and stores the positional information as a program.
- **Off-line programming**: The sewing cycle is digitised from a drawn pattern and the data, plus information on seam width and stitch density, are entered manually into the computer which converts them into the control program.

The picture shows a system for assembling collars. The components are positioned on a feeding device. Automatic feeding means that while one collar is being sewn the next is being prepared manually. The required collar style, and size can be selected at a control console. Electronic monitoring devices for needle and looper threads are programmed to stop the machine if a fault arises or if the underthread spool needs replenishing.

Robots[2]

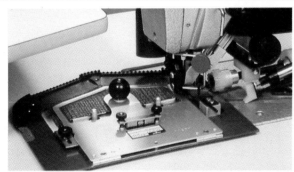

3: Sewing a back seam

Research in automation concentrates on providing motor driven devices to replace manual operations such as picking and positioning the components to be sewn, or removal and stacking of sewn work. A major aim is the development of mechanical handling systems in which the movements of the robots can easily be reprogrammed at will. Handling and guiding functions can be carried out by grippers. The picture shows a pair of robots presenting material to a sewing head for a back seam to be inserted.

Problems in the automation of sewing processes
- Products: fashionable variety, small number of pieces and short delivery times.
- Materials: low bending resistance, surface structure, thickness, mixed materials.
- Sewing technology: manual change of top and bottom thread, visual monitoring of the processes.

[1] CNC: computerised numerical control
[2] robot: independent, powered, mechanical device capable of performing automatically a function normally performed manually

Seam Puckering

Puckering is a result of the particular sewing conditions, as well as differences in raw materials, constructions, and finishing of the materials being sewn. Distinctions can be drawn between puckering caused by the separate effects of material feeding, fabric structure, and thread tensions.

1:   **Feeding pucker**

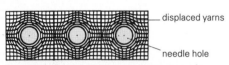

displaced yarns

needle hole

2:   **Distortion of the yarns in a fabric**

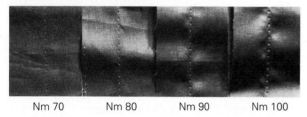

Nm 70   Nm 80   Nm 90   Nm 100

3:   **Influence of needle size on structural puckering**

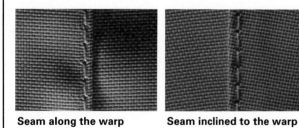

Seam along the warp   **Seam inclined to the warp**

4:   **Influence of seam orientation on puckering**

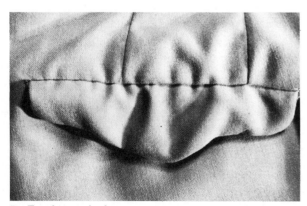

5:   **Tension puckering**

Feeding Effects

Feeding pucker is caused by a displacement between the top and the bottom fabric plies. The bottom ply is pushed forward by the feed dog while the upper ply is restrained by the presser foot (**Figure 1**).

The problem is addressed by the use of special feeder mechanisms, by adjustments to the feed dog or presser foot, by using a special presser foot, e.g. teflon-covered or wheel types, or by reducing the sewing speed.

Structural Effects

Structural puckering is the result of the fabric structure becoming jammed, due to the introduction of sewing needle and thread.

Penetration of the fabric by the needle, and the insertion of the sewing thread, causes adjacent warp and weft yarns in the fabric to be displaced; the fabric structure may become jammed. This can produce small bulges in the fabric, close to the seam (**Figure 2**).

Structural pucker tends to be more obvious with lockstitch than with chain stitch.

It can be reduced by using finer needles, finer threads, lower sewing thread tension and a lower stitch density (**Figure 3**).

Usually, the density and the extensibility of the fabric being sewn is different in the warp and weft directions. Seams which run parallel to the warp will often show more puckering than those sewn along the weft, or on the bias.

This type of problem can often be helped by making the seam at an angle of about 15° to the warp (**Figure 4**).

Thread Tension Effects

Puckering can be caused by excessive sewing thread tensions (**Figure 5**).

Threads which are sewn under high tension will be stretched. This extension will later be recovered to some extent; the yarn will tend to return to its original length, forcing a reduction in the length of the seam, which may then pucker. Synthetic threads, especially, have a high elastic recovery and will tend to show this problem more than cotton.

The recovery does not occur immediately; there can be considerable delay so that the problem may not become apparent until after the garments have been delivered.

To prevent tension puckering:

- the underthread should be wound at low tension.
- tension settings for both needle and underthread should be set as low as possible.
- high quality threads should be used.

Fabric Damage

A material which is difficult to feed, or which is subjected to high pressure during feeding, can be damaged during sewing. The yarns in the material may be weakened or broken. Damage also can be caused by needles of inappropriate size or type, or needles with worn or damaged points. This can cause holes to appear in the fabric (**Figure 1**). Needle points can be tested on the fingernail. A flawless needle point, without a burr, does not produce scratch marks.

Needle damage in a woven fabric may detract from its appearance but generally does not have further serious consequences (**Figure 2**). In a knitted fabric, needle damage may lead to the generation of ladders when the seam is stressed. In high speed sewing, the heat generated by friction at the needle can be enough to melt a synthetic yarn (**Figure 3**).

Fabric damage can prevented by:

- improved fabric finishing
- using the finest possible needles
- selecting special needle points
- moistening the fabric
- using special needles
- cooling the needle with compressed air

1: Damaged loops caused by a worn needle point

2: Damaged woven fabric right: seams with thread, left: without thread; needles: Nm 80, Nm 90, Nm 100 (from left to right)

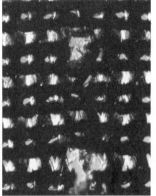

3: Holes caused by melting in a knitted fabric made from synthetic yarn

Sewing Faults and their Causes

4: Thread break

Fault	Cause
Thread break	• Incorrect thread path. • Thread waste fouling the looper. • Worn or damaged hole in the throat plate. • Thread contains knots or has low strength. • Worn or damaged needle eye or groove.
Needle break	• Thread too thick and strong for the needle. • Needle deflected onto the throat plate by the operative pulling on the fabric. • Spool case incorrectly fixed. • Needle is bent and is caught by the looper. • Inadequate needle quality.
Irregular seam	• Needle incorrectly installed. • Underthread badly wound. • Bent needle. • Incorrect looper settings. • Inappropriate needle system. • Poor fabric feed.
Poor fabric feed	• Presser foot pressure too low. • Worn, damaged, or contaminated feed dog. • Feed dog set too low - inadequate penetration through the throat plate. • Inappropriate feeder mechanism.
Missed stitches	• The looper does not catch the needle thread loop because of e.g. a bent needle, an inappropriate needle or thread, or faulty looper settings, threading up or needle installation.

8.5.1   Pressing

Pressing means shaping a textile material. There are three general pressing operations:

- **Under pressing:** operations performed on garment parts during making up.
- **Moulding:** imparting a three dimensional shape without using darts.
- **Top pressing:** final finishing operations on the fully assembled garment.

Pressing is effected by the application of heat and pressure during a certain time. Steam, compressed air and suction can assist the process. Steam is an efficient medium for heating and also delivers the moisture which is required for setting materials such as wool. The setting effect is fixed by cooling, which can be accelerated by suction or compressed air.

Dry Pressing

Electric iron 	The heat is produced by an electric heating element. The temperature can be adjusted from 60 to 220 °C to accommodate the characteristics of the material being pressed. If moisture is required, it has to be sprayed onto the material.

Steam Pressing

Steam generation Temperature of steam at different pressures	Steam is generated and utilised in one of two ways: • At atmospheric pressure. • At high pressure. At normal air pressure water boils at 100 °C. In a self-contained electric steam iron (e.g. domestic irons) water is dripped onto the hot ironing plate and evaporates. The escaping steam has a temperature of about 100 °C. A higher steam temperature can be achieved if the water is heated in a pressure vessel. The graph shows the relationship between steam temperature and pressure. In the garment industry steam pressures of 5 to 10 bar and temperatures from 150 to 170 °C are utilised. The higher temperature accelerates the pressing process.

Graph: Temperature in °C (y-axis: 100, 105, 120, 135, 150, 165, 180) versus Pressure in bar (x-axis: 0 to 10). Data points: 120, 133, 143, 151, 158, 164, 169, 174.

Self-contained steam iron 	**Steam iron with separate steam generator** 	The steam is generated either in the iron itself (left) or in a separate station (right). The latter system allows a longer working time, between replenishment, due to its larger reservoir. Electric heating elements evaporate the water and the steam escapes through perforations in the sole of the iron. The temperature of the sole can be regulated.

High pressure steam iron and teflon shoe  	High pressure steam is supplied continuously to the iron through a tube and is regulated by a valve. The steam issues through holes in the sole. The temperature of the sole is adjustable from 100 to 235 °C. High efficiency heating elements and integrated steam chambers provide steam without condensate. The teflon ironing shoe prevents singing and shiny marks when pressing the face side of sensitive fabrics.

Pressing unit with high pressure steam iron 	The pressing department will often contain work stations for manual pressing designed to suit particular types of garment e.g. skirts, or flat work. These units consist of an electric steam iron with an ergonomic holding device (gibbet) and a pressing area provided with suction. This construction makes it possible to draw air through, or blow air onto the material being pressed. The pressing process is optimized because of the rapid absorption of heat and moisture. A possible disadvantage of suction is that impressions can be left behind on the material; this is avoided by blowing. An advantage is that suction before and during pressing allows the work to be aligned accurately and held firmly in place. The swinging arm can be shaped to accept particular garment parts for different pressing operations. The various actions of the equipment can be controlled by pedals.

Accessories

1: Ironing board

The ironing board is used for pressing larger surfaces. Openings in the board allow the steam to escape.

2: Sleeve board

The sleeve board is for pressing small, tubular items.

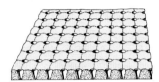

3: Underlay

Special heat reflecting pads, or simple felt materials can be used as underlays for pressing. They spread the pressure and absorb the steam.

4: Hand buck

Hand-held pads are a useful aid in top pressing garments which are difficult to lay flat.

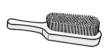

5: Brush

Brushes are used in top pressing surfaces with nap or pile.

6: Needle bed

Needle beds are helpful when dealing with sensitive pile fabrics (velvet).

7: Collar anvil   **8: Edge anvil**

Anvils allow a firmer pressing of particular garment parts.

9: Ironing cushion   **10: Moulded buck**

Various shaped cushions and bucks facilitate the pressing and moulding of three-dimensional garment areas.

Pressing at Different Stages in Manufacture

Under pressing	During garment assembly, various parts may need to be pressed before proceeding to the next stage, to improve the ease or accuracy of sewing e.g. flattening of seams or edges before hemming. Under pressing is also required in cases where it would not be possible to achieve the required effect during top pressing, e.g. collars and cuffs before back-stitching.
Top pressing	This refers to all of the final finishing operations performed on the completed garment. The product is made ready for sale. Also known as finishing.

Pressing Techniques

Flat pressing	Removal of wrinkles before cutting, before sewing, or on the finished product.
Steaming	May be carried out to relax the fabric, to avoid shrinkage during subsequent pressing.
Moulding	Moulding is the creation and fixing of three-dimensional shape in a garment. The location and the extent of the shaping are determined by the cutting pattern. Moulding is most effective on wool fabrics. It involves: Stretching - Rounded forms are imposed by introducing and fixing localised extensions in the fabric e.g at the shoulder, bust and collar. Pressing in - Superfluous width is gathered and fixed, e.g. centre back, centre waist, and sleeves.

Mechanical Presses

Specialised pressing units are produced in many different forms for pressing and durable shaping of particular items, such as collars, shoulders and trousers.

Pressing is effected between a stationary buck and a movable head, both of which are provided with special covering materials. After the head has been lowered steam is supplied from above and/or below. Pressure, temperature and pressing time are adjustable. Suction may be available from the buck.

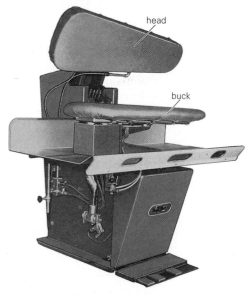

1: Flat press

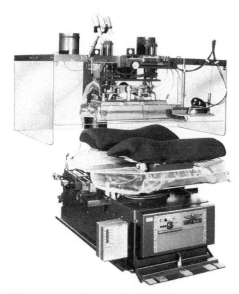

2: Moulding press

Steam Dolly and Tunnel Finisher

3. Steam dolly

4. Tunnel finisher

Whole garments can be finished with steam dollies, although small parts such as collars and cuffs may have to be pre-pressed. The garment is put on the form which is then inflated by blowing with steam and air for 5 to 20 seconds, followed by cooling with air.

The garments are placed on hangers or frames which are conveyed through a chamber in which they are steamed and dried.

For the highest quality finish, small parts may need to be after-pressed.

The total dwell time and temperature, as well as the amount of steam and the drying time can be adjusted according to the particular materials being processed.

Fusing literally means melting. In clothing manufacture, it refers to the bonding of an interlining material to a top cloth by means of an adhesive, previously applied to the interlining, which melts under certain pressing conditions.

Interlining fabrics of this type are called fusibles, or fusible interlinings. They comprise a substrate and an adhesive (resin). The substrate may be a woven, knitted, or nonwoven fabric. The resin is almost always a synthetic polymer material which melts and flows within a defined temperature range. The adhesive may be applied to the substrate in a variety of ways, e.g. powder scattering, dot printing, paste printing, laminating, melt coating.

Fusing technology, therefore, is concerned with the materials, equipment, and methods by means of which a lining may be durably bonded to a top cloth.

The quality of the bond, in terms of fastness to washing, ironing, and dry cleaning, depends on the substrate, the adhesive, the top cloth, and the fusing conditions. These have to be matched to the specific requirements of the garment. There are some types of top cloth for which it is rather difficult to provide a satisfactory fusible interlining. The bond should be formed without detracting seriously from the look, the structure, the comfort and the utility of a garment.

A range of fusible systems has been developed to meet these requirements.

Fusing Equipment and Methods

1: **Electric iron**

2: **Moveable flat bed press**

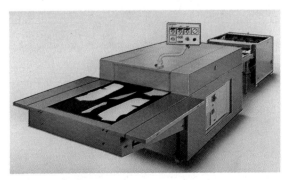

3: **Conveyor fusing press**

Hand fusing with an iron relies on the operator to control the pressure and the time.
The temperature is rather variable.
With polyamide resins, bond formation is assisted by providing steam. The result is better if a damp cloth is used, rather than a steam iron, because the steam is distributed more uniformly.

With a modern **flat bed press**, the pressure, temperature and time can be closely controlled. Advanced models are equipped with moveable beds, or feeding trays which allow for the next workpiece to be loaded whilst one is being fused. The operator works in a seated position.

These devices are especially suitable for fusing short runs of small parts.

Fusing presses are purpose designed. A relatively high pressure is required, which is applied either pneumatically or hydraulically. Steam pressing units, which generate relatively low temperatures and pressures, are not really suitable for fusing.

A **conveyor fusing press** can work either discontinuously or continuously. Temperature, pressure, and time are infinitely variable within the working ranges. The enclosed construction allows for any vapours given off by the fusible to be exhausted safely. The short pressing time gives a relatively gentle process.

In recent years, attempts have been made to develop fusing processes based on **high frequency** (dielectric[1]) heating. In this system, heat is generated within the materials to be fused by passing them through a high frequency alternating electric field. Due to their differing dielectric properties, the adhesive attains a higher temperature than the cloth. Thus, it is claimed, fusing can be achieved with a significantly lower temperature of the top cloth, which helps to avoid heat stress in the fabric. Fully automatic machines using this technology have been demonstrated. They are capable of fusing stacks of components about 10 cm deep (multiple sandwich method). The machine is very productive and, if the technology were to become successful, would be suitable for very long runs in large companies.

[1] dielectric heating: heat produced within a material by frictional losses during vibration of molecules in an alternating electric field

Every manager and supervisor has a legal obligation to protect the **health and safety** of the operatives at work. Every source of danger has to be removed or at least recognized and marked as one. Safety procedures have to be written down in a safety manual, and included in the training of operatives.

All responsible companies will be members of an **industry association**, with a defined code of working practices, and will carry commercial accident insurance on behalf of their employees.

In most countries, health and **safety at work legislation** has been enacted and the rules are compulsory for managers, supervisors and all employees. Observance of the regulations is often controlled by local and regional inspectorates who can recommend or require the implementation of improvements to machinery, processes, or working practices. They also may have the power to impose fines, or close the factory in the event of non-compliance.

Effective elimination of health hazards, and prevention of industrial accidents requires strict attention to safety procedures by all employees.

Hazards and Potential Accidents	Safety Measures
Sewing Finger and hand injury during cleaning and repair work	The machine must be switched off, with the plug removed, and must be stationary before any cleaning or repair work is started.
Eye injury from broken parts	Proper adjustment of the eye guard should be checked before work starts. Safety glasses should be issued.
Finger injury from the needle	Setting of the finger guard should be checked before work starts.
Injury from ancillary equipment	Shears and needles should be put away properly after use.
Spreading and cutting Finger and hand injuries from spreading machines	Disengage the spreader carriage when doing correcting work on the lay.
Finger and hand injury from moving or idle cutting devices	Ensure that the finger guard is adjusted to the correct height of the fabric layers before starting to cut. Learn and use the correct handling techniques for the tool.
Finger and hand injury from pressing mechanisms	Never reach into the danger zone whilst the device is operating. The devices must be designed so that the operator has to use both hands to activate the press. An optical sensor must be provided so that the machine is automatically stopped in the open position if the danger zone is infringed.
Fusing Finger and hand injury in the press	Safety guards should be checked daily for correct operation.
Burns from hot beds	Never attempt to retrieve, or adjust the position of components whilst they are being fed, or are on the bed.
Finger and hand injury in feeding and unloading	A press which has to be controlled using both hands must be operated by only one person. Operators must be well trained and practised in laying the parts on the feeding belt conveyor.
Pressing Scalding from steam	Steam must not be supplied until after the press is closed.
Finger and hand injury from the press	A machine which requires two hands to operate it must never be operated by two people. Never attempt to retrieve or adjust the position of parts after the closing process has started. A safety bar must be fitted which stops and raises the head when it is touched.
Stain removal Health hazard from solvent vapours	Ensure adequate ventilation. Spray guns must be used only where exhaustion is provided.
General working area Tripping and falling	Work area must be kept clean and tidy.
Internal injury from swallowed items	Never store items temporarily in the mouth. Place needles etc. into the proper containers.
Electrical injury	Never use a machine with damaged covers, cables, switches etc. Report the damage at once. Never try to repair it yourself.
Materials handling	Never carry too much at once. Make sure you can see where you are going. When picking up a load, bend the knees, not the back. Use mechanical aids wherever possible.

8.7 Quality Assurance

To the end-purchaser of a product, quality means fitness for purpose, and the major components of quality are price, technical performance, and aesthetic appeal. To a manufacturer, quality means conformance to a specification. The specification may be issued, wholly or in part, by a customer, or may be developed by the manufacturer himself. Differences in garment specifications are reflected in differences in the type of fabric, the exclusivity of design, the cut, the processing and the accessories which are used. In general, a high level of specification in design, manufacture, and performance will result in a garment with a higher price and quality level.

Five levels of price and quality are often distinguished.

- exclusive
- high
- medium
- lower
- discount

Quality assurance is the management system, employed by a manufacturer, to ensure that the required specification is met. For every stage in the manufacturing process, from product design and materials purchase through to packaging and customer service, explicit procedures have to be developed, and followed, which will ensure that the product will conform to requirements and will give satisfaction to the customer.

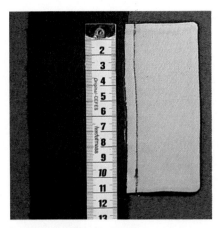

1: Intermediate inspection

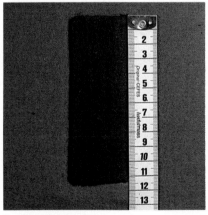

2: Final inspection

Quality control is a set of test methods, inspection and analytical procedures which are applied to raw materials, intermediate products, and final products, to provide feedback to the quality assurance system and to ensure that the system is working correctly. Each department has its particular methods of testing and inspection.

Raw materials are inspected on reception. Top cloth and interlinings are checked for e.g. weaving faults, printing faults, correct width, and distortions. Interlinings, buttons, zips, ribbons etc. may also be tested for various aspects of performance. The wearing and aftercare properties of the top cloth may need to be established to determine the aftercare label which will be appropriate for the garment. The fabric may be tested for its behaviour towards heat, pressure and moisture. Shrinkage during fusing and pressing may be determined (see page 98).

In the **design** department, instructions are developed for each garment, in collaboration with the production planning department, which specify the technical details of garment assembly. This will include items such as seam and hem allowances, seam margins, pattern matching, notch depths, etc. For each value specified, a tolerance will also be given.

The **production planning and control** department designs and documents the procedures for checking conformance to garment size and shape specification and for the final inspection. They also develop and maintain the forms which are used to register daily and weekly fault rates.

The **cutting** department prepares instructions which will identify and accompany the pattern markers: e.g. "lay to be sectioned twice", "top cloth", "lining".

During **preparation for sewing**, each part is individually labelled to prevent mixing and to identify fabric face and back.

In the **sewing room**, devices are installed which aid the achievement of consistent quality, and operators are helped to work to the required standards by clearly defined working methods and by appropriately detailed, methodical training.

Intermediate inspection is concentrated mostly, though not exclusively in the sewing room. **Final inspection** is concerned with the size, fit, and overall impression of the finished garment.

The **cost of quality** is composed of two parts, namely the **cost of conformance** and the **cost of non-conformance**. The cost of conformance is the cost of all of the procedures, such as documentation, analysis, inspection and testing, which are necessary to run the quality assurance system, and to ensure that faulty goods are never, or seldom made. The cost of non-conformance is the cost which results from errors, faults, additional inspection and testing, reworking and repairing, unnecessary waste, downgrading of faulty garments to second grade, returns of faulty garments from customers, loss of goodwill and market opportunity. A manufacturer who is supplying to a low quality specification will usually have a low cost of conformance but a high cost of non-conformance. A manufacturer who is successfully supplying to a high specification market will usually have a relatively sophisticated and expensive quality assurance system, but will be rewarded by a low cost of non-conformance and higher selling prices for his products.

A low-quality operation is typified by high levels of final inspection, reworking, and repairs. A high-quality operation is typified by high levels of training and skill, prevention of faults (rather than correction), and low levels of final inspection.

Electronic data processing (EDP) is common in sophisticated quality assurance systems.

The clothing industry ranges from small, hand-made (bespoke) operations up to large industrial garment making enterprises.

Industrial production is divided according to target groups (women's, men's, and children's wear), according to applications (underwear, shirtings, foundation garments, workwear, and sportswear) or according to the materials used (flat knits, circular knits).

Bespoke operations are divided along technical lines into men's tailoring, women's tailoring, shirtings, and underwear.

Comparison between Bespoke and Industrial Production

Bespoke Clothing Production

Production on behalf of individual clients, according to individual size and requirements.

Particular characteristics of the client, such as hollow back or rounded back, can be taken into account during cutting and sewing, so as to ameliorate the appearance in the garment.

The client selects the material and the design, e.g. from sample swatches and illustrated styles, and by discussion with the tailor, before cutting begins.

Bespoke tailoring involves a much higher investment of time for each garment, and is correspondingly more expensive than industrial manufacture. However, the client is usually rewarded by a more individual design and a higher quality of material and workmanship.

Industrial Clothing Manufacture

Production is geared to an anonymous, statistically and/or demographically and culturally defined target consumer group.

Cutting patterns and sizes are based on size charts, derived from statistical analysis of anthropometric[1] surveys. Garments are produced in a limited range of sizes.

Standardised cutting and making procedures mean that all garments have the same shape; allowances for uncommon body shapes can not be made.

The consumer has the choice between a wide range of different garment styles but has no direct influence over their design and cut.

Large-scale manufacturing techniques allow a wide range of garments to be produced in a fraction of the time required for bespoke tailoring of individual items.

[1] anthropometric: measurements on humans

Product Groups with a Selection of Product Types (Apparel Fabrics)

Menswear and Boyswear	Womenswear	Shirtings and Underwear	Workwear and Sportswear
jackets	blouses	dress shirts	workwear
trousers	dresses	casual shirts	sportswear
suits	skirts	babywear	leisure wear
formal wear	cardigans	nightwear	ski wear
uniforms	costumes	underwear	jeans
waistcoats	trousers & trouser-suits		
coats	evening wear		
traditional costume	wedding dresses		
	traditional costume		
	coats		

Circular Knits	Flat Knits	Foundation and Swimwear	Children's wear
underwear	pullovers	brassières	girls dresses
babywear	twin-sets	corsetry	jackets
T-shirts	jackets & cardigans	support stockings	trousers
body stockings	knitted dresses	swim suits	coats
leggings	stockings	bikinis	anoraks
sweatshirts	socks	swimming trunks	jump suits
	scarfs & caps		blouses

As with any manufactured product, there are different ways to organise the actual production of garments, according to the type, the amount and the diversity of products to be made.

The **type of production system** is determined by the quantity of articles to be made and the required rate of delivery. Individual production, batch production, and mass production are the main types.

In industrial garment manufacture, there are three main **systems of organisation**, namely the synchronised system, the section system and the progressive bundle system.

Types of Production System

Individual production, known as making through, is the traditional method, in which the entire garment is assembled by one operator. Each product is made only once, or in very small quantities. The system requires highly skilled, experienced operators and versatile machinery.

Batch production is used for larger, though fixed, quantities of identical articles either for stock or to order.

Mass production means that large quantities of identical products are made continuously. The high utilisation of machinery and labour allows a high level of automation and specialisation.

Production Organisation Systems

Synchronised System

The synchronised, or straight-line system is suitable for large volume production (mass production or large batches). As the name suggests, the work flows in a straight line through a series of work stations, each of which is synchronised to the next by ensuring that the time spent at each station is exactly the same. This requires that each individual step in the assembly of the product has to be analysed carefully and the steps distributed in a balanced way over the available work stations. Each operator then performs exactly the same operation(s) over and over again on the identical parts of successive garments. Detailed work plans have to be drawn up to facilitate this balancing of the line (see page 183).

Advantages of the synchronised line system include short distances between stations, low volume of work in process, precise planning of production times, highly visible production progress and predictable production quantity.

Disadvantages include the need for intensive detailed pre-planning, high cost of style changes, sensitivity to disruption by production difficulties or absenteeism, and the dependence of productivity on maintaining a strict rhythm of work.

1: **Straight-line system with hanger transport**

2: **Bundle assembly system**

Section System

This system is used by factories with frequent style changes and small numbers of items per style. The sewing room has a number of sections, each of which specialises in the assembly of a major garment component, which is then passed on to the next section. The spatial arrangement of the sections is such that the output end of one section is close to the input end of the section which requires that component.

The **advantages** of this system include a small influence of personnel changes and easy style changes. **Disadvantages** include large space requirement, imprecise production time planning, and longer throughput time.

Progressive Bundle System

The progressive bundle system of garment assembly embraces some of the features and advantages of both the straight-line and the section systems. Machines and operatives are organised into sections, according to basic functions, which produce sub-components e.g. small parts, sleeves, pockets, joining. Within each section the work is balanced according to the time required for each sub-function. The combination of small bundles and a line system (**Figure 2**) provides the best solution to the problems of frequent style changes, small lot sizes, and short delivery deadlines.

Material flow means the way that raw materials, accessories, intermediate and final products move through the various processing stations in the factory. Smooth flow patterns are important for economic manufacturing.

Material and Information Flow in a Factory

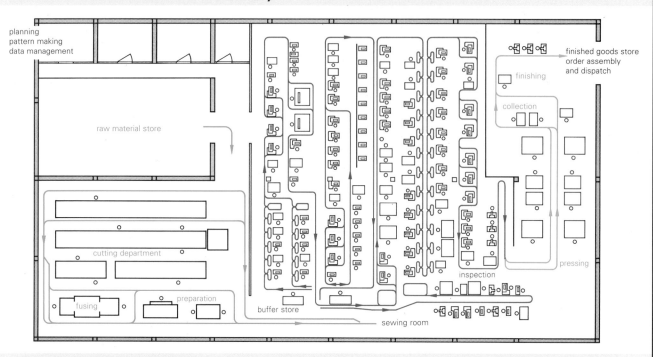

Materials Handling Equipment

In a garment making factory, various **handling systems** are used, according to requirements (**Figures 1 to 5**).

1: Fabric trolley in the warehouse

2: Roll handling at the spreader creel

3: Overhead transport of components in the cutting department

4: Automatic hanger distribution system in the sewing room

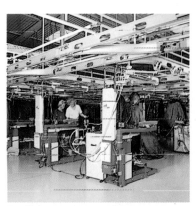

5: Hanger transport in the pressing area

6: Computer controlled warehouse for hanging garments

9 Organisation of Clothing Manufacture	9.4 Organisational Structure

An organisation is a group of people working together towards a common objective. In order to promote efficient cooperation, it is first necessary to arrange a clear organisational structure, and then to create efficient management systems. The various functions and operations have to be shared out among the workers, specific responsibilities assigned, and lines of authority and communication established.

The **organisational structure** sets out the formal lines of responsibility and communication. The **management systems** are what actually make the organisation work effectively.

Organisation

Most companies are organised in a hierarchical structure, along functional lines. At the top of the hierarchy are the operating divisions or departments. Each department is divided into sections, and each section into specific functions or operations. Each department has its manager, each section its supervisor, and each function its individual operator(s).

Hierarchical Organisation

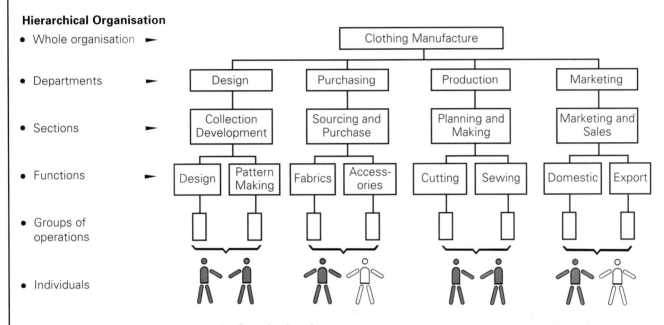

- Whole organisation
- Departments
- Sections
- Functions
- Groups of operations
- Individuals

1: **Organisation chart**

Within the organisational structure, it is necessary to define clearly the patterns of responsibility and communication, especially where responsibilities may cross the functional or sectional boundaries. There are many different ways that the lines of authority and communication can be organised.

System	Patriarchal	Direct Line	Augmented Line	Multiple Line, Functional	Network, Teamwork
Application	small enterprise	small, medium enterprise	large enterprise	clothing industry	idealised form
Schematic					
Advantages	clear lines	discrete responsibility	support services provided to line managers	specialists available for each function	solution of difficult special problems
Disadvantages	inflexible, undemocratic	rigid, slow	too expensive for small and medium enterprises	divided responsibilities and over-specialisation	time-consuming due to extended discussion
Flexibility	low	low	fairly high	medium	high

Lines of Authority and Communication

The Functional system of organisation, in which responsibility and authority are divided according to functional expertise, is often used in the clothing industry (see also page 132). Decision making and freedom of action are increased in the departmental sections, taking some of the burden away from the top management.

Management Systems

Management systems ensure the timely provision of the necessary materials, services, equipment, and information, as well as the proper execution of the various functions and operations. Standard forms are used to convey the technical information required for each production operation (see page 183).

The **Operations** department has a most important role in planning and control. It has to determine the equipment, methods and material requirements for making each order, and the time that will be allocated. It will develop manufacturing plans, parts lists, cutting and sewing plans, and progress tickets.

The **Making** (making-up) department has to actually make the order. Production systems, machine requirements, ancillary devices, and material flow all have to be organised accordingly.

Costs are kept under control by ensuring standard working procedures, low fault rates, timely operations, and well trained operators.

Production Planning and Control (PPC)

Production planning and control is based on the collection and analysis of data. These data will be derived partly from internal sources, such as planning data for the components to be made, partly from the materials and equipment to be used, and partly from the customer requirements. Planning can be greatly assisted by computers (EDP), since all of the required data are available at the various locations in the factory (see page 188).

Beside PPC, the Operations department includes the planning of the production program, time and capacity utilisation, pre-production and introduction of orders, and order progress chasing.

Production program	The company decides on a production program of specific products and product groups, based on information which is fed in from the marketing and sales departments. Usually, at least some of the products will be newly developed for the season, based upon ideas generated in the design department. Several of these will be gathered into a Collection, for marketing as a group.
Quantity planning	Marketing begins with the presentation of the Collection. Predictions will be made of projected sales and the required sizes and colours, so that production can begin immediately. Calculations will be made for quantities of fabrics, accessories etc. so that the necessary supplies can be obtained.
Time and Capacity planning	The predictions are used to calculate production times and delivery schedules, based on the available machinery and labour capacity. The production is assigned to a particular factory.
Order introduction	At the appropriate time, the order is introduced into the factory by issuing a production order. The required materials, together with all of the production instructions (production plan, parts list, cutting and sewing plans) will be released to the making-up department.
Order chasing	Progress, timing, and capacity utilisation are monitored throughout the production. If delays or bottle-necks are encountered, action will be taken to attempt to relieve them. Incoming materials are inspected. Quality control data are monitored to ensure the minimum of faulty products.

```
                        CLOTHING COMPANY

  ┌───────────────┐  ┌────────────────────────────────────────┐  ┌─────────────────┐
  │ DESIGN        │  │        OPERATIONS DEPARTMENT           │  │ MARKETING       │
  │ DEPARTMENT    │  │ sourcing      parts lists    make in-house │  │ DEPARTMENT      │
  │ design        │  │               making-up plans make outside │  │ customer files  │
  │ pattern making│  │ production time costings     machine utilisation │ order processing│
  │ grading       │  │ calculation   progress tickets labour planning │ price lists     │
  │ lay plan      │  │                                        │  │ marketing       │
  └───────────────┘  └────────────────────────────────────────┘  └─────────────────┘

         ┌──────────────────────────────────────────────────────────────┐
         │                   MAKING-UP DEPARTMENT                         │
 Order → │ fabric store > cutting > accessories store > sewing > pressing > finishing > finished goods store │ → Customer
         │        quality assurance, delivery dates, EDP throughout production │
         └──────────────────────────────────────────────────────────────┘
```

1: Interlocking of departments in clothing manufacture

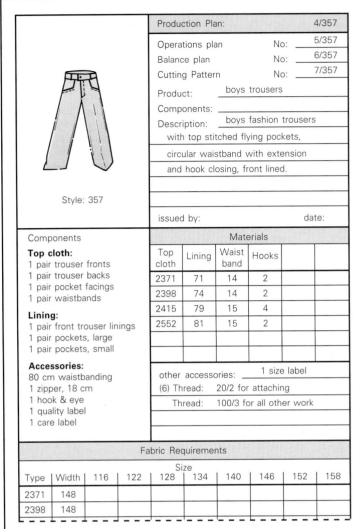

Production Plan:				4/357
Operations plan		No:		5/357
Balance plan		No:		6/357
Cutting Pattern		No:		7/357
Product:	boys trousers			
Components:				
Description:	boys fashion trousers			
with top stitched flying pockets,				
circular waistband with extension				
and hook closing, front lined.				
issued by:			date:	

Style: 357

Components	Materials				
Top cloth:	Top cloth	Lining	Waist band	Hooks	
1 pair trouser fronts	2371	71	14	2	
1 pair trouser backs	2398	74	14	2	
1 pair pocket facings	2415	79	15	4	
1 pair waistbands	2552	81	15	2	
Lining:					
1 pair front trouser linings					
1 pair pockets, large					
1 pair pockets, small					
Accessories:	other accessories:		1 size label		
80 cm waistbanding	(6) Thread:		20/2 for attaching		
1 zipper, 18 cm	Thread:		100/3 for all other work		
1 hook & eye					
1 quality label					
1 care label					

Fabric Requirements									
		Size							
Type	Width	116	122	128	134	140	146	152	158
2371	148								
2398	148								

1: Production plan

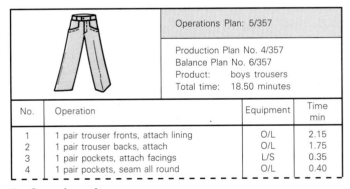

Operations Plan: 5/357			
Production Plan No. 4/357			
Balance Plan No. 6/357			
Product: boys trousers			
Total time: 18.50 minutes			

No.	Operation	Equipment	Time min
1	1 pair trouser fronts, attach lining	O/L	2.15
2	1 pair trouser backs, attach	O/L	1.75
3	1 pair pockets, attach facings	L/S	0.35
4	1 pair pockets, seam all round	O/L	0.40

2: Operations plan

Quality Control		Style: 5/357			Inspector: J. Smith			
Day	Number of samples	Major (withdraw)	Medium (press)	Minor (objectionable)	Cause			
					Operator	Material	Defective procedure	Machine
Mon	10	2	-	1	3	-	-	-
Tue	10	-	1	-	-	1	-	-
Wed	10	-	-	-	-	-	-	-

3: Quality Control form

Operations

Operations is a part of the Production department. Its main functions are to reconcile the orders received from the Marketing department with the technical capability of the factory and to achieve the corresponding production at the optimum quality and minimum cost.

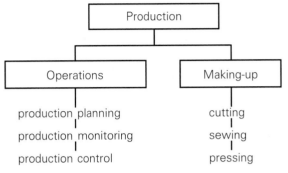

The Operations department plans, monitors, and controls the production. This requires a large amount of documentation, such as production plans, cutting plans, sewing plans, and work allocation plans. Electronic data processing (EDP) is a great help in making all of these plans.

The **production plan** for a given product includes a description of the article, lists for all of the individual components, information on the materials required and their quantities (**Figure 1**).

The individual **component lists** are used as the basis for preparing the operations plan, for calculating fabric and accessory requirements, and for the cost calculation.

The **operations plan** is a list of all of the operations which will be carried out, in the correct sequence, together with the equipment required and the time necessary for each operation. The actual operatives to be used may also be indicated (**Figure 2**).

The **balance plan** is an allocation of all of the operations to specific work stations and operators, in a way which equalises, or balances the time spent at each station so that the work can flow at a uniform pace.

The operations and balancing plans allow easy control of the work in progress, optimum capacity utilisation, and accurate cost and timing calculations.

Production control involves continuous monitoring of actual against target performances. Reasons are immediately sought for deviations and corrective action is taken (**Figure 3**).

A constant watch is kept over the actual levels of quality, cost, and progress in all areas.

Work measurement is a part of Work Study. Its objective is to improve profitability through better organisation and higher efficiency. This involves a close study of the needs and the performance of the workers. Various systematic methods have been devised to analyse the time content of work. An example is the methodology developed by the REFA Work Study Association, in Germany.

In addition to time measurements, work study provides the basis for: cost calculations, method studies, demand calculations, incentive schemes and training schemes.

Work Measurement after REFA

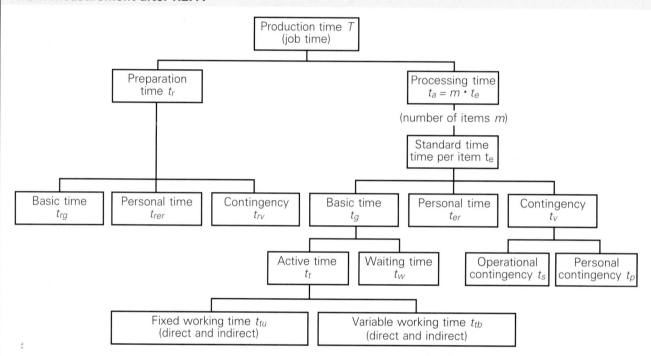

	Time classification	Definition	Example
T	**Production time** (job time)	The total time allowed for the complete operation. It comprises preparation time and processing time.	Sew 5 button holes in each of 100 components, after first setting up the machine for the new button hole length.
t_a	**Processing time**	Time required to carry out the operation on all m components. In general, $t_a = m \cdot t_e$.	Sew 500 button holes
t_e	**Standard time** (time per item)	Time allowed for each individual operation.	Sew 5 buttonholes in one component.
t_g	**Basic time**	Time required for the actual operation.	Pick component, offer to needle, sew seam, place sewn component.
t_{er}	**Personal time**	Interruption of work to relieve fatigue.	Rest after heavy work, relaxation after close concentration.
t_v	**Contingency time**	Interruptions at irregular intervals which are necessary from time to time. They are usually allowed for as a percentage of the basic time.	**Operational contingencies:** include bobbin changes and thread changes. **Personal contingencies:** include visits to the toilets.
t_{rg}	**Basic preparation time**	Time allowed for necessary preparation work.	Read order form, set up sewing machine, enter data on work ticket.
t_{rer}	**Personal preparation time**	Interruptions to preparation work to relieve fatigue.	Rest, relaxation.
t_{rv}	**Preparation contingency**	Interruptions at irregular intervals which are necessary from time to time.	Consulting mechanic.
t_t	**Active time**	Direct work is when the product itself is being worked on. Indirect work is when some auxiliary function is performed. Active time may contain periods whose duration can not be influenced directly by the operator.	Time used to close a seam. Picking and placing components. Fixed: automatic operations. Variable: laying in the thread.
t_w	**Waiting time**	Waiting for work to be delivered from the preceding station.	Waiting for the next component in a straight-line system, or for the completion of an automatic, unmanned process.

To evaluate the **Total Time** required for an operation, actual timings may be made.

All of the relevant data about the operation are entered onto the front of a standard form, including the operator, the equipment and the task. The operation is analysed and broken down into logical sub-units, each of which is timed repeatedly and the results are entered onto the back of the form. Analysis of all of the data allows the Observed Time to be calculated. Meanwhile, the operator will have been assigned a **Performance Rating** which is used together with the Observed Time to calculate the Basic Time for the operation.

Example:

Observed Time t_i = 3.5 min; Performance Rating L = 120%

Basic Time $t_g = \dfrac{L \cdot t_i}{100} = \dfrac{120 \cdot 3.5}{100} = 4.2$ min

This Basic Time (t_g) is entered on the front of the form. Allowances for Personal Time and Contingency are estimated as a percentage and are added. The result is the **Standard Time** (t_e) for the operation. The Standard time is used as an aid to management and to make predictions, for production planning, for setting wage rates, and for determining capacity utilization and production times.

1: Front of a Work Measurement form

2: Back of a Work Measurement form

Other methods of work measurement include PMTS (Pre-determined Motion Time System), MTM (Method Time Measurement) and WFM (Work Factor Measurement). The latter two methods contain lists of the smallest units of movement together with their time requirements. Any piece of work can be analysed into a series of these small movements so that the method, and hence the time, can be synthesized without the need for making actual measurements. These systems also avoid the difficult problem of establishing performance ratings. The PMTS system can be very time-consuming to develop but this disadvantage has now been largely overcome by the availability of tables or computer databases for all the standard times.

Method study is the systematic investigation of a particular operation or function with the objective of finding an improved way of achieving its objectives. It considers the interactions between people, equipment and environment and attempts to increase efficiency and productivity, whilst reducing the burden on the human operator.

Six-Step Method

Method study investigations often make use of a six-step procedure.

1. Specify precise objective
2. Define boundaries
3. Consider theoretical solutions
4. Collect data and propose options
5. Select best option
6. Introduce and monitor option

Objectives of Method Study

Method study is concerned with the improvement, or development, of working methods, equipment, products, and working environments.

In studying **working methods**, one is attempting to improve the flow of products, to ensure better control of production, and to make the best use of equipment, e.g. transport of components by an overhead rail in trouser manufacture.

The study of **equipment** seeks to match the machinery and equipment to the particular task and the procedure, e.g. providing a larger working area for large components.

The study of **products** is often a collaboration carried out between the design and production planning departments, e.g. establish whether the existing profile sewer jigs can be used, or whether new jigs have to be built, or whether the design can be changed to accommodate the existing jigs.

The study of the **work station** is the section of method study which affects the operators most directly.

```
                        Work Station Design
        ┌──────────────────────┼──────────────────────┐
  Working Methods        Working Equipment        Working Conditions
      optimise                improve                  provide
   manual operations    machinery and technology    ergonomic lay-out
```

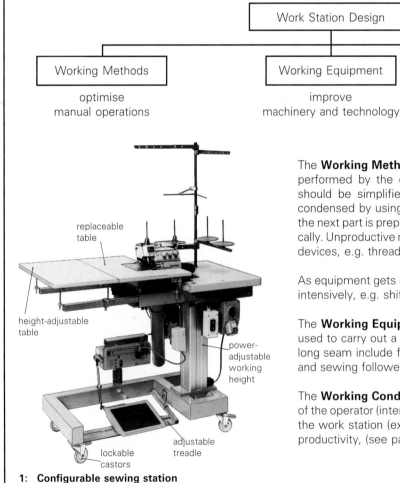

replaceable table

height-adjustable table

power-adjustable working height

lockable castors

adjustable treadle

1: Configurable sewing station

The **Working Method** means the sequence of manual operations performed by the operator. Picking and placing of components should be simplified and shortened. Manual operations can be condensed by using both hands or by overlapping operations e.g. the next part is prepared for feeding whilst one is handled automatically. Unproductive manual operations can be replaced by automatic devices, e.g. thread cutters.

As equipment gets ever more expensive, it has to be utilised more intensively, e.g. shift working for automatic cutting machines.

The **Working Equipment** includes the machinery and technology used to carry out a procedure. Possible technologies for closing a long seam include fusing, sewing with an automatic long-seamer, and sewing followed by fusing or gluing.

The **Working Conditions** include the motivation and competence of the operator (internal conditions) and the physical environment of the work station (external conditions). Both have a large effect on productivity, (see page 187).

Ergonomics

Ergonomics is the study of the efficiency of the person in the working environment. Research is carried out on the influence of machinery and equipment design and disposition upon the comfort, health, productivity and production potential of the human operator, in order to be able to fit the person to the work or, better, to fit the work to the person.

Fitting the work to the person:
- design of work station and equipment
- comfortable working environment
- sensible organisation of work

Fitting the person to the work:
- rational personnel selection according to individual capabilities, age, constitution, etc.
- proper instruction and training for the job

The objective of ergonomics is to measure stress, and to discover how to maximise the particular potential of human operators with the minimum of stress. Quite apart from any moral obligations, the fact is that when production conditions and equipment are designed to reduce stress in the operators, then the result is generally higher productivity, greater satisfaction, and a smoother pace of work. This is sometimes called humanisation of the workplace.

Human Productivity

The productivity of a person depends on his motivation and the way that he copes with stress. How a person copes with stress depends on his capability. Capability depends on education, training, experience, and practice. In addition, productivity depends on general disposition, current health, and fatigue.

Fatigue may be due to physical exhaustion or to boredom; both must be relieved by adequate rest periods. Frequent brief rest periods are normally planned and are included, as personal time, in the time established for a given operation.

Loading and Stress

Loading is determined by the physical nature of the work; it describes the heaviness of the work. Stress is more to do with the individual response of a person to the loads imposed by a specific work environment.

Stress in a working person is analysed with respect to the loads which are placed on different bodily functions, from various sources:

1. Loading the muscle system, e.g. attaching a lining to a winter coat.
2. Loading the senses, e.g. computer-based pattern construction and grading.
3. Environmental loading, e.g. from steam and vapours.

Ergonomic Work Station Design

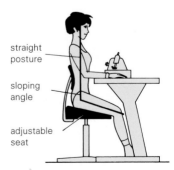

1: **Poor seating posture**

rounded back

straight posture

sloping angle

adjustable seat

2: **Proper seating posture with spinal support**

Ergonomically designed sewing work stations can improve concentration, delay fatigue, and reduce accidents.

Anthropometric design is the design of work stations in such a way as to conform to the natural dimensions of the human body. This includes the working height of tables and the lay-out of working areas. The space required for comfortable working depends on the operation to be performed and the technology. The seated posture during sewing should not be displaced by more than 20 cm away from the upright; the eyes should be about 40 cm from the needle point. The table should have a surface area appropriate to the size of the components being sewn and the method to be used.

Environmental control is concerned with the duration and the heaviness of the work. Attention is paid to the reduction and elimination of negative external influences such as noise, radiation, and waste materials. Lighting and air conditioning are also important in this connection.

The objective is to provide a pleasant and comfortable environment, including colour, music, flowering plants, etc.

Health and safety is an important part of work place design. Measures are taken to avoid work-related illness and accidents.

The **provision of information** is also subject to design considerations: easy-to-use forms, tabulated data, scales, etc.

Electronic data processing (EDP), using computers, can be an effective way of organising information flow in a manufacturing company. The rapid availability of information from many points, both inside and outside the factory, can reduce unnecessary delays, and ensure that the right goods are in the right place at the right time. A computer network is used to integrate the various types of information emanating from different departments of the company.

Usually, each separate department will have its own internal network, and software which is specialised for its own functions. The data on the departmental networks are mostly not relevant to, and not available in other departments. However, depending on the size and technical capability of the company, it may be possible for some of the sales and production data to be combined. An advance on this is the partially integrated system, in which some functions which cross departmental boundaries can be linked.

In principle, a fully integrated (CIM) system would be possible, in which all of the separate departmental networks are combined under the control of a central computer. This has not yet been achieved.

Information Systems

CIM = Computer Integrated Manufacturing
CAA = Computer Aided Administration
CAD = Computer Aided Design
PPC = Production Planning and Control
CAM = Computer Aided Manufacturing

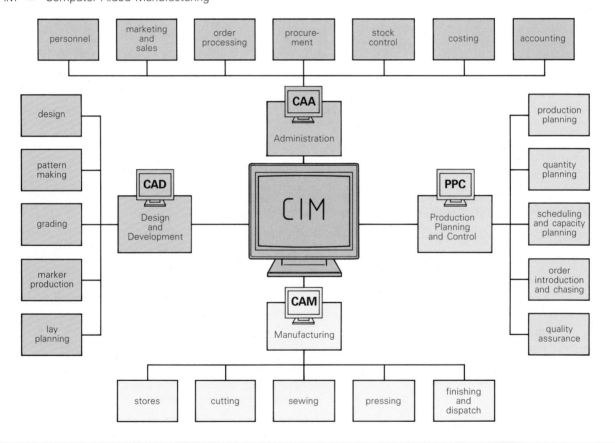

CIM - Computer Integrated Manufacture

CIM is the ultimate integration of information flow in a company. Specialists in every department have instant access to technical and organisational data as and when needed. CIM implies totally automatic, seamless integration of all production stages and access to all data (orders, costings, designs, machinery and process control etc.).

CAA - Computer Aided Administration

Computer-based company administration is the area with which the clothing industry has the most experience (e.g. stock control, accountancy, wages).

CAD - Computer Aided Design and Pattern Development

In the clothing industry, CAD embraces the creative design of new styles as well as the technical functions of pattern construction, grading, production of cutting markers and lay planning.

Design

New garment styles are developed using the computer, colour monitor and pointing devices (**Figure 1**). Any required fabric designs and colours can be introduced, modified, and stored for later use (**Figure 2**). Usually, designs are made in two dimensions. This is partly because textile materials are two dimensional and partly because the standard size charts, derived from body measurements, have been developed for working with two dimensional patterns (see page 133).

1: Design sketches overlaid with colour

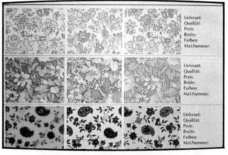

2: Patterns held on computer files

A wire model in the form of a human body (**Figure 3**) can be used to realise three-dimensional representations. On the monitor screen, they can be enlarged, reduced, rotated, compressed, or stretched. The individual garment parts are transposed into two-dimensional drawings (**Figure 3**). The structure and drape of textile materials can also be represented visually (**Figure 4**). Nevertheless, in contrast to the automobile, engineering, and shoe industry, the clothing industry has not yet realised a complete three-dimensional design system.

3: Transformation from three-dimensional design to flat garment parts

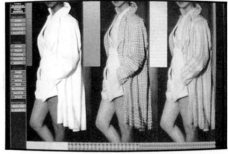

4: Three-dimensional material simulations

Pattern Construction

The basic pattern is either constructed on the screen, or an existing pattern is digitised (**Figure 5**). The basic pattern is then graded into a full pattern set using predefined rules (**Figure 6**). All of the results can be saved for later recall at will. This allows more cost effective product development and lay planning, as well as shorter delivery times (see page 133 and 134).

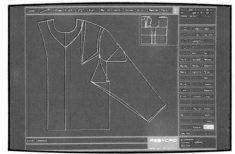

5: Basic pattern construction

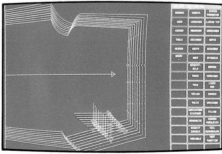

6: Grading

PPC - Production Planning and Control

Planning, monitoring, and control of production can be supported by computers. This can help a company to react more rapidly to market opportunities. In addition, the different sections and departments can communicate information more rapidly, through networking (see page 182).

CAM - Computer Aided Manufacturing

Computer Aided Lay Planning

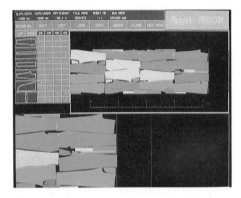

After grading, a lay plan has to be devised which makes maximum use of the material.

The cutting markers can be reproduced in full size at a plotter. They are placed on top of the fabric lay, followed by manual cutting (see page 136).

Computer Controlled Cutting

The lay plan is sent directly (on-line) to a computer-controlled cutting device which cuts the fabric lay automatically (see page 140).

It is not necessary to produce cutting markers.

Computer Controlled Sewing

This device allows automatic sewing of the long seams in trousers. 30 different sewing programmes can be stored and recalled at will.

Computer Controlled Pressing

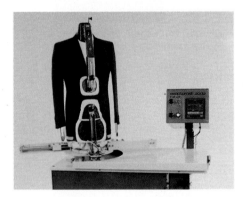

The illustration shows a form finisher for jackets. 15 different pressing routines can be programmed, corresponding to different materials, styles, and button placings.

Computer Controlled Materials Distribution

The various material transport systems which link the different production sections, from fabric rolls through cut parts, to half and fully finished products, can all be controlled by computers. Material flow can be made smoother and waiting times can be reduced. Information on the progress of manufacturing can be called up from the system at any time (see page 180).

10 Garment Sizing   10.1 Proportion

Proportion is the relation of one part to a whole or to other parts. An appreciation of natural proportions is essential to the representation of the human figure, and therefore to clothing manufacture.

Two concepts which have proved useful in representing human body proportions are the Golden Section (or Golden Mean) and Division into Eighths.

The Golden Section (Golden Mean)

When dividing a line into unequal sections, harmonious proportions can be constructed by using the golden section.

Principle:

The shorter section (a) is to the larger section (b) as the larger section (b) is to the whole line (a+b).

$$\frac{a}{b} = \frac{b}{a + b} = 0.618$$

This proportion is found very frequently in works of art.

Construction of the Golden Section:

1. The perpendicular BC is erected at B, with BC = ½ AB.
2. C is joined to A.
3. D is marked on CA so that CD = CB = ½ AB.
4. E is marked on AB so that AE = AD.
5. E divides AB into the golden section.

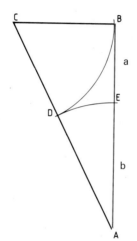

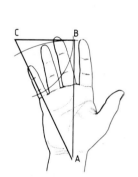

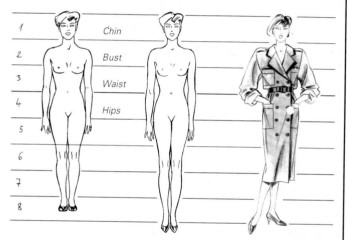

1: Division of a line into the golden section

2: Proportion of a hand

3: Female proportions

4: Ideal proportions for clothing

Division into Eighths

The ratio of the golden section works out in practice to 0.618 which is quite close to 5/8. The total height of a full-grown woman is about 7½ times the vertical size of the head. Therefore, the body is provided with **ideal proportions**, and sketching of it is made easier, by dividing it into eight equal parts, whereby the waistline is placed at about 5/8 of the total height, and the crotch is at about half the height. For fashion sketches, the proportion is often extended to between eight and eight and a half times the head, with the extra length being given to the legs (**Figures 3 and 4**).

Departures from the Ideal Figure

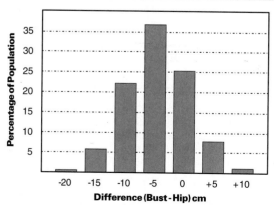

5: Difference between Bust girth and Hip girth

Every individual has his or her individual body size and proportions. Large, small, slender, or stocky figures do not always have the ideal proportions. **Figure 5** illustrates the wide range of female body proportions found in a typical population[1].

It can be seen that most of the women had a bust girth which was smaller than the hip girth. For about 37% of the population, this difference averaged about 5 cm; for a further 23% the difference averaged about 10 cm and for a further 25%, bust and hip girths were about the same. The total range of hip girth in that survey was from about 81 to 132 cm and, for a large portion of that range (86 to 122 cm), the range in bust size at constant hip size was 20 to 25 cm. Similar surveys have been made in other countries, for example France, Germany, Sweden, and the USA, with similar results.

[1] "Women's Measurements and Sizes"; H.M. Stationary Office, U.K., 1957

10.2   Body Size Tables (1)

Basic Considerations

Clothing has to be made so that it fits the size and the shape of the body as well as possible, but industrial manufacturing does not allow for the economic production of a vast range of different garment shapes and sizes. Somehow, the data obtained from population measurement surveys have to be grouped into a manageable number of body types and sizes and then tabulated in a form that can be used by the industry to meet the requirements of particular target markets.

The division of statistical survey measurements into a manageable number of body types and sizes has usually been a largely empirical process. In a given country, it is constrained by the practical limitations of the clothing industry and by local attitudes and preferences. Therefore it is not surprising that different countries construct different body type and size groupings, even when starting from similar statistical data.

In all cases, however, the construction of body size tables is founded on just a few basic concepts, such as:

- The **percentage of the population** which has to be satisfied.
- The **control dimensions** which define different **body types**.
- The **size intervals** between different body types and different sizes within the same body type.

Percentage of the Population

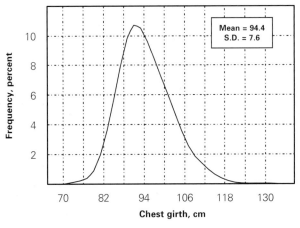

1: Distribution of adult male Chest girth

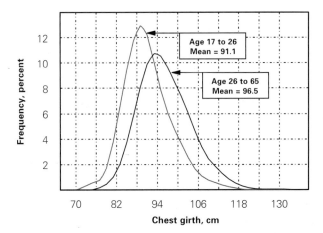

2: Adult male Chest girth in different age groups

Within a given population, most body dimensions are distributed in a pattern similar to **Figure 1**, which shows the distribution of chest girth in a certain population of British males in the late 1970's[1]. The standard deviation of that distribution was about 7.6 cm, which means that about 95% of the population could be accommodated by a range of chest sizes spanning about 4 x 7.6 = 30.4 cm.

In a different population the average girth and the standard deviation may both be different. Even within a single population the distributions may be different for different age groups (**Figure 2**) or other social groups. Once the basic statistics are available, the range of measurements which covers a given percentage of the target population can easily be discovered.

Control Dimensions

In body measurement surveys, there may be more than 40 different body measurements made on each individual[2]. It is clearly impractical to develop body size tables taking all of these measurements into account individually. It is necessary to select a few control dimensions which will serve to make the major distinctions between body types and sizes. The other dimensions have to be related to the control dimensions, within a given body type, usually by averaging. Thus, the control dimensions serve several functions:

- They provide the basis for establishing the **total range** in body measurements.
- They provide the basis for defining different **body types** (proportions) within the population.
- They provide the basis for creating the **size intervals** between different sizes within the same body type.

Obviously, the control dimensions which are selected must be ones which largely determine the fit of a garment to a given body size. For a woman's dress, the hip girth, the bust girth, and possibly the length are most important; for a skirt, the waist girth, the hip girth, and the length are dominant. For a man's jacket, the chest and the waist girths are most important; for trousers, the waist, hips, and inside-leg length must be considered. The same control dimensions which are used to divide population statistics will later be used to specify the key dimensions of garments.

---

[1] "British Male Body Measurements", WIRA Clothing Services, U.K., 1980   [2] ISO 8559: 1989

Definition of Separate Body Types

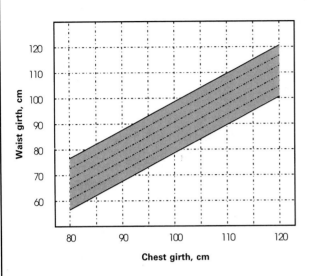

1: **Adult male Waist girth versus Chest girth**

General Principle:

Figure 1 illustrates the general relation between male chest girth and waist girth. It shows that, for any given chest girth, the waist girth may vary by up to about 20 cm, because of the differences in body proportions. If a range in chest girth of, say 5 cm is taken to represent a specific chest size, then the total range of corresponding waist girths is increased to about 25 cm.

An area of approximately constant body proportion is defined by a band which is parallel to the two lines which outline the total range. Different body types (different proportions) are found by moving vertically through the range of waist girths at a given chest girth. To delineate different body types, the total range can be divided into parallel, sloping bands. In this case, with equal size intervals of 4 cm for the waist girth, there would be five parallel bands, i.e. 5 different body types. Taking the average waist girth within a band to be representative of that body type then, over the whole range of chest girths, there will be a constant difference between chest girth and waist girth. This is called the **drop value**. Each body type would have a different drop value, representing the five different body shapes in the population. Thus a given body type can be specified by the chest girth and the drop value.

Example: **Men's whole body outerwear garments (after ISO/TR 10652: 1991)**

Body Type: Name	Athletic	Regular	Portly	Stout	Corpulent
Mean drop value (chest-waist), cm	16	12	6	0	-6

This is not the end of the matter, because the population is also distributed according to **stature** (total body height). Often, the total range of stature will be divided into three; "short", "medium", and "tall". In the male population illustrated in **Figure 1**, the average stature was about 174 cm with a standard deviation of about 7 cm. As an example, therefore, "short" could be defined as less than 167 cm; "medium" could be 167 to 181 cm; "tall" could be greater than 181 cm. A larger number of height divisions is, of course, possible and may be considered necessary for clothing items where the length is of great importance.

Following this classification, each of the 5 chest/waist groups may be divided into the three (or more) stature types to make 15 (or more) different chest/waist/stature body types, e.g. Tall-athletic, Medium-athletic, Short-athletic, etc.

Size Intervals

Size intervals fulfil three major functions:

- They provide the basis for assigning the boundaries for the different body types, as discussed above.
- They provide the numerical basis for grading sizes, and hence garment cutting patterns, from one size to the next within a given body type (grading intervals).
- They provide the purchaser of the garment with a guide for which garment, within a range on offer, is likely to be the most suitable for his/her figure.

To keep the number of different sizes to a manageable quantity, the size interval should not be too small. To provide a simple, practical, and consistent means of pattern grading, the size interval ideally would be constant throughout the whole range. To serve the customer, the size interval ideally would be small enough so that no customer is expected to purchase a garment which is too large, or out of proportion. The ideal situation is not always achieved.

A size interval of between 4 and 6 cm for girths seems to satisfy most of these requirements for a wide range of adult garments, although local industry preferences may dictate a variable size interval or an interval outside this range. Changes in body proportions and/or size intervals may be required for outsize ranges or for garments designed specifically for the elderly. Children's garments are based on different sets of tables and proportions.

Looking again at **Figure 1**, if a size interval of 4 cm for chest girth (the primary control dimension) is chosen then, within each body type, there would be about 10 different sizes. Thus the total number of body type/size groups would be at least 15 x 10 = 150. In practice, a good number of the theoretically possible body type/sizes will not actually exist within the population, or will contain only a few members, so that the final number of different body type/size groups actually selected will be significantly fewer than the theoretical maximum.

Size Charts

Once the population has been classified into major types and sizes according to the chosen control dimensions and size intervals, then all of the measurements from all of the individuals contained within each type/size group can be averaged to provide the basic set of body measurement tables for each body type and size. Minor adjustments to these raw tables are then made empirically to provide consistency within types and between sizes and to give practical numbers (whole numbers, even numbers). In the body size tables issued by the US Department of Commerce in 1971, there were 7 body type tables for women. The seven body types were named "Junior Petite", "Juniors", "Misses Petite", "Misses", "Misses Talls", "Womens", and "Half Sizes". Each table contained 45 body measurements for between 6 and 10 different sizes, making a total of 55 type/size groups.

To develop garment patterns using these tables, allowances must be applied to the basic body dimensions. These will depend on the style of garment and type of fabric to be used. For stable woven fabrics and loose styles in knitted fabrics space must be provided between the garment and the body to allow for movement and for changes in body dimensions (e.g. spreading of the hips when seated). This is called the **ease allowance** or **tolerance**. For close fitting garments or support styles using stretch fabrics, the allowance may be zero or negative. In any case an additional allowance is made for the width of the seams. Further modifications may also be made to allow for fashion and styling details.

Size charts are tables which have been constructed from the basic body measurement tables and which include ease allowance and other allowances necessary for the production of a particular type of garment.

Designation of Sizes, Size Codes

Each of the body type/size groups contained within the body size tables or size charts is given a simple size designation or **size code** to identify it. The size code performs two main functions.

For the manufacturing industry, it indicates which size table is being (has been) used to construct the master cutting patterns for the garment in question. For the consumer, it indicates the body type and size which the displayed garment is intended to fit.

At present, there is no universal system for size designation that is used world-wide to indicate the same or similar body sizes in different countries. This is partly because the body size tables developed in each country are based on different body type boundaries and different size intervals, but also because many countries use different coding systems to indicate similar sizes.

As an example of the differences in size designations between systems, the US standard size codes for women can be compared to those for Germany, for similar body measurements. A few of these are shown in the table, where the US body measurements have been converted from inches and rounded to the nearest half centimetre.

Comparison of some US and German Size Designations

Size Code	Short				Medium				Tall			
	US 22½	G 25	US 12	G 19	US 22	G 48	US 16	G 42	US 22T	G 596	US 18T	G 588
Bust, cm	117	116	89	88	112	110	96.5	96	112	110	101.5	100
Hip, cm	119.5	119.5	94	94.5	117	114	101.5	101.5	117	120	106.5	111
Hip-Bust, drop	2.5	3.5	5	6.5	5	4	5	5.5	5	10	5	11
Stature, cm	160	160	162.5	160	168.5	168	165	168	179	176	176.5	176

Because of the lack of standardization in size codes, the ISO has recommended that size designation for garment labels should refer primarily to body measurements[1] rather than size codes. Several national standards bodies have adopted this format to a greater or lesser degree.

The **ISO discussion document**[2] specifies the use of a pictogram showing the control dimensions and/or a box with the control dimensions for the recommended body size indicated in words and numerals. The control dimensions to be used for different types of garments are also specified. Additional information, such as other body dimensions, garment dimensions, or size codes may also be given but should be indicated separately and should not reduce the prominence of the main control dimensions.

Example 1: Man's Suit

Control dimensions are Chest girth, Waist girth, and Height.

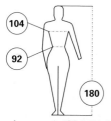

OR

| CHEST GIRTH 104 |
| WAIST GIRTH 92 |
| HEIGHT   180 |
| INSIDE LEG   78 |
| SIZE CODE   52 |

Example 2: Woman's Coat

Control dimensions are Bust girth, Hip girth, and Height.

OR

| BUST GIRTH 92 |
| HIP GIRTH   98 |
| HEIGHT   168 |
| SIZE CODE   40 |

[1] see for example ISO 3636, 3637, 4415, 4416   [2] see ISO Technical Report 10652: 1991

A collection is a range of garment styles, designed for a particular market.

In developing a collection, the following factors have to be considered.

- Assessment of **fashion trends**
- Analysis of **consumer behaviour**
- Identification of **target groups**
- Economic **scale of production**

The company's **Marketing** department will be active in market research, market analysis, and sales research. All of this information will be used to develop, produce and promote new products. The company objective is to develop the maximum sales potential with the minimum of risk.

Stages in the Development of a Collection (example)

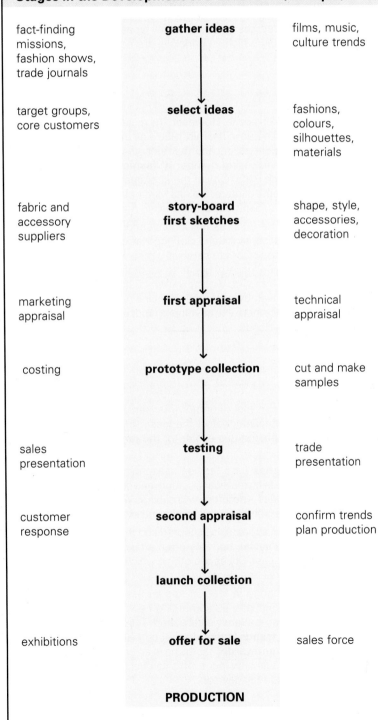

fact-finding missions, fashion shows, trade journals	**gather ideas**	films, music, culture trends
target groups, core customers	**select ideas**	fashions, colours, silhouettes, materials
fabric and accessory suppliers	**story-board first sketches**	shape, style, accessories, decoration
marketing appraisal	**first appraisal**	technical appraisal
costing	**prototype collection**	cut and make samples
sales presentation	**testing**	trade presentation
customer response	**second appraisal**	confirm trends plan production
	launch collection	
exhibitions	**offer for sale**	sales force
	PRODUCTION	

Development starts with the assimilation of **market intelligence** from a wide range of sources. Seasonal trend information on colours, silhouettes, and materials is available from haute couture, textile and fibre companies, trade journals and independent consultants. Inspiration is drawn also from social and cultural trends, the arts, movies etc. and from history. From this information, broad styling themes are distilled, refined and re-interpreted into specific garment styles suited to the requirements of existing customers and target groups. Target groups will be chosen according to age, quality demands, leisure activities, life styles, fashion awareness, etc.

Preliminary design sketches are made and assembled together with selected materials and indications of fashion themes to create a **story board.**

These initial design ideas are discussed at a **first appraisal meeting**, in which the scope, balance, and image of the collection, as well as the quality standard is decided. The whole management team - design, marketing, and technical - is involved in these decisions.

Samples of each chosen style are cut and assembled in the sample room to create **garment prototypes**. Preliminary costings for material, labour and appropriate profit margins are calculated and compared with established selling prices.

The finished **prototype collection** is tested for sales appeal and, if necessary, modified. (**second appraisal**). Styles which lack competitive potential are either eliminated or have their design features altered to better reflect the perceived requirements of potential customers. At this stage a preliminary **production and scheduling plan** will be made.

Traditionally, separate collections were developed for the two main seasons, Autumn/Winter and Spring/Summer. Nowadays, because the turnover in styles is more rapid close attention must be paid to market developments so that additional styles, or mini collections can be produced at short notice.

The whole collection may be replicated for agents, exhibitions, displays, and presentations.

Production begins as the orders are generated.

Concepts of Fashion in Clothing

The term **fashion** describes the current prevailing trends in a society, for example concerning a particular way of dressing, lifestyle, pattern of thought and the development of the arts.

Fashion in the narrow sense of the word means the changing forms of clothing. These originate from people's need to be adorned and admired but also allow the opportunity to enhance personal style or indicate a position in society e.g. membership of a particular group.

Originally, the term fashion was used for a very short-lived trend, whilst something which prevailed over a longer period and developed on a cultural and artistic level was described as style.

Today, many of the terms used to describe the various trends in clothing generally mean the same, for example "**fashion**", "**style**", "**look**", "**line**".

A particular style of clothing adopted by ethnic or religious groups over a long period is called **traditional dress** or **regional costume**. Clothing or fashions of a bye-gone age are often referred to as **period costume**. Clothing which identifies members of e.g. a civil or military service, commercial organisation, or sporting club are described as **uniforms**.

The terms dress, costume and uniform are often used almost interchangeably for many types of specialised styles of clothing which, in principle, are not subject to fashion changes.

The Development and Significance of Fashion

In the past, power and wealth, social distinction and belonging to a particular class were emphasised by clothing. Customs and moral conventions were often more important than practical utility in shaping clothing styles. Conversely, aesthetic ideas could be expressed or a sense of sexuality could be displayed through clothing.

Until the middle of the nineteenth century, the aristocracy and the courts, or the sophisticated bourgeoisie determined fashion styles. After this, **haute couture** took on the leading role. Fashion designers or fashion houses created **exclusive models** for a chosen look. Paris was the centre of women's fashion, whereas for men the English style was the most popular.

Industrialisation and the emergence of **ready-to-wear** clothing, as well as the development of **synthetic fibres** enabled the gradual participation of all classes of society in the fashion scene. However, the dictates of haute couture still dominated in the mid 1950's as they were imitated by the bespoke tailors and the ready-to-wear clothing industry. An increasing number of **fashion centres** grew up along side Paris. One of the strongest influences was the Italian haute couture, the Alta Moda, challenging the French women's fashion and the English men's fashion.

During the 60's, as an unconventional style of clothing gained acceptance and clothing was seen less as a status symbol but rather to serve as a means of self-expression, the fashion industry began to adapt to the changing situation. The ready-to-wear fashion industry moved to the forefront, driven by consumer demand, whilst haute couture was concerned with developing and refining ready-to-wear clothing trends.

Changing Fashion

Developments in fashion are based on the desire for change, variety or emulation and are influenced by the structure of society, by technical and cultural development as well as political and economic events. In earlier times, fashion clothing remained more or less constant over a long period of time whereas today changes in fashion take place very rapidly.

Fashion designers and Couturiers are inspired, take hold of trends and make suggestions for a forthcoming fashion season. If these suggestions are taken up by a large part of the population, they become the fashion. Strict rules of fashion are disappearing along with the erosion of sharp demarcations in social status. Individuals feel more and more free to compose their own individual styles from the vast diversity of available designs.

International fashion fairs, with **trend shows**, are held regularly in a number of cities around the world, e.g. Paris, Milan, Düsseldorf, London, New York, Hong Kong and Tokyo. Fashion houses, designers and the ready-to-wear clothing industry present their collections for each Spring/Summer season and Autumn/Winter season. These shows are held immediately before the season for haute couture fashion and six months earlier for the ready-to-wear clothing industry.

The **themes** for a fashion season include the cuts, patterns, details, materials, colours and designs as well as the accessories. The interested public is kept informed of fashion events through the media and other publications.

A fashion appears, is accepted and then disappears again (**fashion cycle**), but very often a fashion may be revived from the past. Styles of clothing which achieve long lasting acceptance are descried as classic (timeless).

Every change in fashion has an associated risk for the clothing industry as something new must succeed over that which is already established. The correct prediction of **fashion trends** is therefore of crucial importance. Those with "**avant-garde**" tastes have an enthusiasm to assimilate unusual new ideas. This can help predict how a general trend may develop.

11.3 Fashion Accessories

Accessories are those additional items of adornment which extend and round off an image. They have played an important role in every fashion age and were often as characteristic as designs or colour.

Previously, great importance was attached to the harmonious matching of the accessory and the style of clothing. Today's fashion allows for combinations of different styles and contrasting accessories. Every season the fashion industry offers co-ordinating accessories in current colours and materials for different fashion themes.

Only a few accessories offer **decoration** alone, for example, jewellery. Above all shoes, but also headwear and handbags have a specific **function** to fulfil. What is fashionable is often not strictly advisable. An example of this is the stiletto heel.

Accessories today are:

- headwear
- shawls, scarfs, ties
- stockings and shoes
- handbags, umbrellas
- belts, sashes
- artificial flowers
- costume jewellery
- glasses, watches

1: Accessories - Fashion's final touch

2: Formal dress accessories for men

Headwear

Style, material and trimmings are aimed at the occasion. The headbands and brim on hats can be greatly varied in design.

Caps and woolly hats are generally not reinforced, have no brims, but do sometimes have a peak.

Materials may be: felt, straw, leather, fur, woven fabric, knitted products

Possible trimmings: ribbons, feathers, veils, cords, flowers, leather and felt strips

3: Beret

4: Veiled hat

5: Trilby

6: Hunter

7: Turban

8: Boater

Fashion is not the only consideration in developing a garment for a market. The overall appearance (style) as well as the utility value (fitness for purpose, aftercare) also have to be appropriate. The style, colour, decoration, material, trimmings and technique are fundamental elements of clothing design.

Styling

A fashionable cut, good fit and comfort in wearing arise mostly from the structure of the design. This includes e.g.

- the position and direction of vertical and horizontal components
- length-width proportion
- shaping
- details, e.g. sleeves, collars, fastenings, pockets

Distinctive **silhouettes** are attained from particular designs. These are denoted by letters (**Figures 1 to 7**) or according to their shape (**Figures 8 to 11**) or after particular periods (**Figures 12,13**).

A distinct **sectioning** of the garment is obtained from the disposition of seam lines and edges (**Figures 15 to 18**).

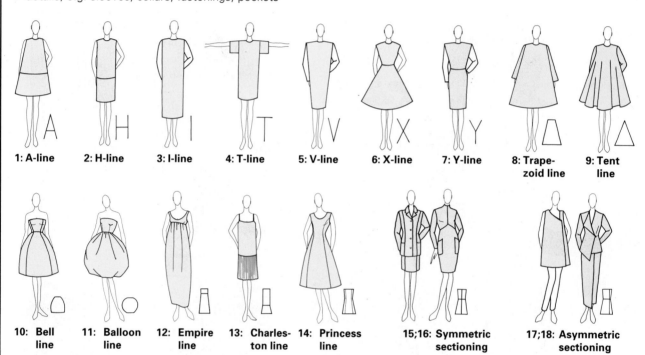

| 1: A-line | 2: H-line | 3: I-line | 4: T-line | 5: V-line | 6: X-line | 7: Y-line | 8: Trapezoid line | 9: Tent line |

| 10: Bell line | 11: Balloon line | 12: Empire line | 13: Charleston line | 14: Princess line | 15;16: Symmetric sectioning | 17;18: Asymmetric sectioning |

Decoration

Decoration can emphasize the **style** of a particular item of clothing and can, for example, give an elegant, casual, business-like, or romantic feel to the clothing.

Decoration can take the form of:

- decorative stitching and embroidery
- pleats and tucks
- frills and flounces
- piping and binding
- trimming and braid edging
- appliqué and incrustation

Material

The material greatly influences the **character** of an item of clothing and also determines its **possible end-use**.

On the one hand, the visual qualities such as how the material hangs, the colour, pattern and surface texture are important when chosing a material. On the other hand the comfort, wearing, and care characteristics which depend on the fibres, type of yarn, fabric and finishing, must also be taken into account.

Trimmings and Technique

The trimmings and the technique considerably influence the **utility** or the functional performance of the clothing. Apart from the material, they are crucial to the overall **quality level**.

Trimmings include the application of linings and interlinings, padding and fastenings.

Technique includes technical aspects of sewing, such as the quality and structure of the seams, reinforcement of edges, and securing of pockets and flies.

11.5   Design Influences

Many factors need to be considered when designing clothing. The major influences are fashion and style trends, the purpose of the clothing and the characteristics of the wearer.

Fashion

Fashion sets the **accent**. The major features which are determined by fashion are:

- basic silhouette and accentuations
- length and width
- details and decoration
- colour, pattern, drape and texture of the material

Style Trends

Clothing is an **expression of personality**. Clothes only feel good when they express the wearer's own attitudes. The great variety of styles which exist side by side in today's fashion clothes allows for individual expression. The style that is favoured at a given time depends on both the venue and the personality of the wearer. Typical styles are:

- casual, informal
- classic, timeless
- business-like, masculine
- conservative, formal
- romantic, pretty
- traditional, rustic
- casual, elegant
- refined, elegant
- feminine
- extravagant
- avant-garde
- frivolous

1: Casual leisure wear

2: Feminine style

3: Casual-elegant style

4: Youthful style

5: Winter fashions

6: Formal morning dress

7: Party dress in traditional style

Purpose

Clothing has different **requirements** according to its purpose.

Sports, leisure and work clothes are primarily functional. Formal dress should stand out from day clothes and appear elegant or festive.

Clothing for Summer wear will have different requirements, in terms of its ventilation and insulation capabilities, moisture absorption and transference, than clothing intended for Winter (see page 129).

The Personality of the Wearer

The characteristics of the wearer include the combined aspects of figure, stature, age and personality.

For a satisfactory **overall effect** the clothing must be adapted not only to the individual body measurements but also to the different requirements of a particular age group. The bespoke tailor can accommodate these individual aspects whereas the ready-to-wear clothing industry must endeavour to consider the broad distinctions between particular target groups (see page 195).

12 Clothing Styles   12.1   Skirts (1)

Nowadays, the term skirt is used for an item of clothing worn from the waist down and which is the basic element of women's and girl's clothing.
A matching jacket with a skirt makes a suit, or costume.

Many styles of skirt are subject to changes in fashion. Other styles are considered classics, or timeless. Individual styles are distinguished by length, width, silhouette, cut and details.

1: Skirt lengths

| **micro** thigh length | **mini** above the knee | **knee length** | **below the knee** | **midi** calf length | **maxi** below the calf | **ankle length** above the shoes | **floor length** covers the shoes |

2: Narrow

The hem of the skirt is narrower than the width at the hips.

3: Straight

The slim silhouette is obtained from the straight side seams.

4: Semi-flared

A comfortable width is obtained from the diverging side seams.

5: Flared panelled

This style is close at the hips with a wide hem obtained by shaped vertical panels.

6: Bell

The circular or semi-circular cut produces a swinging hem.

7: Full

The large amount of material gathered at the waist makes the skirt billow out to a greater or lesser extent.

8: Gored

The symmetrical panels become broader towards the hem.

9: Straight panelled

The clearly defined seams make the straight skirt appear box-like.

10: Godet[1]

Either bell-shaped panels or inserted additional material allow the hem to swing out.

11: Tiered

The successive horizontal panels increase in width towards the hem.

12: Flounced

A succession of horizontal flounces is sewn onto the skirt and drape freely.

13: Frilled hemline

The ruffled hem edging can be either straight or flounced.

[1] godet (Fr.) = flared, fluted

200

14: Yoke style

A straight sect-
ion is added from
the waist to
about hip height.

15: Fit and flare

A skirt, narrow at
the hips, with a
flared, gathered
section attached
near the bottom.

16: Tiered, pleated

Attractive tiered
effect with multiple
layers of sun-ray
pleats.

17: Puff Ball

The skirt is
drawn in at the
waist and at the
hem and puffs
out in between.

**18: Handkerchief
     hemline**

An asymmetric
or uneven hem
gives an elegant
or traditional
style.

19: Draped

An elegant, soph-
isticated skirt
with soft folds.
Here with a wrap
-around effect.

**20: Accordian
     pleats**

The skirt drapes
to a narrow sil-
houette because
of the straight,
narrow pleats.

**21: Sun-ray
     pleats (fine)**

**22: Sun-ray
     pleats (broad)**

Flared skirts with pressed stiff pleats
which widen towards the hem. Very
broad sun-ray styles are sometimes
called umbrella pleats.

23: Inverted pleats   **24: Knife pleats**   **25: Knife pleats**

Pleats allow freedom of movement whilst maintaining a
slim silhouette. They are also an attractive styling feature which can be inserted at the front, at the back or at
the side of a narrow skirt.

26: Country style

The high centre
pleat and side
pockets charac-
terise the casual
country style
skirt.

27: Soft pleat

A soft and
comfortable
style of skirt is
obtained from
an un-pressed
roll pleat.

28: Wrap-around

The open edge is
overlapped a long
way and is often
fastened only at the
waist band.

29: Kilt

The character-
istics are flat
pleats on one
side, a wrap-
around style
and a checked
pattern.

30: Casual style

Big pockets and
a button-through
front are typical
details in a
casual skirt.

31: Culottes

Front and back
trousers fit to-
gether exactly
at the crotch
seam and are
as wide as a
skirt.

The blouse is a soft and loose garment for the upper body which is worn by women and girls together with skirts or trousers. In today's fashion, there is a large variety of blouse styles.

The different features of individual designs, e.g. the neckline and collar, length, cut, details and decoration, together with the material produce a particular style.

1: Shirt style

The straight cut, cuffed sleeves and button placket are borrowed from the men's shirt style.

2: Revere collar

3: Stand collar

Button-through blouses can be designed with a wide range of different collars and neck-lines. The buttons can be visible or covered.

4: Polo shirt

A casual blouse made of knitted fabric with an open collar and a short button placket.

5: Tie neck

The bands on the neck line are loosely knotted or tied into a bow.

6: Slip-on

A short opening at the kneck makes slip-on blouses easier to put on over the head.

7: Tunic

This very long and ample blouse is worn loose or belted.

8: Camisole

This flimsy item is reminiscent of the top half of an underslip.

9: Cossak, tunic

The long, straight blouse often has side slits and is usually belted.

10: Blouson

A blouse with a full bodice and a close fitting waistband.

11: Peplum

Top with a short skirt (peplum) which is either sewn on or shaped.

12: Wrap-over

The front section is loosely overlapped and tied at the side.

13: Traditional style

14: Traditional style

Typical characteristics are frills on the neckline and sleeves, embroidery, border trimmings, lace insets, small pleats and flowers.

15: Carmen

Features of the Carmen blouse are an off-the-shoulder low-cut neckline with frilled or flounced trimmings.

16: Safari style

Breast pockets, epaulettes and rolled-up sleeves emphasise the casual style.

17: Jumper

Casual outer clothing in a slip-on style with a waistband; usually made from knitted fabric.

18: Cap sleeve

A comfortable slip-on blouse made of light knitted or woven material.

The dress is a basic item of female outer clothing. In its original form, a shift or smock, it was worn in ancient times.

In the narrow sense, the term is used for a single piece of clothing comprising an upper body part and a skirt section, either cut from the same panels or sewn on. In a "two piece" the matching top and skirt are made separately (see page 208).

Individual styles of dresses differ in width, silhouette, cut, details and decoration.

1: Fitted
The dress is figure-hugging without being restricting.

2: Shift
The shirt-like straight cut without a waist is characteristic of this dress.

3: Flared
A loosely falling dress with a swinging hem.

4: Princess
Long vertical seams form a close-fitting top but a wide, free swinging skirt.

5: Empire
The high, gathered under-bust seam is characteristic of the empire style.

6: Straight
A flared or pleated skirt is fitted to an elongated straight top.

7: Shirt dress
This has a loose cut, cuffed sleeves and a shirt collar. It is buttoned all the way through and is belted.

8: Coat dress
This is usually made of strong material. It is always buttoned all the way down and is mostly worn with a belt.

9: Strapless
The closely fitted, low-cut, sleeveless top is shaped and supported with bones. It sometimes also has thin straps.

10: Day dress
An elegant, high neck, long sleeved dress, worn during the day or also during the evening to semi-formal occasions.

11: Traditional   12: Traditional
Common features of traditional styles are: generous bodice, sleeves and skirts; aprons; embroidery, frills and flounces; a belt to emphasise the waist.

Knitted outerwear is highly popular as it is very comfortable. Nowadays, it is indispensable in sportswear, leisure wear and casual clothing.

Bulky knitted fabrics are particularly suited for warm outer clothing. Their resistance to wrinkling and creasing can also be an advantage.

   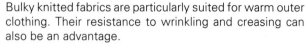 

| 1: T-shirt with round neck | 2: T-shirt with button placket | 3: T-shirt with long shoulders | 4: Polo shirt | 5: Sweatshirt with round neck | 6: Sweatshirt with zip and collar |

The term **T-shirt** is used generally for casual tops with a narrow neckline, short sleeves and no collar, usually made from cotton. Originally made as under shirts.

The **polo shirt** is similar to a shirt or blouse and is made from a light knitted material in a slip-on design. It always has a collar and a short button placket. It can have either short or long sleeves.

A long-sleeved, warm shirt with a waistband is called a **sweatshirt**. The inside is often fleecy. There are many possible collars and necklines.

| 7: Slash neck pullover | 8: V-neck pullover | 9: Round neck pullover | 10: Sweater | 11: V-neck tank top | 12: Round neck tank top |

The **pullover or jumper** is a knitted top with sleeves and a waistband and is put on over the head.

Sweater was an earlier term for the pullover. It is still used today for heavier casual pullovers with long sleeves.

The **tank top**, a sleeveless pullover, is usually waist length and is worn over a blouse or shirt.

| 13: Cardigan | 14: Cardigan with zip | 15: Short knitted waistcoat | 16: Long knitted waistcoat | 17: Tank top | 18: Twinset |

Cardigans are open at the front and are fastened with a zip or buttons. They usually have a waistband.

Long or short sleeveless jackets are regarded as **waistcoats**. They can be provided either with buttons or a zipper.

An over-sized variant with large armholes.

A combination of a classic pullover and cardigan for women.

Until relatively recently, trousers were worn exclusively by males. Today they are commonly found in the female wardrobe. The various styles of trousers have developed mainly from different functional uses, but they are also influenced to a greater or lesser extent by fashion.

Length, width and silhouette, cut and details distinguish the different styles.

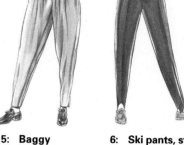

1: Tapered

Narrow trousers. The legs are significantly narrower at the bottom.

2: Straight

Narrow at the hips; legs the same width all the way down.

3: Flared

Closely fitted at the top but legs wider at the foot than at the knee.

4: Wide legs, bags

These have a very wide and straight cut.

5: Baggy

Very full at the hips but the legs narrow at the ankle.

6: Ski pants, stirrup trousers

The foot stirrups hold the ski pant style trousers tight.

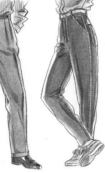

7: Pleated

A comfortable width is obtained by pleats inserted below the waist.

8: Turn-ups

Turn-ups give a casual feel.

9: Jeans

Characteristics are bold top-stitched seams, studs and leather patches.

10: Knee breeches   **11: Knickerbockers**

Knee to calf-length trousers with buttoned cuffs are traditional designs which survive to some extent as plus-fours in golf and country sports.

12: Harem pants

Very long, wide trousers with a tight cuff.

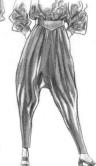

13: Shorts

Very short trousers. Hot pants are skin-tight women's shorts.

14: Bermuda shorts

Wide shorts reaching to just above the knee.

15: Capri pants

These are tight and just cover the knee. (Pirate trousers).

16: Three- quarter length

Three-quarter length trousers with a comfortable width.

17: Gaucho's [1]

These are calf-length with a wide cut, similar to culottes.

18: Salvar, Chalvar [2]

These are wide like a skirt, with a deep crotch seam and a tight band at the bottom of the leg.

[1] gaucho: South American cowboy   [2] chalvar: oriental trousers

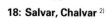

The jacket is a basic item of outerwear and is worn by men, women and children alike.

The distinguishing features between individual designs for example, length, width, silhouette, cut and details are determined by the style and purpose, as are the material, production and finish.

1: Bolero

This small, open jacket is generally waist length and usually has no collar or sleeves.

2: Waistcoat (Gilet)

This reaches to just below the waist, is fitted and sleeveless. The back panel is often of lining fabric.

3: Short jacket

A short, loose jacket which is also described as a jacket-top.

4: Spencer

A waist length jacket with a fitted cut. The front is often shaped.

5: Blouson, Lumber

A short jacket with a comfortable width and waistband. It usually has cuffed sleeves.

6: Tyrolean

This has a straight cut. It often does not have a collar or has a stand collar.

7: Long waistcoat

A long, narrow women's jacket which is sleeveless and worn unfastened.

8: Cardigan style

A hip length, shaped jacket with a long neck and no collar.

9: Donkey jacket

A long jacket with a straight cut and well defined shoulders.

10: Flared

A jacket, narrow on the shoulders, which flares out at the bottom.

11: Long blouson

The tight bottom of the jacket sits below the hips on this long blouson style.

12: Coat jacket

A long, fitted jacket with broad lapels, often double-breasted.

13: Tailored

A dainty women's jacket, fitted at the waist with a classic lapel.

14: Blazer

A sporty elegant jacket with a shaped style, single or double-breasted with lapels.

15: Shirt jacket

A loose jacket, often without padding. Typical details are a shirt collar and cuffed sleeves.

16: Safari style

A belted jacket with large sewn-on pockets, pleats and epaulettes.

17: Parka

Voluminous, long weather-proof jacket with roomy pockets, a hood and draw-strings at the waist and hem.

18: Anorak

This windcheater with a hood and waistband often slips on or has a zip.

The coat is an item of outer clothing and is an essential part of women's, men's and children's clothing. It is longer than a jacket and is also more generously cut. The cut and material determine different styles, which in turn are fitted to different functions. The various styles are distinguished by the length, width, silhouette, cut and details.

1:   Straight

A coat with a straight or slightly flared cut which hangs loosely.

2:   Flared

Features narrow shoulders and a wide swinging hem.

3   Blazer style

This coat is in the style of a men's suit jacket, has a fitted cut, lapels and is single or double breasted.

4:   Redingote

A fitted women's coat with lapels and long vertical seams which widen to provide a flared or semi-flared hem.

5:   Wrap

This generally has a comfortable width and is held together simply by a belt. Popular details are raglan sleeves and shawl collars.

6:   Cape

The cape is a wide, sleeveless cloak of various lengths. The coat-style design usually has holes for the arms.

7:   Trench coat

An all-weather coat with a loose cut, mostly double-breasted with broad lapels. It is worn belted. Epaulettes, shoulder pads and wrist straps are typical details.

8:   Sport coat

A knee length weather-proof coat in a box-like cut with straight defined seams. They are mostly single-breasted, often with a covered zip. They can be worn loose or belted.

9:   Duffle coat

A casual short coat with a box-like cut, large patch pockets, toggle fastenings and a hood.

10: Raglan

A loose men's coat with raglan sleeves or shoulder seams, often with concealed buttons. A broad collar and a short lapel are characteristic.

11: Great coat

A heavy, thick men's coat with a wide lapel cut downwards. They are usually double-breasted.

12: Chesterfield

An elegant, fitted coat with a suit-like lapel pointing upwards. They are usually double-breasted. Other details are flap pockets and a vent.

Since the end of the nineteenth century, putting together several items of clothing to form a whole outfit has been part of the sophisticated female wardrobe. Whilst the earlier classic combinations such as the ensemble and the complet always formed a complete outfit and were also mainly made of the same material, today's unconventional combination fashion allows outfits to be put together according to individual taste.

The **suit** or **costume** consists of a skirt and jacket and is possibly accompanied by a waistcoat.

The strong, masculine finish as well as high quality classic material are characteristics of the **tailored suit**. The fitted jacket with lapels is single or double breasted, has double-seamed sleeves and fitted pockets. The skirt has a narrow cut and is always made of the same material as the jacket.

Casual suits generally have a less severe finish as well as popular technical details in the cut. Combinations of material and decoration are frequently used. The suits are usually described according to the design of the jacket or the style.

1: Tailored suit   **2: Chanel suit** [1]   **3: Casual suit**   **4: Two-piece**   **5: Trouser suit**

4: Two-piece
A suit in the style of a dress. The jacket dress consists of a skirt and a soft jacket top.

5: Trouser suit
The combination of trousers and a jacket or top is now an essential part of the wardrobe.

The term **coordinates** is used for combinations which are made out of matching material.

Matching material can have the same pattern but be of different fabric.

Alternatively, it can have the same pattern on a different scale or in different colours.

Finally, the fabric can also be patterned differently but have the same colouring.

6: Coordinates   **7: Separates**   **8: Ensemble** [2]   **9: Complet** [3]   **10: Composé** [4]

7: Separates
A collection of coordinating garments, displayed and sold as separate items. The purchaser selects from the range to produce an outfit.

8: Ensemble [2]
The ensemble puts together items of clothing which complement each other in style and material to form a whole outfit.

9: Complet [3]
The complet is a combination of a skirt, dress, suit, or trouser suit with a coat or long jacket.

10: Composé [4]
The composé consists of single items of different yet complementary fabrics which can also be decorated.

[1] Coco Chanel: French couturier   [2] ensemble (Fr.) = together, harmoniously   [3] complet (Fr.) = complete   [4] composé (Fr.) = combined

The basic men's outfit consists of a combination of jacket and trousers. Material, cut and details are chosen according to the purpose. Conventional designs dominate but the influence of fashion is nevertheless evident.

The two-piece outfit can be supplemented with a waist-coat to form a three-piece.

If the same fabric is used for both pieces, then the result is a **suit**. If not, then the individual parts will normally be chosen to be complementary in colour, pattern, cut and details.

| 1: Single-breasted with one button | 2: Single-breasted with two buttons | 3: Single-breasted with three buttons | 4: Double-breasted with rounded lapels | 5: Double-breasted with pointed lapels |

A jacket which has only one row of buttons is described as single breasted. They can have one, two or three buttons. The lapels usually point downwards. The pockets are either integral (flap pockets) or sewn on (patch pockets) according to the style. The single breasted suit appears more elegant with a waistcoat.

The double-breasted suit can have one, two or three pairs of buttons on the jacket. The lapels generally point upwards (pointed design) and the pockets are always integral. The double-breasted suit is normally worn fastened and this design is rather smart and formal.

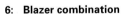

| 6: Blazer combination | 7: Business suit | 8: Sports suit | 9: Leisure suit | 10: Traditional suits |

6: Blazer combination

The casual, but smart jacket is usually of one colour and has metal buttons. There are both single and double-breasted designs.

7: Business suit

A single-breasted suit, often with a waistcoat, or a double-breasted suit with pointed lapels; usually made of dark, elegant fabric.

8: Sports suit

Rustic fabrics and sporty details such as prominent, oversewn seams, yokes, patch pockets and a back strap are favoured.

9: Leisure suit

The blouson style jacket with a button placket and cuffed sleeves is generally chosen. They are often unlined.

10: Traditional suits

The characteristics of the jacket reflect local or regional historical-cultural traditional styles. The illustration is based on alpine traditions.

Formal dress describes men's and women's clothing for official or festive occasions. Distinctions are made between the wardrobes for the day and the evening. Apart from the classic or formal styles of clothing, modern or unconventional styles have developed. Although these styles are not as severe, they are nevertheless clearly distinguishable from day wear.

The **formal day suit** consists of a dark jacket, striped trousers without turn-ups and a grey waistcoat. The tie can be discreetly patterned.

Women wear an elegant suit or two-piece to official occasions.

The **cutaway** or **morning suit** is the very formal daytime attire. The tails of the black jacket are cut back in a curve from the single, fastened button. It is worn with striped trousers, a grey waistcoat and a broad silver-grey silk tie, or cravat. Alternatively, the whole outfit can be grey.

1: **Formal suit**   2: **Peplum suit**   3: **Cutaway**   4: **Wedding dress**   5: **Spencer suit**

The Spencer suit is gaining popularity among the younger generation, as an unconventional wedding suit. The waist length Spencer has a fitted cut.

The black single-breasted **dinner jacket** (**tuxedo**) is part of the classic evening dress suit. The characteristics are silk covered, straight or pointed lapels and silk stripes (galloons) down the sides of the trousers without turn-ups. The suit is traditionally worn with a white-on-white embroidered or fancy-woven dress shirt, a cumberbund (sash) and a black bow tie.

6: **White tuxedo**   7: **Jump suit**   8: **Dinner jacket**   9: **Tail coat**   10: **Evening dress**

Nowadays, the formal tuxedo can be white or cream and double-breasted but, nevertheless, is always worn with dark trousers and a black bow tie. More adventurous versions, in a variety of striking colours and materials, with silk-covered lapels, have also appeared. Accessories, such as fancy shirts and neckwear, are chosen to match the colour, but the black trousers are usually retained.

Women choose a party suit, a party dress, a cocktail dress or evening dress according to the occasion.

The very formal evening suit is the **black tail coat** which has tails on the back beginning from the side seams. The front is only waist length, the pointed lapels are covered with silk and the trousers have a silk stripe down the sides. The tail coat is worn open and is accompanied by a white waistcoat, a dress shirt with a wing collar and a white bow tie.

The women's very **formal evening dress** is always full length.

Year	Period and its Clothing Styles		
3000 BC	**Ancient Egypt**	**Germanic**	Stone Age
2000	Egyptian costume	**Prehistory and Early Times**	
1000	**Ancient Greece**		Bronze Age
	Greek costume	Germanic costume	
0	**Ancient Rome**		
100 AD			Iron Age
200	Roman costume		
300			
400	**Byzantine**		Migration
500	**Middle Ages**		of the Tribes
600	Byzantine costume		
700		Frankish costume	
800			Carolingian period
900	**Romanesque**		
1000			
1100			High Middle Ages
1200		The Age	
1300		of Chivalry	
1400	**Gothic**		Late Gothic
1500		Burgundian fashion	
		Renaissance fashion — Reformation	
	Renaissance	The Landsknecht	
1600		Spanish fashion	Counter Reformation
	Baroque	Netherlands fashion	30 Years War
		Rhineland fashion	Early Baroque
1700		French fashion	High Baroque
	Rococo	Rococo fashion	Late Baroque
1800	**Neoclassicism**	English fashion	French Revolution
		Directoire and Empire	
		Biedermeier	
	Romanticism	Neo-Rococo	
		The Victorian era	
1900	**Art Nouveau**	Belle Epoque	
1910		Reform, Art Nouveau	
1920			
1930		The Twenties	
1940		The Thirties	
1950		The Forties	
1960	**The 20th Century**	The Fifties	
1970		The Sixties	
1980		The Seventies	
1990		The Eighties	
2000			

Row labels (left column): Ancient History, Middle Ages, Modern Age, Recent Times, Present Day

Characteristics of the Age

1: Egyptian building style (Sphinx and Pyramids of the Pharaohs, Giza)

The ancient Egyptians had a well developed culture. Their architecture, in particular, was technically highly advanced. Large temples and powerful pyramids, the tombs of the Pharaohs (kings), have survived to the present. Characteristics of the Egyptian **style** were a strong regularity and rhythmic repetition. Wall paintings, reliefs, sculptures, and hieroglyphics (pictographic writing system) yield information about the life and customs of the Egyptians. Religion and tradition were very important. There was enormous interest in life after death in another world.

Only light **clothing** was necessary because of the mild climate. Originally, all levels of society dressed the same but later clothing became an indicator for social standing and wealth.

Men and women wore similar items of clothing. The preferred material was a fine white linen. However, fabrics with colourful patterns or with gold thread incorporated were also popular. The garments were often transparent and finely pleated.

2: Kalasiris in both pleated and narrow styles

3: Shenti and narrow kalasiris

Women's Clothing

Originally the women wore a simple linen cloth which was wrapped around the lower body and knotted together at the waist. The upper body remained uncovered. Only members of the upper class wore a cape which came down to the elbows and was gathered into crossways folds.

The **kalasiris** appeared later and was worn in many different ways. Worn as a calf or ankle length garment, it was close-fitting on the body leaving the breasts uncovered and was secured by a shoulder band or broad straps. They were often richly decorated.

The kalasiris in shift form came up to the neck or had different necklines. It was either sleeveless or was provided with sleeves. It was worn loose or belted, and was usually transparent and finely pleated.

Under the influence of Asia, a sort of coat was developed. A broad piece of fabric, double the length of the body, had a button hole and side seams from the waist to the hem. It was gathered under the breasts so that the top was like a cape. A sash was often added.

1: Narrow women's kalasiris and different styles of the shenti (shown on gods; a mixture of human, animal, plant and the forces of nature).

2: The men's pleated kalasiris, women's tight kalasiris

Men's Clothing

The men wore a loin cloth or hip cloth, the **shenti**. The cloth was wrapped around the lower body and was tied in front or kept up by a belt. Kings and dignitaries wore cloths which were gathered, had many pleats and were decorated. Several cloths were often worn one on top of the other. The outermost was the longest and was similar to a skirt.

Originally, the shenti was the only item of clothing and the upper body remained bare. Later men also wore a shift-style **kalasiris** usually over, seldom under, the loin-cloth.

The wide, cloak-like drape, which was pulled on over the head, was held at the waist by a knot. The **haik**, a transparent coat wrapped around the body, was reserved for the ruler.

3: Men and women's wigs

4: Crown head-dress

5: Egyptian sandal

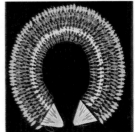

6: Shoulder collar

Accessories

Natural hair and the large **wigs** had a straight chin-length cut and was smooth or braided into many small plaits.

As symbols of power, the rulers wore **headbands**, **crowns** and elaborate **head-dresses**, for example the snake diadem (**uraeus**) or the sphinx head-dress (**khat**).

The Egyptians generally went barefoot. Only the upper class wore **sandals** with toe straps and long points.

Circular or shoulder collars were worn as jewellery and as protection from the sun and were a permanent part of Egyptian clothing. They were made out of leather, metal or fabric and were painted in many colours or were studded with precious stones.

Men and women wore costly jewellery made of gold and precious stones, enamel and ivory: armbands, necklaces, ankle bracelets, earings, finger rings, belts. Great value was placed on cosmetics.

Characteristics of the Age

1: **Greek architecture (Erechtheum, Acropolis, Athens)**

The ancient Greeks had a high level of culture. They made significant achievements in the areas of architecture, art and craft. Greek philosophy is considered as the foundation of scientific thought. Their highest goal was to achieve harmony of body, soul, and lifestyle.

The characteristics of Greek **architecture** were serenity, clarity, balanced proportions and a strict order. Vertical sections of buildings stood in harmony with the horizontal sections.

Clothing was airy and wide. It consisted of pieces of fabric elaborately draped around the body. Individual gathering and the arrangement of the belt were the main forms of decoration. Men and women wore similar clothes.

The woven fabrics were made of linen and wool, then later out of cotton. Rich strong colours and edges decorated with braid trimming were valued highly.

2: **Noble Greek women, a priestess in the background**

3: **Belted peplos**

4: **Chiton**

5: **Chiton and himation**

Women's Clothing

The **peplos** consisted of a rectangular woollen cloth which was laid around the body, under the arms, and then lifted over the shoulders where it was secured by brooches, clasps **(fibula)**, buttons or knots. The upper edge of the fabric was folded over, down to the waist or the hips; the right side remained open. This long straight garment was often worn unbelted although sometimes it was belted at the waist either under or over the folded-down material.

The lighter **chiton**, made from linen, was usually sewn up at the sides. The narrow design, reaching from elbow to elbow with outstretched arms, was simply placed on the shoulders and, consequently, was sleeveless. The wide chiton stretched from fingertip to fingertip and had sleeves

of a sort. They resulted from gaps in the sides (arm holes), or the uppermost edges were knotted over the arms. The top drape could be greatly varied, for example cut unevenly or round. The typical chiton was arranged with a multiplicity of pleats and folds produced by one or several belts at the waist, or the hips, or under the breast.

In later times, both types of garments were combined. They were also worn together, the chiton as an under garment, the peplos as an outer garment.

The **himation**, a large rectangular woollen cloth wrapped around the body, was worn as a coat. Sometimes it also covered the head.

1: **Men's chiton**   2: **Exomis**   3: **Himation**   4: **Himation** 5: **Chlamys**   6: **Men's long chiton**

Men's Clothing

The men's **chlaina** corresponded to the women's peplos. The rectangular woollen cloth was placed over the back and shoulders and held together at the front, or on the right shoulder, by a clasp.

The men's **chiton** ended, like the chlaina, above the knee and was belted at the waist. The ankle-length chiton which was belted under the chest was only put on for festive occasions and was reserved for high-ranking men and priests.

The short garment which left one shoulder bare was called the **exomis**. It gave more freedom of movement.

The **himation** was elaborately draped around the body and sometimes was the only item of clothing.

Horsemen, travellers and soldiers preferred to wear the **chlamys** as a coat. This short, woollen drape was put over the left shoulder and pinned over the right shoulder, so that the right arm was free.

8: **Petasos**

9: **Pilos**

7: **Disc shaped hat**
    with pointed top

10: **Greek garment clasps**

11: **Greek necklace**

Accessories

Headgear was only worn by the Greeks when travelling. The most popular was the flat round felt hat with a brim, the **petasos**. Men also wore a tight fitting cap made of leather or felt, the **pilos**. The elaborate wavy and often knotted hair of the women was secured by **hair bands**, **circlets** and **ribbons**. Occasionally, head scarfs were worn. The round hat with a pointed top presumably offered protection against the sun.

The Greeks went barefoot in the house; in the streets **sandals** were worn. These were often laced up high. Women's sandals were decorated.

Tasteful jewellery was made out of precious metals. Necklaces, rings, earrings, diadems, decorative brooches and bangles were produced from very fine filigree made out of gold wire.

Characteristics of the Age

1: Roman architecture (The Colosseum, Rome)

The Romans made significant advances in the organisation of government and in town planning. Their supremacy and high level of self-confidence was also reflected in their lavish life style and imposing buildings.

The style of **architecture** was characterised by the sympathetic blend of prestige and functionality. Monumental and functional buildings, such as palaces, theatres, aqueducts, and viaducts, were constructed with arches and domes.

The influence of Greek culture was particularly evident in **clothing** which, however, was governed more by tradition than by individuality. Clothing sometimes appeared rather formal and impersonal but, nevertheless, was very lavish and imposing; often even luxurious and elaborate. Design, colour and decoration were indicators of rank and status.

Originally the garments were made of natural coloured wool with decorated edges. Later, more showy and colourful garments were favoured. Women generally preferred lighter materials such as cotton and the expensive silk.

2: Noble Roman women and slave (right)

3: Roman woman in a stola and palla

4: Roman woman in a stola and palla

5: Roman woman in a stola and palla

Women's Clothing

The **tunic**, a shift-like, floor length house dress or under-dress, was two pieces of material sewn together with a slit for the head and openings for the arms. Sleeves were occasionally sewn on or cut out. The tunic was usually belted under the bust and decorated on the shoulders with buttons or brooches. Early versions were made of wool; later fine linen, cotton or even silk was used.

The outer garment, the **stola**, had the same cut as the tunic and was similar to the Greek chiton. It was wide and often trailing. The **strophium**, a kind of bust-bodice, was put on before the stola. Belts were worn under the breast, at the waist or at the hips. Occasionally the stola was worn with no belt. Expensive materials were used and decorations such as pearls, fringes, gold spangles and embroidery were added.

For outdoors wear, the **palla**, a rectangular woollen cloth, was draped around the body. This usually covered the head although occasionally it was only wrapped around the hips.

The **paenula**, a circular or diamond-shaped drape made from thick woollen material or fine leather, was worn in bad weather. It was either worn open at the front or closed all around. It often had a hood.

1: Roman emperor (centre)
   and nobleman (right)

2: Roman in tunic and toga

3: Speaker in tunic and
   the earliest style of toga

Men's Clothing

The men's **tunic** reached to just below the knees and was belted at the hips. Later, and on ceremonial occasions it was ankle length. Several tunics were often put one on top of the other. Many had insignia on them, for example purple bands. In these cases, the tunic was worn without a belt.

The **toga**, the impressive state and honorary dress of the Roman people, was draped over the body in elaborate folds and occasionally covered the head. It consisted of an oval woollen cloth which was folded lengthways. The length corresponded to the height of three men, the width about two men.

The **pallium** was more practical and comfortable than the toga. The rectangular robe was wrapped around the body. Later it was draped only over the left shoulder and fastened at the right shoulder.

When travelling or in bad weather, the men also wore the **paenula**.

4: Roman sandal

Accessories

The women wore a **veil** outdoors. The elaborately curled hair was put into **nets** woven from gold and silver and secured by clasps and tiaras. Men rarely wore headgear and then only for a specific purpose. Farmers, hunters and workers wore a close fitting **cap**. The free citizens preferred a **hat** with a narrow rim. The upper class citizens used the **toga** to cover their heads.

Footwear also indicated to which class a Roman belonged. The occasion determined the footwear. There were many variations of **sandals**, enclosed and slipper-like shoes and also **boots** for men. Women's shoes made out of fine leather were richly decorated.

Tiaras, rings, armbands, ankle bracelets, necklaces and earrings were worn as jewellery. These were manufactured from precious metals, enamel, ivory and pearls.

5: Roman boots

Characteristics of the Age

**1: Architecture in the Bronze Age
(pile buildings by Lake Constance)**

The ancient Germanic (Teutonic) tribes originally inhabited the central and northern areas of Europe. With their advance to the Alps, after about 800 BC, they came into contact with the ancient people of the Mediterranean and their highly developed culture. During the period of the migration of the tribes in the second to the sixth centuries AD, the Teutonic peoples contributed to the decline of Roman power in southern and western Europe.

Very few **buildings** from this time have been preserved. Those that do had been built from logs.

Techniques for spinning, weaving and basket work were already known during the **Stone Age**, the earliest known age of human cultural development (up to about 1800 BC). Clothing was made with the aid of flint and bone tools.

Clothing from the **Bronze Age** (about 1800 to 800 BC), with its own distinctive character, has been found preserved in graves. In the **Iron Age** which followed (about 800 BC to 600 AD), an ancient influence was evident, particularly in women's clothing, as indicated by relics recovered from peat bogs.

The **clothing** of the Teutonic peoples was suited to the cold northern climate. Wool, linen, and especially animal skins were used. Woven patterns, coloured borders and edgings, as well as fringes enlivened the simple garments.

2: Bronze Age Teutons

**3: Bronze Age girl's clothing;
smock, cord skirt**

**4: Iron Age Teutons,
3rd to 4th century AD**

Women's Clothing

Women's garments during the Bronze Age consisted of a **skirt** and **blouse**. The wide skirt was ankle length and came up to just under the breast. The skirt was gathered at the waist, secured by a braided fringed belt or cord and decorated with an ornamental belt disc. The blouse had kimono-like sleeves, was made out of one piece of material and had an opening for head and neck. It was worn inside the skirt and fastened with a decorated brooch.

Young girls wore a knee length **cord skirt** which consisted of numerous, closely packed cords suspended from a waistband.

The Iron Age brought the **tunic dress** which was put on over the head, held together on the shoulders by pins or clasps and belted once or twice. It draped in many folds and was sleeveless but was often worn under or over a blouse with sleeves. Later, it was provided with short or long sleeves.

Chest, leg and thigh bindings were worn under the dress.

A large cloth served as an outer garment. It was wrapped around like a cloak, covered the head, and was held together by pins or clasps (**fibula**).

13.5 Germanic Prehistory and Early Times (2)
ca. 2000 BC to 600 AD

1: Bronze Age men's clothing

2: Iron Age trousers

3: Iron Age smock

4: Iron Age men's clothing

Men's Clothing

During the Bronze Age, the men wore a **tunic** wrapped around the body and belted at the waist. It reached from the armpits to the knee and was held by a strap which ran over the shoulder and was secured at the back by a button. Under the tunic, a rectangular belted loincloth was commonly worn.

Trousers were developed in the Iron Age. The long style of trouser might be tied at the lower leg. Short trousers were extended by leg pieces or bindings. The trousers were held up by a belt which ran through loops.

A knee length **smock** which was put on over the head was worn with the trousers. It was originally sleeveless, although later it was provided with short or long sleeves. It was usually belted and occasionally had a hood.

A **cloak** was worn over the smock; a linen **shirt** was worn under.

5: Thonged shoe

Accessories

Women put their hair, which was pinned up or knotted, into **nets**. Girls wore their hair loose held by a circlet. Cloths, veils and caps served as headwear. Men mostly had long hair which either was worn loose, or was knotted or tied into a bunch. Helmets with animal heads were common in battle, otherwise tall or hemispherical **caps** were made out of hide or knotted wool.

Thonged shoes were usually worn on the feet. These were made out of a piece of hide with the fur on the inside. The network of straps was held together by a shoelace.

Richly decorated jewellery was also regarded as part of the clothing. The magnificent belt discs, garment clasps, arm and leg bangles, ear and finger rings were made out of bronze or precious metal and decorated with precious stones, glass beads, enamel or amber.

6: Amber chain

13.6 Byzantine Middle Ages (1)
ca. 300 to 1400 AD

Characteristics of the Age

**1: Byzantine architecture
Hagia Sophia, Istanbul (earlier
Constantinople or Byzantium)**

After the division of the Roman empire around 300 AD, Byzantium, the capital of the Eastern Empire, became the economic and cultural centre. Christianity became the state religion. The Greco-Roman culture developed a new form, shaped by both Christian and oriental influences. From then on the Church had a crucial role not only in cultural life but also in society; the emperor was head of everything both secular and spiritual.

The Byzantine style of **architecture** represented wealth and power. Characteristics were round arches and domes, as were gloriously colourful mosaics which covered the insides of the powerful churches.

Clothing developed into a sumptuous formal costume which enveloped the body completely, covering its natural shape. The ruling class preferred heavily coloured silk fabrics and brocades, richly embroidered with precious stones and pearls. Insignia were important. The ordinary people however, wore unobtrusive wool and linen materials.

Even today the vestments of the Church are based on Byzantine clothing. For a long time, the coronation robes of emperors and kings also followed the Byzantine model.

**2: 6th century Byzantine court
costume: Empress and retainers**

**3: Byzantine Empress and princess,
servant in the background**

4: 6th century Byzantine nobles

Women's Clothing

A white ankle length **tunic** served as an under garment. This was belted, had long sleeves and was often made of silk.

The outer garment, the long or short sleeved **stola**, originally reached to the floor but was later shortened to show the under garment. It was worn either belted or loose, depending on the weight of the material.

The **paenula** served as a top garment. The front edge of the circular cut, closed robe was often lifted up and placed over the shoulder.

Members of the ruling house wore a **shoulder cloak** which was secured on the right shoulder by a decorated clasp.

1: Byzantine Emperor and Empress

2: 6th century Byzantine court costume

3: Byzantine Emperor and noble youth

Men's Clothing

The long sleeved **tunic** was either knee or ankle length and was usually belted. Length, width, colour and material revealed rank and status. The tunic was normally worn over tight leg-wear.

The **dalmatic**, a long unbelted robe with wide sleeves was reserved as an outer garment for rulers and high ranking dignitaries. Colourful lengthways stripes, called **clavi**, decorated the front and back as well as the hem of the sleeves.

The **cloak** was either rectangular or rounded and was fastened with a clasp at the front or on the right shoulder. A fabric appliqué, the **tablion**, was sewn on at chest height to show rank. For the ruler, it was gold and richly decorated; for high ranking officials, it was Tyrian purple.

The robe which was put on over the head, the **paenula**, was adopted by the Church and became the **chasule**.

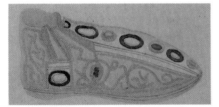

4: Coronation shoe of the German Emperor

Accessories

Women combed their hair into a sort of **rolled style** and adorned it with a **tiara** onto which a **veil** was secured. **Head-dresses** and turban-like caps were popular, as was the **caul**, a cap of silk or wool covered with a net of coloured silk, wool, gold, or silver thread, sometimes jewelled at the intersections. Men usually wore nothing on their heads. Members of the ruling class occasionally wore a flat **cap**. The emperor wore a **crown**.

Footwear also depended on status and the occasion, and was always determined by the garment. Apart from **sandals** with an enclosed heel and pointed toe, richly decorated **slippers** were common. Men often favoured high, laced shoes, and **leather socks**.

The diverse and luxurious jewellery made out of different metals and enamel was richly studded with pearls and precious stones. Large earrings, collar-like neck rings, finger rings and striking ornamental brooches were worn.

5: Collar-shaped necklace

Characteristics of the Age

1: Romanesque architecture (St. Michael, Fulda)

The cultural period of the Romanesque Middle Ages was characterised by a strong display of power by the ruling nobility and a struggle for power between Church and State. The founding of cities contributed to the development of business and trade.

The Romanesque style of architecture developed from a fusion of Teutonic elements and the art of the Romans. The characteristics were: clear, calm execution, round arches, powerful masonry, supporting columns and pillars.

During the **Carolingian** period (about 700 to 1000 AD), France under Charlemagne gained supremacy over central Europe. The clothing of this period, **Frankish costume**, was derived from Teutonic or Roman clothing. It was also influenced by the Church which demanded that the body be covered up.

Chivalry, or **Knighthood** played a significant political and cultural role in the twelfth and thirteenth centuries. Lifestyles improved and clothing became more worldly and disguised the body less.

The clothing of the courts was colourful. Delicate linen, fine cotton, velvet, silk and brocade were valued. The borders of the garments were decorated with expensive trimmings. However, the clothing of the ordinary people was prescribed by decree. Only coarse fabrics in dark colours were to be used; trimmings and jewellery were to be avoided.

2: 10th century Frankish noblewomen

3) 12th century German noblewomen and female citizen

4: 13th century German prince and noblewomen

Women's Clothing

Until the 11th century, the women's dress had a tunic-like cut and was generally long sleeved, belted and richly decorated with trimmings. The shift-like, pleated under garment was often visible at the neckline and sleeves. It reached the floor and had long, narrow sleeves. In time, the outer dress was shortened and made narrower which emphasised the female figure. The sleeves, however, became very wide at the wrists.

A piece of material, placed around the shoulders and fastened at the side or front with a clasp, served as a cloak.

In the 12th century, the top part of the dress, called the **cotte**, was made to fit closely to the body. This was achieved by the shaped cut of the front and back sections, and by lacing on the side or back. The skirt trailed and an inserted gusset maintained a wide hem. A belt accentuated the low waist.

Noblewomen often wore a luxurious outer garment over the cotte, called a **surcot**. This was usually unbelted and sleeveless. In the 13th century it was excessively long and was held up when walking. The cotte also became very long, and less closely fitted and then also worn without a belt.

The shoulder cloak, cut in a semi-circle, was fastened at the front with a clasp, or with a cord or chain between two decorative discs (**tassels**).

1: 9th century Frankish court costume   2: 10th century Frankish royal couple   3: 11th century Frankish royal couple

Men's Clothing

The **Frankish costume** for men consisted of a shirt, hose, tunic and cloak. The knee length tunic had long straight sleeves and a round or square neckline. The shirt worn underneath was wide and long. The hose consisted of two long legs over which bindings were wrapped around the lower leg. Short hose were also common. The legs were secured onto a belt.

The rectangular shaped and usually long cloak was placed round the left shoulder and pinned on the right with a clasp.

During the age of chivalry, from the 11th until the 13th century, men's clothing differed very little from courtly women's clothing. It simply had fewer folds and was always above the feet. The shorter and sleeveless **surcot** was worn over the **cotte**, the long-sleeved and belted shift-like dress. The surcot was slit at the front or at the side, was often lined with fur or had fur trimming around the neck. The tight, stocking-like hose or **nether-stocks** served only as under clothes. The **cord** and **tassel cloak** was also worn by men as an outer garment.

4: Shoe from around 1000 AD (reconstruction)   5: Frankish gold foil clasps   6: Jewellery from the tribal migration period

Accessories

Married women had to cover their hair in public. They pulled the cloak over their head or wore the **headrail** (or couvrechef = coverchief = kerchief), a shoulder length or longer draped head square, with or without a head band. Later, the **wimple** appeared. This was a linen strip wrapped around the chin and head and was often topped by a pointed crown. Young girls decorated their loose or plaited hair with a **fillet**, a brow or head circlet made of metal or flowers.

Originally, men seldom wore headgear, except when at

war. Later they wore caps, turban-like hats and a hat with a tall point. Young men also wore the **fillet** or **circlet** on their chin-length hair.

Footwear included ankle high **thonged shoes**, **slippers** and **leather socks**. The pointed shoe with no heel appeared in the 12th century.

Jewellery consisted of belts, clasps, chains, sword decoration and circlets. These were made out of gold or enamel and richly studded with precious stones, real pearls or glass beads.

Characteristics of the Age

1: Gothic architecture (Cathedral, Ulm)

Culture in the late Middle Ages was determined not only by the church and the nobility but also by the rising bourgeoisie and the city states. The German Empire crumbled, and France gained political and cultural superiority in Europe. The Gothic style of **architecture** also originated in France. Characteristic features were towering spires, pointed arches, strong vertical divisions and delicate tracery.

Clothing was graceful and elegant, but also complicated and lavish. It was then made by "garment tailors". Typical characteristics were long, slender designs with an emphasis on the waist and bright colours. Men's clothing lost its similarity to women's clothing.

The 14th century saw the emergence of relatively rapid changes in fashion. Fashion was spread by travelling bards and traders.

Around 1450 a peculiar **exaggerated fashion** emerged from the court of the wealthy dukedom of Burgundy. Apart from exaggerated designs of head-wear and shoes, the most conspicuous features of Burgundian fashion were deeply-serrated garment borders, called **dagges**, decorations of small bells and diamonds, padding and quilting. The mi-parti[1] or **parti-coloured** fashion was also very popular: different coloured legs, or garments in which differently coloured fabrics were joined together.

2: 14th century princess and noblewoman

3: German noblewomen, early 15th century

4: 14th century knight and noblemaiden

Women's Clothing

In the 13th century, the women's **cotte** was still close fitting and was worn either loose or belted. It was gently waisted and the skirt was very long, with many gathers and folds. The sleeves were narrow for the full length, or became very wide at the wrists.

In the 14th century the top of the dress became tightly laced, with a very wide neckline and button fastenings. The skirt widened from the hips, which were often accentuated by a belt. Short sleeves which had long trailing strips of material secured at the back, called hanging sleeves, also came into fashion.

The garment was gradually divided into a skirt and top or bodice. The bodice could then be made very tight-fitting.

The join with the long trailing skirt was covered by a belt.

The sleeveless **surcot** was popular as an outer garment. The deeply cut armhole, which often reached the hips and allowed the waist to be visible, was called the **devil's window**. Sometimes the surcot would be only hip length, with fur-trimmed edges.

The **houppelande**, a cloak-like outer garment, also became fashionable. It was open at the front or closed all round and was usually worn belted. It had various styles of sleeves which were often dagged around the edges.

The circular-cut **clasp cloak** was fastened at the front by a decorative clasp.

[1] mi-parti : divided in half

1: Early 15th century
   German court costume

2: Burgundian fashion,
   around 1450

3: Burgundian court costume,
   around 1450

Women's Clothing at the time of Burgundian Fashion

In the late Gothic period, the **silhouette** of the women's dress became very **slender**. The tight bodice had a very deep pointed neckline. The waist seam and the belt moved up to just under the breasts. The **train** at the back of the skirt became very long. The front of the bodice was often provided with a breast bib and a shawl collar. Tight-fitting pipe sleeves, wide at the wrists were popular, as were bag sleeves with arm slits, very long loose sleeves and open hanging sleeves.

4: English court clothing
   around 1400

5: Burgundian men's clothing
   around 1450

6: Early 15th century
   French court costume

Men's Clothing

The tunic became narrow and short and was provided with a fastener at the front. The front and back sections, the skirt part descending from the waist, and also the long, narrow sleeves were tailored to fit.

The outer garment which was originally calf length developed into a jacket, the **doublet**, and only came down to the hips. The doublet was narrow at the waist, tight fitting at the front, buttoned up or deeply cut. The back and skirt section were gathered in folds. The chest section and the upper sleeves were well padded. The collar came up to the chin. Open sleeves often had long falling folds of cloth, whilst the closed sleeves were often widened at the wrist. The belt sat on the hips and became an item of decoration.

1: English court clothing
   around 1400

2: 15th century English
   court clothing

3: 15th century French
   men's clothing

Men's Clothing (continued)

The stocking-like **hose** made of leather or stretchy fabrics were often **parti-coloured**. These were fastened behind the skirt of the doublet. Towards the end of the 14th century they were joined at the top so they created trousers which now covered the stomach. The codpiece was developed, both for protection and for emphasis.

Over time, the doublet became very short. However, older men preferred long over garments, especially for formal occasions. The **houppelande** was gathered into the waist and was belted. It was often slashed at the sides and usually had a stand-up collar. The long, wide conical sleeves and also the puffed sleeves were often provided with additional arm slashes. The long, or knee length **tabard** (a rectangular garment adapted from crusader knights armour covering) was worn draped loosely back and front over the tunic.

Cloaks of various length were worn; sometimes long and trailing, sometimes only hip length.

4: Chaperon hood and
   shoulder cape

Accessories

Married women always covered their hair, which was plaited or worn up, when in public. Apart from **headrails**, many different kinds of **head-dresses** were popular. These were very important at the time of the Burgundian fashion. The **steeple**, a tall conical head-dress with a long flapping veil, the rolled **heart-shaped** head-dress and the stiffened **frilled** head-dress were particularly characteristic of this period.

Young girls and boys wore a **circlet** over loose hair. In the course of time, long hair for men went out of fashion. However, hair crimped with tongs was popular. The preferred head covering in the 14th century was the **chaperon**, a close fitting hood with collar-like shoulder pieces and tail. Today this is a part of a jester's clothing; a fool's or trickster's cap. Apart from caps and tall felt hats, the **turban** and the **silk roll**, a flat cap or a roll of fabric with trailing strips of material, also came into fashion.

5: Piked shoe and patten

Typical footwear of the late Middle Ages included shoes with long, extended (piked) toes, known as **poulaines**[1]. Their toes were often so long that they had to be tied up when walking. In addition, undershoes made of wood, called **pattens** were worn outdoors. Turned over shoes, like boots were introduced for men.

Gloves and fans completed women's clothing. Gold necklaces set with precious stones, clasps and belts as well as gold and silver bells, buttons and bangles were worn as jewellery and decoration.

[1] Poulaine (Fr.) = Poland; hence Polish style shoes

Characteristics of the Age

1: **Renaissance architecture**
   (Old castle, Stuttgart)

The beginning of the **Modern Age** marked a turning point in all areas of life and culture. A Humanistic philosophy of life promoted individual personality and sought a freer spirit reminiscent of Greek and Roman culture. Meanwhile the Reformation started a movement towards the renewal of the Church. **Architecture** also was influenced by ancient models. Greek columns and Roman arches were combined. In contrast with the vertical lines of the Gothic, an emphasis on horizontal structuring was favoured.

Clothing of the early Renaissance or Reformation period reflected the individual taste of the newly influential, self-aware and prosperous bourgeoisie. The colourful garments made from expensive materials, such as brocade, damask and velvet were richly patterned and lavishly decorated with ribbons, braids, trimmings, embroidery and lace. The striking costume of the **Landsknecht** (mercenaries), with puffs and colour-contrasting slashes, had a strong influence.

Around the middle of the 16th century, Spain rose as a strong political power after the discovery of America and the establishment of a colonial empire. Consequently, the Spanish court also set the trend for styles of clothing.

Spanish fashion expressed the austere spirituality of the Counter-Reformation and dictated colours, designs and details quite precisely. Although the clothes were sometimes elegant and showy, they were also stiff, uncomfortable and often in sombre colours.

2: **German patricians**
   Early 16th century

3: **German patricians**
   Early 16th century

4: **German patricians**
   Early 16th century

Women's Clothing during the Reformation

The **tight bodice** was separate from the skirt, often laced-up at the front and provided with a breast bib. The round or square neckline was broadened and was usually filled with a fine pleated undershirt, with a ruche close to the neck. The **sumptuous sleeves** were tied on and were therefore interchangeable. By using draw strings and inserting strips, numerous subdivisions and puffs were obtained. They were also often provided with slashes which were lined with differently coloured fabric. The cuffs and ruched edges often covered half of the hand.

The wide **trailing skirt** was gathered in folds and was accented crossways by braid and other trimmings. Whilst walking, the skirt was held up to reveal the pleated underskirt. Occasionally a long and richly embroidered **apron** was worn which later also served as a replacement for the outer skirt.

The **partlet**, a round shoulder collar, was placed on top of the low-cut bodice. It usually had a stand-up collar, was made out of velvet or silk and was often decorated with embroidery.

Laced bodices, partlets and aprons are still seen today, in traditional rural costumes.

The long, wide **chamarre** with a broad collar and arm slits was worn as a coat.

1: German Landsknecht (mercenaries)
Early 16th century

2: German magistrate and knight
Early 16th century

3: French court costume
16th century

Men's Clothing during the Reformation

The tight-fitting doublet reached just to the hips. A shirt with finely pleated neckline and cuffs was worn underneath. A knee length coat, with a gathered and pleated lower section was worn over, or instead of the doublet. It could either be open to the belt or high-necked. The **doublet and skirt** had **broad bulging sleeves** which could be exchanged, had slashes with coloured linings, and were bound many times in order to create puffs.

The legs were clothed in **wide knee breeches** and stockings which were either fastened or sewn on. Often, the tight hose were secured to a belt. Many of them were differently coloured or **parti-coloured**. Later, baggy breeches with puffs and slashes, called **slops** or **pluder hose** or **trunk hose** were borrowed from the Landsknecht mercenaries costume.

The typical outer garment of the Reformation was the **chamarre**[1], a decorative coat with shawl collars. It was open at the front and usually unbelted. It was often lined or trimmed with fur. Sometimes it was ankle length, sometimes just above the knee. The wide sleeves often had additional openings for inserting the arms. The chamarre is worn today as a robe or gown by judges and protestant priests.

Accessories during the Reformation

4: Duck bill shoe
(reconstruction)

The flat **biretta**, richly decorated with feathers and cords, was the typical headwear for men and women during the Renaissance period. This was usually secured onto a **calotte**, a tight fitting skull cap. Men preferred their hair to have a round cut with no parting. The women wore their hair up, and would often use a net of gold and silver cords as the calotte. Apart from the biretta, head-dresses also came back into fashion.

The flat shoes were very broad but were supported by a raised heel. The **duck bill** shoe was round at the front and excessively broad. The **horn shoe** had padded pointed toes.

Heavy rings, chains, medallions and gold circlets were popular as jewellery. While the men wore wide leather belts, fashionable accessories for women were gloves and lace edged ornamental handkerchiefs.

The Spanish Fashion in Women's Clothing

The tight **bodice** was always high-necked and reinforced by bone and wire to press the upper body flat. At the front it had a pointed or rounded lengthening, the **stomacher**. The waist was laced very narrow by a corset worn underneath. The neck ruche of pleated white linen or lace developed gradually into a circular **ruff**. The Stuart[2] collar, or **collet monté**, made from stiffened lace surrounding the head in a fan shape, also became fashionable.

[1] chamarré (Fr.) = bedecked, gaudily decorated   [2] after Mary Stuart, Queen of Scotland

The Spanish Fashion in Women's Clothing   (continued)

A white ruff was also formed at the ends of the long sleeves. Wide over-sleeves, and emphasis of the upper arms by puffs and rolls were popular.

The floor length underskirt was stretched over a conical frame. The first **hoop skirt** of fashion history was called a "farthingale"[1].

The top skirt lost all its folds, was usually open at the front and decorated with trimmings on the edges. The hips were broadened by means of padding which was tied on.

Occasionally, a coat-like over-dress with a straight cut, the **ropa** was also worn.

1:   Spanish fashion in France, 16th century

2:   Spanish nobles, late 16th century

3:   Spanish fashion in England, 16th century

The Spanish Fashion in Men's Clothing

The **doublet** was kept very short, was tight-fitting and deeply padded. The padding on the chest created a ridge running all down the middle of the chest, called a **peasecod-belly**. The high-necked doublet had a long, stiff stand-up collar over which projected the shirt ruff. The neck ruff grew increasingly larger and stiffer and eventually became a separate item of clothing. The long sleeves were padded, puffed and slashed, and were provided with shoulder pads; they also had stiff ruffs at the ends.

Sleeveless doublets were often provided with loose decorative sleeves.

The full, well padded breeches, which sometimes had slashes, were short and extended only to the middle of the thighs. They had tight bands at the waist and on the legs. The front flap, or codpiece was also padded. Below these **trunk hose**, tight fitting **nether stocks**, or leggings fastened with ribbons were worn.

The very short, bell-shaped cape of velvet or silk, the **Spanish cape**, was only placed around the shoulders. It had a high standing collar and occasionally a hood.

The Spanish Fashion in Accessories

The high neck ruff of the Spanish fashion meant a shorter haircut for men. The women combed their hair into severe upswept hairstyles. Headgear was stiff. The **toque**, a small hat with or without a narrow brim was popular, as was the **Spanish hat**, a tall felt hat with a narrow brim.

4:   Shoe in the Spanish fashion

The soft, close fitting **leather shoes** often had rich decorations of holes or embossed patterns. The women's shoe was often of brocade or embroidered velvet and sometimes was even provided with a high sole. These stilted shoes were known as **chopines**.

The exquisite jewellery consisted mainly of rings and necklaces. Fringed sashes placed over the chest, gold chains worn around the waist, as well as **fine gloves**, **decorative handkerchiefs** and **fans** were also popular.

[1] farthingale: from verdugo (Sp.) = hoop of pliant wood

Characteristics of the Age

**1: Baroque architecture
(Monastery Church, Ottobeuren)**

A struggle for European supremacy developed during the **Thirty Years War** (1618 to 1648), fuelled by differences in religious doctrines. Spain lost her leading role and, for a short time, the Netherlands became the dominant economic and trading power.

However, under the dictatorship of Louis XIV (from about 1670), France determined the political and cultural scene. The splendid court of the "sun king" at Versailles had a leading role. The strong need for display was exemplified in the **architecture**. Magnificent palaces, churches and parks were constructed. Behind curved and ornate façades, the buildings had richly decorated interiors. Further features of the architecture were complete symmetry, twisting columns, onion towers and domes.

After the bourgeois **Netherlands fashions** of the early Baroque the **French fashion** of the High Baroque period was once again very elegant and luxurious. Men's clothing was even extravagant and pompous. Heavy fabrics such as damask, velvet and brocade were preferred and garments were lavishly trimmed and embroidered. Lace became the most important fashion accent. From then on, the people of the courts had to be dressed "à la mode"[1] - according to the French dictate. News of the latest fashions, the way of dressing and the latest luxuries, now changing faster than ever before, was spread by the first fashion magazines, and by means of dolls, dressed according to the latest "ladies fashion" and "men's fashion".

**2: Mid 17th century
Netherlands Fashion**

**3: Late 17th century French
aristocrats in court costume**

**4: Court costume in the
Fontange period,
late 17th - early 18th century**

Women's Clothing

When fashion was led from the **Netherlands**, the bodice had a comfortable width. It was kept short or had divided skirts. The wide neckline was framed or covered by a flat lace collar. The shortened puffed sleeves ended with lace cuffs and were sometimes decorated with ribbons. The skirt, under which many underskirts were worn, fell in soft folds and trailed. The small decorative apron came into fashion.

With the arrival of **French fashion**, the waist was once more tightly laced. The reinforced stomacher with a pointed lower edge, was held together at the front over a richly decorated insert called a **tucker** or **modesty piece**. The low neckline, the **décolletage**, was edged with trim-

mings and lace, and the short sleeves also were sometimes provided with several lace flounces (**engagéantes**). The long trailing outer skirt was made of the same material as the bodice. Together they made a complete outer garment, called the **manteau** or **robe**. The skirt was open at the front and the edges were folded over and pulled back at the sides. Later the sides were pulled up high at the back and were puffed out over seat padding (bustle) into the so-called **French tail**. The visible underskirt (**jupe**) was made from material of a different colour and was richly decorated with e.g. braid, cord, lace, ribbons and embroidery.

[1] à la mode (Fr.) = in the latest fashion

1: Late 17th century
   German aristocrats

2: Court costume and Rheingrafen
   fashion; France, late 17th century

3: French aristocrats at the court of
   Louis XIV, early 18th century

Men's Clothing

During the Thirty Years War, the loose fitting doublet and skirt had a high neck. The open seams of the wide sleeves allowed the richly decorated shirt to be seen. A flat lace collar (**falling band**) and also lace cuffs on the sleeves were popular. At first the calf-length trousers were wide and fastened under the knee. They later became narrow at the bottom. Occasionally, a leather jerkin served as an outer jacket. This was either sleeveless or had sleeves fastened by cords.

Around 1650, men's clothing became more feminine. The fashion of the Rhineland Counts (**Rheingrafen**) consisted of a short open jacket with short sleeves and wide skirt-breeches, the **rhinegraves** or **petticoat breeches**, which were narrow at the hips, fastened under the knee and provided with lace cuffs.

The shirt which was embroidered and decorated with lace bulged out at the chest, waist and sleeves. Everything was lavishly decorated with ribbons and bows.

The knee-length, tight fitting outer coat, or **justaucorps**[1], came into fashion around 1670. It was made out of brocade and decorated with gold or silver braids and metal buttons. The lavish lace cuffs were visible under the broad cuffs of the straight sleeves. The vest worn underneath was a little shorter and had the same cut. The coat covered almost all of the fairly wide knee length trousers, the **culottes**.

With the introduction of the justaucorps, the falling band gave way to a loosely tied, fancy lace cravat.

Accessories

4: Woman's shoe

5: Man's shoe

Originally, men and women wore the soft felt hat with a broad brim and ribbons or feather decoration on their chin-length curled hair. Later, women piled their hair high and decorated it with the **fontange** which was typical of those times. This head-dress had stiff pleated lace ruches on the front which stood up like organ pipes.

When wigs came into fashion, men wore the **tricorn** hat over the **full bottomed wig** which was piled high and had long falling curls.

After the wide bucket-top and goblet boots, which were often filled out with lace cuffs, **shoes with heels** came into fashion for men. They were often made like those for women, of brocade or damask, fastened with a buckle and decorated with interchangeable rosettes or bows. The coloured silk stockings were secured with ribbons.

Both men and women wore expensive bracelets, necklaces and earrings. **Long gloves**, **muffs** and **canes** all were part of the fashionable image. Apart from these, **fans** and beauty spots were important items of decoration for women.

[1] justaucorps (Fr.) = close to the body

Characteristics of the Age

1: Rococo architecture
(Falken House, Würzburg)

The Rococo period concluded the style of Baroque in the 18th century. Lifestyles became more refined. Composure and gestures revealed a serene, gallant and rather affected character. Aristocratic society was only slightly influenced by the great spiritual movement of this period, the Enlightenment.

Architecture kept the basic curved shape of the Baroque period. However, the lines were softer, lighter and more elegant. The characteristics were mainly shown in the decorative, dainty and proliferous decor and the lavish interiors of the buildings. Grandeur became cluttered. Shell ornaments and Asian subjects were popular.

Clothing also moved away from the stiff showy Baroque fashions to a lighter, graceful and occasionally frivolous style. The luxurious silk fabrics were in single colours, delicately patterned or elaborately embroidered, and in the typical pastel shades of the time. Women's robes were extravagantly full and decorated with flounces, ruches, bows, lace and artificial flowers.

Towards the end of the Rococo period, the influence of English fashion began to be felt. Clothing became more bourgeois and more practical.

2: "Madame Pompadour" by François Boucher

3: "The Declaration of Love" by Jean-François de Troy

Women's Clothing

Women from all levels of society wore the **hoop skirt**. It was originally dome-shaped. The graduated hoops of wire or wood were secured with oil cloth. They were later flattened at the front and back to give the typical ellipse shape and were constructed from whalebone. The framework or **panier** became so large that it was only possible to go through doors sideways.

The under skirt (**jupe**) lay quite flat over the hoop skirt and was richly decorated with flounces, bows, garlands and flower arrangements. The outer skirt was of a different colour, open at the front in the shape of a triangle and with elaborated edges. From about 1775, when it became fashionable for skirts to be above the feet, they were gathered up at the sides and back and puffed out over a frame or padding - the **bustle**.

The **stomacher** was pointed at the front and had a deep neckline which was often decorated with frills. The **modesty piece** was lavishly decorated. The narrow elbow-length sleeves were provided with many frills, **engageantes**, and bows.

The outer skirt and bodice were of the same material and together comprised the **manteau**. The desired wasp waist was obtained by a laced under bodice.

The **contouche**, the bourgeois and comfortable indoor, outdoor and travelling dress, had a straight cut and fell loosely over the hoop skirt. It was held together at the front by ribbons. At the back there were deep inserted folds, called **Watteau pleats** (supposedly named after the painter, Watteau).

13.11 Rococo (2)
ca. 1720 to 1785

1: Woman in hoop skirt, mid 18th century

2: Fashion around 1780

3: French fashion around 1780

Men's Clothing

The elegant **justaucorps** with decorated borders reached the knee and usually allowed the long **vest** to be seen. Pockets with slashes were provided at the sides and at the back. The richly decorated shirt, with a lace frill (jabot) at the front and wide lace cuffs, was also visible. As time went by, the skirts of the coat and vest were stiffened with whalebone and horsehair so that they stood away from the hips.

The semi-wide knee breeches, the **culottes**, were usu-ally made of velvet. These were originally worn with white knee-length stockings. Later the trouser legs were pro-vided with button holes at the side and were fastened with a clasp over the stockings.

Overcoats were uncommon in this period. Short, sleeve-less cloaks were worn when the need arose.

The cravat evolved into the **stock**, a wrapped neckcloth fastened or tied at the back.

Accessories

Women wore a **lace head-dress** or a small confection of feathers, flowers and lace on their decorative curled hairstyles. Later, hair was styled over tall frames and was richly decorated. Men twisted the hair on the sides of their wigs into rolls, back-combed the hair on the crown very high, and wore the hair at the back in a net or plaited. The **tricorn** was carried under the arm. It was seldom worn.

Heavy powdering and make-up as well as men's wigs were a privilege of sta-tus. Grey or white powdered hair was a characteristic of the Rococo period.

Women preferred the **stiletto shoe** with a very pointed toe and curved high heels. These were usually made out of embroidered fabric and provided with interchangeable buckles and bows. Embroidered slippers with heels were worn indoors. The men's **buckled shoe**, usually made of leather, had heels and was rounded at the front.

Whilst the women's décolletage was often embellished only with a ribbon ruche or ribbons with lockets, the dress and hairstyle were studded with pearls and precious stones. Multi-stranded pearl bracelets and diamond studded earrings were also popular. **Fans**, **gloves**, draw-string purses and a **muff** were essential. The men arrayed themselves with long watch chains. The rapier became an essential part of the cavalier's clothing.

4: Woman's shoe

5: Man's shoe

Characteristics of the Age

1: Neoclassical architecture (The Brandenburg Gate, Berlin)

The **French Revolution** (1789) created the preconditions for a bourgeois society, after the abolition of the feudal system and the pronouncement of human and civil rights.

Art turned towards Classicism. The clear and simple designs of ancient Greece and Rome were revived. **Architecture** was characterised by columns and strong symmetrically structured facades. Museums, theatres, residences and monuments were built.

Clothing also expressed a striving towards a new freer lifestyle. This was made possible through the abolition of classes and therefore also clothing dictates. Before and after the period of the Revolution, the bourgeois and functional **English fashions** came to the fore, influencing also the **Werther costume**[1] developed later in Germany.

At the time of the **Directoire**[2] (around 1795), women's clothing developed classical overtones and became exclusive. Pre-eminent were the finest cotton fabrics in fashionable white. In the following **Empire**[3] period, clothing returned to greater ostentation. Robes were of velvet and heavy silk and had the typical high waistline. Men's clothing, originally unobtrusive and made of dark woollen fabrics or leather, also gradually became more sophisticated for the ruling classes. The uniform played a significant role.

2: English fashion around 1790

3: French fashion around 1800

4: Empire fashion, early 19th century

Women's Clothing

For the **English fashion**, the long, wide skirt fell in soft folds and, instead of a hoop skirt, a bustle was tied on. A bodice top or the **caraco**, a short jacket of a similar style to the tailcoat, was worn with the skirt. The long coat, or **redingote** (riding coat), had the skirt cut away at the front. The neckline was covered with a small shawl, the **fichu**.

The light **chemise** appeared in the **Directoire** period. The waistline moved up to below the breast and was held, like the large neckline, by a gathered seam. The transparent garment with many folds, either sleeveless or with short sleeves, had a long train. Underneath was simply a skin coloured knitted shift. Sumptuous cashmere shawls were draped around the body when it was cold or in bad weather.

Top dresses reappeared later. They were worn open over the long, trailing under garment which was a different colour. Otherwise they ended at the knee as a tunic. The edges were decorated with embroidered trimmings. The décolletage was covered by a small, long sleeved, spencer-style jacket, the **canezou**.

During the **Empire** period, the high bodice was separated from the skirt and was shaped into a corsage to fit the body very closely. The neckline was often emphasised by a tall lace collar. The sleeves were usually short and were puffed or slashed.

The skirt became stiffer, narrower and shorter. By 1808 it was above the feet, by 1810 even above the ankles. The hem was often decorated. The train was still worn only at the courts and was fastened on the back as a separate item of clothing.

---

[1] Werther: hero in a book by Goethe   [2] Directoire (Fr.) = Directory : post-revolutionary French government executive   [3] Empire: Napoleonic empire

1: German Werther costume, late 18th century

2: German Empire fashion around 1800

3: French court costume and carrick, early 19th century

Men's Clothing

At the time of the Revolution, the dark frock coat was given a high collar, broad tails and long, narrow sleeves. It gradually developed into the **tailcoat** and became the main item of clothing for the bourgeoisie. The two rows of buttons were fastened, or it was worn open. The waist moved upwards with time.

Bright colours were preferred for the trousers. Long breeches, the **pantaloons**, gradually replaced the tight-fitting knee-length trousers with a fastener at the side. They originally came down to the calf. Later they reached the feet and were held tight by stirrups and braces (suspenders).

The trousers were very narrow with a high waist, and knitted fabric was preferred.

The close-fitting short waistcoat, the **gilet**, was sleeveless and was often worn with a high collar, as was the open shirt. Large neckcloths (stocks) were worn loosely or knotted under the chin. The sash appeared.

The long, double-breasted **redingote**, with overlapping front pieces, and the **carrick**, with several shoulder layers, served as overcoats. The short sleeveless **spencer** was also sometimes worn over the tailcoat.

Accessories

4: Woman's shoe

5: Escarpin:[2]
Man's dancing shoe

At the time of the English fashion, women preferred to wear large round hats with extravagant feather decoration on their magnificent head of curls. During the Directoire and Empire periods, hair was styled according to the ancient models; waved, plaited or knotted after ancient Greek styles or curled like the Romans. They adorned themselves lavishly with combs, bangles, diadems, ribbons and feathers. **Turbans**, **lace head-dresses** and antique **helmets** came into fashion, and later the **poke bonnet**, a hat with a brim and ribbon ties. Windswept hairstyles and classical curls for men were in keeping with the times. The two-corned hat gradually replaced the high round felt hat which then developed into the **top hat**.

After the stiletto shoe, the flat shoe came into fashion for women. Sandals were appropriate to the long flowing robes. However, soft **slipper** shoes (pumps) with low fronts were worn in preference. These were covered in fabric and the colour was matched to the clothes. Later, when skirts rose above the ankles, they were provided with crossed ribbons. The main footwear for men was soft boots, with or without tops. However, flat, low-fronted shoes were also common. **Gamashes**[1] were worn as protection from the weather.

Long gloves were essential for women with short-sleeved dresses. **Muffs, shades** and **reticules**, a kind of small hand bag, were important accessories when going outside. Necklaces of many strands were worn with the low décolletage. Bracelets, rings and large earrings were also popular. Men wore a watch on a chain and would not go out of doors without **gloves**. Decorated cane handles and tobacco pouches were much esteemed.

---

[1] gamashes: stiffened fabric or leather item, usually with buttons, placed over the shoe and lower leg.   [2] escarpin (Fr.) = dancing shoe, pump

Characteristics of the Age

1: Biedermeier room (Düsseldorf)

After the political defeat of Napoleon, the **Vienna Congress** tried to create a new order in Europe and restore the earlier relationships. During this time of the **Restoration**, there was a growing interest in past cultures, revealed particularly in art and literature (romanticism).

Architecture retained its classical forms but a new, more bourgeois style, the **Biedermeier**, developed in the design of living rooms. A homeliness and idyllic atmosphere was attained by simple, clear and soft curving designs.

Clothing fashion was shaped according to the ideas of the **Romantics** and suited the needs of the bourgeois lifestyle. It was highly imaginative and colourful. In contrast to the lavish women's fashion, men's clothing was unobtrusively elegant and functional. Distinctions were made between day clothes and formal dress, Summer and Winter clothing, and materials and colours were chosen accordingly. Stripes, checks and floral patterns, combined with white linens were typical of the Biedermeier period.

2: German fashion around 1820

3: Biedermeier fashion around 1830

4: Biedermeier fashion around 1830

Women's Clothing

For a while, the slim silhouettes of the Empire fashion were retained, although they were modified. The stiff, narrow skirt was ankle length, sewn on under the breast, belted and accented around the lower part by flounces, frills, gathers and ribbons. The small neckline of the tight bodice was framed by a high ruche. The tops of the long, narrow sleeves were puffed.

Around 1820, the waistline moved down once more to its natural place and was tightly laced by a corset. Several underskirts supported the wide skirt which came above the feet. A collar or a **bertha**, a deep collar or trimming, surrounded the broad neckline of the tight fitting bodice. The enormous **leg-of-mutton** (gigot) or **elephant sleeves** had to be supported by a whalebone frame. They were set deeply into the dress and were usually narrow from the elbows to the wrist. Later they were narrow at the top and puffed out below.

Widened shoulders, full sleeves, narrow stomachers and wide skirts produced the so called **hour-glass silhouette**. The dress was also richly decorated with ribbons, bows, embroidery, flounces and artificial flowers.

Around 1840 the floor length skirt returned, but this time stiffened around the circumference by horsehair. Originally, it had only a single flounce at the hem, but gradually it developed many rows of flounces. Sometimes several skirts were worn over each other in graduated lengths.

The **crinoline**[1], a hoop skirt originally stiffened by horsehair then later with wire hoops, developed from the stiffened underskirts. The sleeves became narrow once more.

Because of the bulky sleeves on dresses, shawls and capes were popular. The **pelerine**[2] was like a broad, fringed scarf; the **mantilla** was a triangular shawl. Shoulder collars were developed from the **canezou**, a short, long-sleeved jacket. The long and very wide cloak was called the **rotonde** or **wrap**.

[1] crin (Fr.) = horsehair   [2] pèlerine (Fr.) = pilgrim; hence pilgrim's cape or shawl

1: **Cloak fashion around 1830**

2: **Crinoline fashion 1847**

Men's Clothing

The coat jacket or double-breasted **frock coat**, became the day suit. The **tailcoat** with rounded or cornered lower jacket front served as a formal suit or upper class streetwear. The frock coat and the tailcoat were made of dark or colourful woollen fabric. The knee-length flared tails were sewn on at the waist. The chest and shoulders were padded. Sometimes the men would even wear a corset to attain the required slim waist. The tops of the sleeves were puffed. Later they were sewn flat.

Lighter, or differently coloured knitted material was always preferred for the long trousers called **pantaloons**. The trouser legs were very narrow at the bottom, partly cov-

ered the foot and were held taut by a **stirrup**. The colourfully patterned or embroidered **waistcoat** was also tightly fitted. The tall, stiffened **pointed collar** (cut-throat) and the cuffs of the white shirt were visible. Neckscarves or stocks would be wrapped loose, tied according to individual preferences, or tied into a bow.

The fashion of the cloak was very varied. The **carrick** was worn loose and had several shoulder collars. The **redingote** was fitted in the cut of the frock coat but somewhat longer. The **paletot** was a new design with a straight cut and high neckline, sometimes with a flared skirt.

3: **Woman's boot**

4: **Man's buttoned boot**

Accessories

Women's coiffure was highly imaginative and varied. Elaborate hairstyles with pinned-up plaits, tufts of curls, corkscrew curls and kiss-curls were characteristics of the Biedermeier period, as was the **poke bonnet**. This was made out of straw, felt, or cloth and was richly decorated with flowers, fruit and bows. The broad brim often jutted out over the face and it was tied under the chin with ribbons. The typical headwear for men was the tall **top hat**, both with day clothes and formal dress. Curled hair and mutton-chop side boards were fashionable.

The women's shoe had a thin sole and no heel, was very soft and invariably covered with fabric. **Cross-band** shoes were popular and were often tied up to the calf. Later the women's **short boot** with low heels and laces appeared. The shortened skirts allowed light coloured, often decorated stockings to be seen. The men's laced or buttoned **half boots** also had low heels. Fabric and leather were often combined.

Gloves, reticules[1], **shades, fans** and **muffs** were important accessories for women Necklaces with lockets, long earrings, brooches and lavish belt buckles were popular. Men were equipped with **gloves** and a **walking stick** or **umbrella**. The pocket watch was worn on a long chain, and expensive tie pins and signet rings were favoured.

[1] reticule: dainty fabric handbag, often with draw-cord

Characteristics of the Age

1: **Architecture of the Romantic period (Textile factory, Ochtrup)**

The second half of the 19th century was a period of rapid **industrialisation**. Mechanisation of spinning and weaving and the arrival of the ready-made clothing industry supported by the invention of the sewing machine, now enabled more classes of society to dress fashionably.

However, there were no really new developments in the style of either fashion or architecture, rather a reworking and mixing of earlier styles. The renewed interest in ideas and designs of previous ages was known as **Romanticism**. Elements of especially the Renaissance, Gothic, and Rococo periods were incorporated into churches, civic and prestigious buildings, as well as functional buildings such as factories and railway stations.

The **clothing** of middle-class women presented their status and image, and was lavish with the material and trimmings. However, men's clothing was distinguished by functional, classic and suitable designs in unobtrusive dark colours.

The **Victorian era** in general, and in Germany especially the period after the Franco-Prussian war of 1870/71 and the founding of the German Empire (**Founding Years**), was a time of great industrial expansion.

From 1860 to 1870, women's fashion copied the style at the French Imperial Court of Napoleon III, where the Rococo was popular again (**Neo-rococo**). Later, derivatives of the Baroque were more popular.

2: **Crinoline fashions (Neo-rococo) 1860**

3: **Visiting dress 1879**

4: **Formal dress 1882**

Women's Clothing

During the **Neo-rococo** period, the dome-shaped skirts, supported by a **crinoline**, became enormous. To add to this, the width was emphasised by flounces, frills and embroidery. The **stomacher**, usually buttoned all the way up, was high necked and had a lace collar during the day. For evenings, it was deeply cut and richly embellished. The **pagoda sleeves**, which were narrow at the top and widened into a bell shape from the elbows, were often overloaded with frills, flounces and lace trimmings. Puffed under-sleeves were often worn.

Shawls, capes, mantillas, and jackets with a masculine cut served as over garments.

After 1860, the skirt was flattened at the front, became wider at knee height and trailed at the back in many folds. The bodice emphasised the bodyline down to the hips. The sleeves were also long and tight. The over skirt was eventually lifted up and puffed out at the back over a frame. This **bustle**, or improver, was extravagantly decorated with e.g. cords, braids, bows, flounces and lace.

This fashion also continued during the **Founding Years** until about 1875, when it was replaced by the **slim line**. Skirts became very narrow, the bodice fitted very tightly and the length was emphasised by stripes and seams. The length of the train was determined by the formality of the occasion. Day clothes eventually lost their train.

The costume (suit) appeared, accompanied by a blouse. Colour and material combinations, as well as contrasting trimmings were popular.

Around 1880, once again a drape was attached to the back of the skirts, the **Cul de Paris** (Paris tail).

1: **Outer garments of the crinoline period**

2: **Men's fashion 1875**

Men's Clothing

Men's fashion was completely modelled on the English example and was suited to the professional or social occasion. For a while, outerwear was dominated by the **frock coat** and **tail coat** but, gradually, the more comfortable jacket, the suit jacket, became accepted. The front and back parts had a straight cut and were not very fitted. The double-breasted style, and trimmed edges were popular.

Stirrups went out of fashion. Trousers became wider, with a higher waist, and were often striped or checked. The waistcoat was at first still coloured. The **suit** appeared around 1860; trousers, jacket and waistcoat were all of the same colour and material.

The black tail coat, combined with striped trousers, was worn only for particular occasions. The black tail coat with a white waistcoat was worn only as formal dress.

The **paletot** with a straight cut was the preferred style of coat.

Shirts were often embroidered. Stand-up collars and turned down collars were gradually replaced by stiff buttoned-on collars. Depending on the type of outfit, a narrow tie, a broad cravat or a neckband would be worn.

3: **Woman's boot**

Accessories

Women's head wear continued to evolve with the appearance of **spoon** and **gipsy** bonnets. They were lavishly decorated and sat directly over the forehead or on the back of the head. The sometimes smooth but also sometimes elaborate hairstyles were decorated with fine hairnets, pearls and precious stones, ribbons, feathers and flowers. Men wore tall **top hats** on their slicked down parted hair to go with the tail coat and frock coat. The **bowler**, a felt hat with a stiff rounded top and a small stiff brim, came into fashion for wearing with the suit. The **boater**, a flat straw hat, was worn with the Summer suit.

The women's wardrobe was completed by low or calf-length **boots** with a medium heel, so no part of the leg was to be seen. The boots were often embroidered or had stitched decoration. **Pumps** began to be worn with ball dresses, as skirt lengths became shorter. Laced or buttoned **boots** were also fashionable for men. Only the formal shoe was lower.

Women favoured conspicuous jewellery; large lockets, earrings, brooches and bracelets studded with precious stones and pearls. **Gloves, handbags** and **shades** were necessary when going outdoors. Men displayed prominent tie pins and cuff links. The gold watch was worn on a heavy chain. The correctly dressed man always wore **gloves** and carried a **cane** or walking **umbrella**.

13.15 Belle Epoque[1], Reform, Art Nouveau (1)
ca. 1890 to 1914

Characteristics of the Age

1: Art Nouveau facade (Düsseldorf)

The time before and after the turn of the century saw tremendous developments in science and technology, which had their influence on lifestyles. The fabric, colour and cut of men's and women's clothing was now suited to its purpose and the occasion. Jobs, sport and free time were influential. Attempts at **reform and emancipation** by doctors, artists and women's groups towards the end of the century, meant that women's clothes had to be more functional and easier to wear. They also had to reflect the increased status of women in society.

The English style with a formal business-like design and subdued colours and patterns was still of prime importance to men's fashion.

Women's fashion in the period before the turn of the century, known as the **Belle Epoque** was luxurious and extravagant with the material, the cut, and the finish. Discreet colours were nevertheless retained. The **clothing reform** at the beginning of the 20th century brought simplified designs, lively colours and new decorative patterns, inspired by the **art nouveau**. This art trend (about 1895 to 1914) attempted to harmonize the functional with the natural and aesthetic. This included architecture and above all, craft. Basic characteristics of this style were soft, flowing lines, simple ornaments inspired from nature, and designs which were suited to the materials.

2: Women's fashion around 1898

3: Turn of the century women's fashion

4: Women's fashion, early 20th century

5: Dance dress 1914

Women's Clothing

In 1890, skirts with a **slim silhouette** were preferred. They were narrow at the front and trailed in folds at the back. The flared skirt, cut out of panels appeared. It was tight-fitting at the hips and flared out in many folds from the knee. Lining and underskirts, both silk and trimmed with flounces, gave a fullness to the dress and produced the popular rustle. The long and pointed bodice was always high necked and had a high stand-up collar for day wear. It gradually became more like a blouse and was decorated with a false collar. Generously puffed sleeves, in particular the leg-of-mutton sleeve, were popular.

A skirt and blouse with a belt to **emphasise the waist** were often worn. The **bolero** allowed the attractive finishings of the blouse to be visible. The **costume**, with a men's style jacket, also became firmly established. Straight or fitted coats and longer jackets replaced the cape.

Around 1900, the princess cut came into fashion and the very long sleeves became narrower. The front was made straight and the breasts were emphasised by lacing the body and hips into a corset. From the side, the body then resembled an S-shape. This unhealthy fashion was counteracted by the **reform dress**, which flowed softly to the floor from the shoulders or the breast. At first, it found favour only as formal wear but, gradually daywear also began to be less tightly constricted and higher in the waist. Around 1910, skirts became so narrow that walking became difficult. However, this **hobble skirt** was as unpopular as the trouser skirt.

Around 1914, the shoe-length, straight skirt, often with a draped over skirt (**tunic**), combined with a blouse-like top dominated day wear. An oriental style was preferred for extravagant evening wear.

[1] belle époque (Fr.) = beautiful age

1: Men's and women's riding suits, 1890

2: Formal dress 1910

3: Formal dress 1910

Men's Clothing

Men wore the **suit** in a moderately fitted style with a fairly high front at work and outdoors. Gradually the suit became more fitted and the lapel became longer. The ankle length trousers tapered towards the bottom and had turn-ups (cuffs) and pressed creases.

On formal occasions, in the day time, the frock coat was replaced by the **cutaway** (tail coat) with rounded tails. This was worn with striped trousers with no turn-ups.

The **dinner jacket** (smoking jacket, tuxedo) appeared in formal evening dress and, from then on, tails were not worn in the evening except for large, official occasions.

The overcoat was chosen according to the suit. Apart from the elegant **Chesterfield**, the casual **Ulster**, the comfortable **Raglan** and the **short coat** were favoured. With the arrival of sporting fashions, knickerbockers and plus fours became popular.

4: Woman's strap shoe

5: Man's short boot

Accessories

Women preferred small hats on their tightly waved hairstyles with a knot at the nape of the neck. When the piled up, protruding hairstyles came into fashion, the hat also developed into a "**picture hat**" and was richly decorated with feathers, flowers, ribbons and bows. For men, a soft felt hat, a stiff **bowler**, a smart **top hat** or a summery **boater** were worn, depending on the occasion or the suit.

With the shortening of skirts, the women's shoe entered the fashion arena. The low fronted shoe, the **pump**, gradually replaced the boot which had been the standard daytime footwear. The pumps were pointed, had curved, medium height heels and often a strap. Men wore ankle high **laced** or **buttoned boots** or dark shoes, over which they wore fabric gaiters. Lacquered (patent) shoes had to be worn with formal evening dress.

Hats, **gloves** and **handbags** were essential outdoor accessories for women. In addition, a **sunshade** was required during the Summer, and a **muff** in Winter. Highly imaginative jewellery, feather boas and fans completed the evening dress. **Breast pocket handkerchiefs**, **gloves** and **canes** completed the men's outfit. In addition, tie pins, shirt buttons and cuff links made of expensive materials were displayed. The wrist watch appeared.

13.16 The Twenties (1)
1920 to 1929

Characteristics of the Decade

**1: Bauhaus
(School of Design, Dessau)**

After the first World War (1914 to 1918), women's clothing in particular under went revolutionary changes. One of the most important influences was the movement towards **equal status for women**; in the work place, in private and political life and, increasingly, in sport. A newer, more business-like type of woman emerged and made corresponding demands on **clothing**. The distortion of a corset was no longer desired. Exaggeration of the female form was abjured and more freedom for the legs was demanded. The result was simplified styles and short skirts. Above all, day wear was practical and comfortable. Casual fabrics in muted colours were preferred. On the other hand, evening dress was composed with striking materials in bright colours and extravagant decoration. The new leaders of fashion were to be theatre and movie stars.

The fashion industry began to boom. Art, theatre and music also flourished. Evening entertainment made the pressures of inflation, political unrest and unemployment more bearable. The years from 1924 to 1929 were described as the "roaring twenties".

The Bauhaus, a school of design founded in 1919, heavily influenced the trends in **architecture** in the 20th century. Its goal was the fusion of art and technology. Function and efficiency were most important. Concrete and metal, glass and plaster were the building materials. In contrast, the fantastic ornaments and interior design of the **Art Deco** were reminiscent of Art Nouveau.

2: Sport suit and jumper fashions 1926

3: Evening wear 1925

4: Afternoon wear 1929

5: Formal dress 1929

Women's Clothing

After the wartime fashions, with an emphasised waist and a wide skirt, the narrow, loose, shift dress emerged. The length of the skirt became shorter; by 1920 the mostly one-piece dresses were scarcely calf-length. The loosely swirling dropped waist was emphasised by a belt or sash. Comfortable knitted fabrics and affordable artificial silk fabrics appeared. Long **jumpers** or pullovers were also popular.

By 1924 the skirt was at the knee and by 1927 it had risen **above the knee**. The lengthened top of the dress had a straight cut so that the bust and waist disappeared. The fashion ideal was the **garçonne**[1], a boy-like figure.

Formal dress had the same cut as day wear although the **décolletage** was larger and there was more feminine detail such as swinging flared or pleated skirts and trimmings of pearls, sequins or fringes.

At the end of the decade clothing became more figure hugging and skirts lengthened to the calf. Biassed cuts, drapings, flounces, asymmetrical and uneven hems were popular.

A **masculine cut** was often chosen for suit jackets and day coats. The wrap-around coat with a shawl collar dominated the elegant style of clothing. Fur coats and fur trimmings came into fashion, as well as the **ensemble** (dress and coat).

[1] garçon (Fr.) = boy

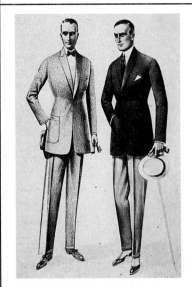

1: Men's fashion 1920

2: Men's fashion 1925

3: Men's fashion 1928

Men's Clothing

Men's day wear was either business-like or sporty. The discreetly coloured fabrics had various patterns, such as checks, stripes and small designs. At first, the **jacket** retained its stiffened front and high waist and was usually single breasted with pointed lapels. The **trousers** became narrower at the bottom.

Around 1925, the suit jacket became less fitted and was not so stiff. The trousers had an even leg width.

Around 1929, the shoulders became well padded. The suit jacket was fairly fitted and close on the hips. Trousers with turn-ups and a wide, straight cut appeared.

Knickerbockers and the sport jacket were no longer worn only for sporting occasions. The waistcoat, essential when dressed correctly, was replaced by a pullover during the day.

The **trench coat** appeared as a casual overcoat. The **Chesterfield** was preferred when more elegance was required.

Formal dress remained similar. The **cutaway**, **dinner jacket**, or **tails** were chosen according to the occasion. The **Stresemann**[1], a combination of a dark jacket and striped trousers, emerged as a semi-formal outfit for day wear.

4: Woman's shoe

5: Man's shoe

Accessories

Women wore the bell-shaped **cloche hat** pulled right down over the forehead over their smoothly styled or wavy short (bobbed) haircuts. The **turban** decorated with feathers was preferred for formal occasions. Men combed their parted hairstyle smooth and slicked it down. Headgear included the soft felt **Trilby**, the elegant stiff **Homburg** or various **sporty caps**, chosen according to the occasion.

Women's shoes were quite pointed, whether elegant **pumps**, high heeled **strap shoes**, or casual **flat shoes**. Short skirts revealed the legs and therefore the stockings. Skin-coloured silk or artificial silk stockings were often decorated. The men wore ankle length **boots** or **shoes**; the latter with gaiters or spats in winter.

Gloves, **handbags**, **shawls**, **shades** and **hats** provided splashes of colour. **Ties**, now colourful and patterned, were also fashion items. Women favoured multi-strand pearl necklaces, bracelets and earrings. Costume jewellery appeared alongside genuine jewellery. The long cigarette holder was also essential. The men wore wrist watches and signet rings as decoration.

[1] Stresemann: German politician of the time

Characteristics of the Decade

The beginning of the decade was marked by the aftermath of the economic crisis (1929). Frugality was enforced by unemployment. **Socialism, Communism, or Fascism** were strengthened in many countries as a reaction to social and economic difficulties.

Art developed very little. Architecture was functional and plain. Public buildings were constructed in the **Neoclassical** style.

Women's fashion was very **feminine**. The emphasis on natural forms was in keeping with the conservatism of the times. With the rise of militarism, daywear became severe and acquired masculine details.

Men's clothing remained conservative, although the everyday fashions became gradually more sporty and casual.

1: Formal dress 1932

2: Coat and Ensemble 1933

3: Evening dress

4: Winter coat 1936

5: Suit 1939

6: Afternoon dress 1939

Women's Clothing

Dresses were made of flowing fabrics, were calf length, accented at the **waist**, narrow at the hips and had a flared hem. Biassed cuts, draping, and the wrap-over effect emphasised the elegant line. The **shoulders** were accentuated by pads and strongly gathered sleeve settings. Formal evening dresses were low-cut and often had a train.

Jackets and coats were also slim-fitting. By the end of the decade, shoulders had become heavily padded. Skirts just covered the knee. Coats were often $^7/_8$ length. Details from **uniforms** such as epaulettes, large sewn on pockets and broad lapels were typical.

Men's Clothing

The fitted jacket lay on the hips, had emphasised shoulders and short, broad lapels. The straight trousers with **turn-ups** had a comfortable width. The **double breasted suit** was popular for special occasions during the day.

The **Norfolk jacket**[1] **and knickerbockers** or blazer and belted slacks were popular casual combinations. Beside the fitted Chesterfield and the straight great-coat, trench coats and raincoats were worn.

Accessories

Women favoured **small** decorated **hats** or close-fitting caps on their chin length curled hair. Shoes with high heels, wedge heels and thick soles appeared. White trimmings, fabric flowers and decorative belts served as finishings.

Soft or stiff felt **trilbys** or sporty **peaked caps** completed the men's wardrobe. Narrow, two-tone shoes were common.

7: Men's casual fashions

8: Chesterfield and Great coat

[1] Norfolk jacket: casual sporty jacket with golfing pleats, oversewn belt, bellows pockets and shoulder saddle

Characteristics of the Decade

During the **Second World War** (1939 to 1945) and the immediate **post-war years**, few developments of clothing fashion were possible. The shortage of fabric and official rationing necessitated frequent alterations and patching. The motto was "waste not - want not". **Women's clothing** was simple and functional but nevertheless flattering. Muted colours were used and expensive trimmings were excluded. In 1947, haute couture was revived in Paris and took up the fashion leadership once more. Christian Dior rose to be "fashion king" with his new, feminine fashion for women, known as the **New Look**.

Women's fashion of the early forties

1: Day and afternoon dresses
2: Day wear
3: Suit

Women's fashion 1949

4: New Look suit
5: Pencil line
6: Bolero suit
7: Afternoon dress

8: Casual coat 1949
9: Elegant day coat 1949
10: Men's fashion

Women's Clothing

Narrow designs with emphasised shoulders and **knee-length** skirts were typical during the war. The dresses stressed the waist; jackets and coats had details of uniforms.

In contrast, the New Look brought calf-length, wide **flared skirts** and tops with rounded shoulders which flattered the figure. An alternative to this youthful, bouncy style was provided by the **pencil line** with its elegant, and feminine tightly fitted top and long, narrow skirts.

Formal evening dress acquired drapings, tunic and peplum effects, and a stylish décolletage. The **tight waistline** brought a revival of the corset and stiffening of the bodice.

Jackets and coats were tailored to fit the figure or had a flared back.

Men's Clothing

Men's fashion changed very little and remained conservative in colours and patterns. The standard suit was **double breasted** which made the waistcoat unnecessary.

In the post war years, the **suit jacket** became longer, and broader on the shoulders, but remained narrow at the hips. **Trousers** were given a wide cut and turn-ups. The casual **duffle coat** appeared.

Accessories

Caps or draped **headscarves** were worn on the long and wavy or upswept hairstyles. Shoes were often heavy, with thick soles. The New Look brought short curled hairstyles and elegant **hats** with either no brim, or a broad brim.

Men wore soft **felt trilbys**, **peaked caps** or **berets**. The crêpe sole for shoes first appeared in the post war years.

Characteristics of the Decade

Tremendous developments were made in the clothing industry due to the boost in the economy and the rise in living standards. The exclusive ideas of haute couture were converted into wearable fashion and made accessible to all levels of society. Position in society was underlined by clothing. Easy-to-wear synthetic fabrics of good value promoted a consumer society.

While **men's clothing** remained conventional, the fashion trends for **women** began to change from season to season. Silhouettes were labelled by letters or shapes. Skirt hems rose from the calf to below the knee.

Apart from **sports** and **leisure** clothing, a separate and uncomplicated fashion developed for the younger generation based on knits, cords, and leather clothing but, most of all, the popularisation of blue jeans. Fashion was modelled on film stars and pop idols; many of the trends came from the USA.

1955:
tulip, cupola, and I-line

1957:
trapeze, A, H, and sack line

1958:
barrel line

1: Fashion lines

2: Coats in X- and V- lines, 1951

3: Afternoon dress, 1951

4: Blouson suit, 1959

5: Cupola line, 1959

6: Tailored suit and double-breasted suit

7: Single-breasted suit, 1954

8: Sport and leisure wear, 1954

Women's Clothing

Slim skirts, narrow waists and styled hips were the elegant, feminine fashions. Typical examples were the **pencil line**, **tulip line**, **Y line** and **Empire line**. The youthful, swinging styles were typified by the **X line** with a princess cut, **cupola** and **balloon** lines with bouncing skirts and petticoats, and also the flared **trapeze** and **A lines**. Emphasis on the hips, a fluid waist line and a blouse-like top were features of the **H line** and **wave line**. The **sack line** was a completely loose cut which concealed the figure and later developed into the **barrel line**.

Men's Clothing

Jackets and coats had a wide cut, broad **padded shoulders** and **no waist**. The trousers were comfortably wide at the top and became narrower towards the bottom.

Around 1955, the suit jacket became **more fitted** and acquired more rounded shoulders. The single breasted jacket with a short, broad lapel and the elegant double breasted jacket were both popular.

Accessories

Headwear, handbags and gloves were carefully matched to the clothing. Broad brimmed or decorative hats sat upon short curly hairstyles. Pointed low-front shoes with **stiletto heels** and whisper thin nylon stockings were in demand. Young girls preferred ponytails and the **ballerina slipper**.

Soft **felt hats** or **sporty caps**, narrow **shoes** or **slip-ons** were worn by men. The **breast pocket handkerchief** and narrow tie or bow-tie were for correct dressing.

Characteristics of the Decade

Clothing in the sixties was characterised by a liberation from constraints and taboos. Young people were allowed to adopt unconventional clothing styles, and the textile industry adapted accordingly. The catchword for advertisers and the media was "**youth**". The prime example of the trend was the **miniskirt fashion**. Jeans, sweaters and T-shirts became universal dress for the young in their late teens and early twenties, who modelled themselves mainly on pop stars. Towards the end of the decade long hair came into fashion.

Space travel and **abstract art** also influenced the fashion scene. Loud colours and new types of materials such as plastic film and coated fabrics appeared. However, there was also an **anti-fashion** movement which expressed the protest of youth against social and political events. The so-called "nostalgic" and "hippy"[1] fashions were directed against the achievement-orientated consumer society just as the deliberately careless "dropout" look was against the conventional style of dress.

Women's fashion of the early sixties

| 1: Princess dress | 2: Fitted dress | 3: Chanel suit | 4: Shirt-waister dress |

Fashion after 1964

| 5: Op-art | 6: Courrèges look[4] | 7: Op-art | 8: Trapeze line |

| 9: Maxi-coat and trouser combination | 10: Mini-coat | 11: Leisure suit 1964 | 12: Single-breasted suit 1964 |

Women's Clothing

The **sporty casual** style of loose jumpers and shirt dresses was popular, alongside feminine and figure-flattering lines such as the decorative princess and fitted styles. Blousons, long waistcoats and pinafore dresses also were popular; the Chanel suit, **miniskirt** and **trousers** for women became accepted once and for all.

Op-art[2] and the **space look** brought a futuristic fashion with geometric patterns and designs in black and white, white and silver. Dresses and coats in the **trapeze** line stressed contrasting trimmings and clearly defined seams.

Trousers with extremely wide flares appeared. Hot pants[3], maxi-coats and the transparent look were unusual variants.

Men's Clothing

At first, suit jackets and coats had a **straight** and comfortable cut. However, after 1965 the silhouette became more **tailored**. Occasionally, the suit jacket was even very strongly waisted. Narrow trousers without turn-ups and knee length coats were preferred. Leisure jackets and pullovers were combined with tight fitting belted trousers.

Accessories

Broad shoes with **large heels** appeared. Fine tights (panty hose) made the miniskirt more acceptable, and it was worn with **boots** of all lengths. Women's hats were seldom to be seen. Large back-combed hairstyles were therefore popular, as were short hair cuts, false hair pieces and wigs.

Apart from colourful shirts, thin polo neck jumpers came into fashion for men. The broad ties were colourfully patterned.

[1] hippies: flower children; hip (USA) = well informed, stylish
[2] op-art: optical art, geometric-abstract patterns   [3] hot pants: skin tight ladies shorts   [4] André Courréges: French fashion designer

Characteristics of the Decade

Fashion was extremely wide ranging, allowing people to compose their own **individual look**. **Combinations** of separately-purchased items were popular (separates), as were **mixtures of materials and patterns** (mix-and-match).

Skirt lengths fluctuated and settled on **midi** style. A wave of **nostalgia** brought back the feminine styles of the thirties as an alternative to the sporty, casual style. The **traditional and romantic** looks also were new trends.

In men's fashion, a rich selection of **leisure or casual** clothing developed alongside the conservative and formal.

Young people preferred denim and jeans. Trainers became the most popular footwear. Disco fashion appeared with loud colours and shiny materials. Punks[1] gave vent to their non-conformist feelings through skin tight leather clothing and shocking hairstyles.

1: Blazer fashions 1972

2: Mix and match 1977

3: Denim fashion 1976

4: Nostalgic fashion 1978

5: Traditional style 1978

6: The exotic look 1977

7: The T line 1979

8: Party fashion 1975

9: Single and double breasted suits 1972

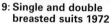

[1] punk (USA) = worthless, naive

Women's Clothing

Day wear was dominated by **mini length** pleated skirts and shirt dresses, trousers with **wide flares**, blousons and **fitted** blazers. Many different styles of blouses, trousers and jackets appeared with the fashion for **combinations**. Skirt hemlines fell to below the knee.

For the new **feminine line**, dresses of flowing fabrics had fitted tops, longer skirts and a belt to emphasise the waist.

Frills, flounces and embroidery characterised the **traditional and romantic** look. There was a strong exotic influence in evening wear.

Finally, a more business-like style arose with the **T line**, which had a straight cut and emphasised shoulders. **Over-size** styles were a clear reflection of the trend towards more casual fashions.

Men's Clothing

For a while, men's fashion was exemplified by the **closely fitted** suit with narrow shoulders and **broad lapels**, together with trousers that were close fitting to the thighs but with **broad flares**. Later came a new style which, though it **looked very slim**, was more comfortable. Typical features were broad shoulders, long lapels and narrow trousers.

Accessories

Bell-shaped and veiled hats came in with the **nostalgic** trend. Shoes with thick soles and heavy heels were popular for a short time. Otherwise many different styles of **boots** dominated footwear.

Men's shirts had discreet small patterns, stripes and checks. Scarfs and cravats were sometimes worn instead of ties. The **handbag for men** (manbag) appeared.

Characteristics of the Decade

Modern clothing fashion is highly **diverse and differentiated**. This is only a reflection of the range of different and individualistic lifestyles as well as the multiplicity of opportunities for wearing different styles of clothes at work, during the day, and at a wide range of leisure pursuits. Awareness of fashion is generally high, and clothing is an expression of higher living standards. Good quality fabrics, high grade garment making, decorative details and a great **diversity of style** are typical.

In **menswear** the traditional suit has to be elegant, with a classic cut, and comfortable. In casual clothing, light materials, a casual cut and elaborate functional details are required.

In **womenswear** the inspiration is the active, self-aware woman. Styles are both classic/elegant as well as casual/functional. Feminine fashion has persisted, however, with refined, seductive and extravagant styles. **Nostalgic influences** are reminiscent of fashions of past decades and have led to the style mix, a combination of greatly contrasting silhouettes. **Skirt lengths are varied** from knee length to ankle length according to the style; the miniskirt has returned.

Youth fashions have shown a distinct tendency to move away from punk and the tattered look towards a neater, more wholesome style which, nevertheless, is combined with original ideas.

1: Feminine fashion

2: Layered look

3: Suit with new proportions

Women's Clothing

Daytime clothing is predominantly **casual** with a simple, comfortable cut. The swirling, slim silhouette and the voluminous, very wide layered look compete with each other. The **casual, elegant** city style, with masculine shape and details has also been retained for suits and coats.

Evening wear is **feminine and elegant**: softly flowing or figure-fitting with a tight, or flared, or full skirt.

The waist is accented or may be raised or lowered. Sleeves are cut generously for freedom of movement. The **shoulders** are very often **emphasised**, and the combination of very different lengths and widths has given rise to **new proportions**.

4: City style

5: Casual, elegant men's fashion

6: Party fashion, "after six"

Men's Clothing

The suit jacket has changed very little. The waist is slightly fitted, shoulders are lightly padded, and lapels are not very broad. **Belted, pleated trousers** are the most common. Quilted and light shell coats are popular. Evening wear is a broad and lively mixture of **party fashions**.

Accessories

There has never been such a great **diversity of accessories**. Fashionable and functional are often combined. The colours, designs, and materials of the latest fashion themes may be used to reinforce a given style, or to contrast with it.

13.23 Glossary of Special Terms

Term	Explanation	Style Era
Berthe, Bertha	Loose collar or neckline insert for women's wear	Biedermeier, Neo-rococo
Biretta	Flat cap, decorated with feathers and cords	Renaissance
Bustle	Wire or whalebone frame over which the rear of the skirt was gathered; also "Cul de Paris"	Baroque, Rococo, Neo-rococo, Victorian
Canezou	Short small jacket, spencer type, for women; later with a wide shoulder collar	Empire, Biedermeier, Neo-rococo
Caraco	Short tailed jacket for women, similar to a tail coat	English
Carrick	Coat with several stepped shoulder layers	Empire, Biedermeier
Chamarre	Decorative loose coat with large collar and broad sleeves	Renaissance
Chaperon	Close fitting hood with shoulder collar and tail	Gothic
Charleston	Women's dress for evening wear with a straight unwaisted line, often with fringes; named after the fashionable dance	Twenties
Chemise	Light women's dress with high waist, puffed sleeves, décolletage, train	Directoire, Empire
Chiton	Women's and men's belted linen robe, gathered into many folds and secured at the shoulders	Ancient Greek
Chlaina	Simple woollen men's robe, draped over the back and shoulders, clasped at the right shoulder	Ancient Greek
Chlamys	Short woollen men's cloak, thrown over the left shoulder and clasped at the right	Ancient Greek
Circlet	Ring of metal or flowers etc, worn around the head or brow	Romanesque, Gothic
Clasp cloak	Circular or rectangular cloak, clasped at the front or shoulder	Romanesque, Gothic
Clavi	Decorative strips used as edge trimmings, mostly purple dyed	Ancient Rome, Byzantine
Codpiece	Pouch in the crotch of men's breeches	Late Gothic, Renaissance
Contouche	Women's outer garment for house, street and travel wear; fully tailored with deep folds at the back (Watteau pleats)	Rococo
Cotte	Long women's dress or men's long tunic	Romanesque, Gothic
Crinoline	Underskirt stiffened with horsehair or wire	Biedermeier, Neo-rococo
Cul de Paris	Emphasised rear of a women's outer dress, using a frame or padding; also "Paris tail", "French tail", "bustle"	Baroque, Rococo, Neo-rococo, Victorian
Culottes	Knee breeches; at first quite broad, later close fitting	Baroque, Rococo
Dagges	Cut out or sewn on flaps of fabric at the edges of a garment	Gothic
Dalmatic	Unbelted outer robe for the ruling classes with wide arms and coloured lengthways strips (clavi)	Ancient Roman, Byzantine
Doublet	Term for the men's close fitting, buttoned jacket; worn over the shirt and under the coat, or as an outer garment	Gothic, Renaissance, Early Baroque
Engageántes	Multiple lace flounces or ruches at the sleeve ends	Baroque, Rococo
Exomis	Short robe, used mainly as men's working clothing, which left the right shoulder bare	Ancient Greek
Farthingale	Earliest hoop dress; a conical frame of thin, flexible switches was worn below the underskirt	Spanish
Fibula	Pinned clasp for holding robes together	Ancient, Middle Ages
Fichu	Cloth square for covering the décolletage	English
Fontange	Head-dress with stiff, folded lace ruches at the front, standing up like organ pipes	Baroque
Full-bottom wig	High, long, curly wig for men	Baroque
Head-dress	Various confections made from stiffened cloth, veils, padded rolls, wire flowers, nets, jewels, brooches, etc.	Burgundian
Headrail	Shoulder draped headsquare	Romanesque, Gothic
Himation	Large, rectangular woollen outer robe for men and women	Ancient Greek
Hobble skirt	Long, very narrow skirt; very difficult to walk in	Art Nouveau
Houppelande	Cloak-like outer garment for men and women; long and heavily folded, mostly open at the front and belted	Gothic
Jerkin	Short, close fitting outer garment for young men, very similar to and worn over the doublet	Gothic, Renaissance
Jupe	Underskirt, made visible by gathering up the overdress (manteau); usually of a different colour and richly decorated	Baroque, Rococo
Justaucorps	Elegant, knee length, close fitted men's coat of velvet or brocade and decorated with cords; later with flying tails	Baroque, Rococo

Term	Explanation	Style Era
Kalasiris	National robes for men and women; narrow shell with straps, richly ornamented; in shift form transparent and finely pleated	Ancient Egypt
Manteau	Courtly women's outer robes; bodice and usually open skirt from the same material	Baroque, Rococo
Mantilla	Shawl, usually triangular covering the shoulders and sometimes the head	Biedermeier, Neo-rococo
Modesty piece	Decorated, triangular insert for the neckline of a bodice	Baroque, Rococo
Paenula	Oval or diamond shaped cape with head opening, closed all round or slit at the front; often with a hood	Ancient Rome, Byzantine
Palla	Rectangular woollen cloth used as a robe by women out of doors; often covered the head	Ancient Rome
Pallium	Men's rectangular woollen cloth outer robe, wrapped around the body, over the tunic	Ancient Rome
Panier	18th century hooped skirt; typically very wide, but flattened at the front and back	Rococo
Pantaloons	Originally, calf or ankle length narrow breeches, later full length and held with stirrups	Directoire, Empire, Biedermeier
Parti-coloured	Hose of different colours, or garments with panels of different colours	Gothic, Renaissance
Partlet	Women's broad shoulder collar used to cover a wide neckline	Renaissance
Peasecod-belly	Doublet with heavily padded breast, with a ridge down the middle	Spanish
Pelerine	Collar-shaped shawl or large shoulder collar on a cape	Biedermeier
Peplos	Women's rectangular woollen cloth robe, wrapped around the body and fastened over the shoulders	Ancient Greece
Petticoat	Stiff, dome-shaped underskirt, usually layered and decorated	Fifties
Poke bonnet	Richly decorated bonnet-hat with a broad brim; tied with ribbons under the chin	Empire, Biedermeier, Neo-rococo
Poulaine	Shoes with extended (piked) toes	Gothic
Redingote	Waisted coat with full skirts or a back vent, usually double breasted; riding coat	English, Empire, Biedermeier
Reform dress	Loose, freely draping dress, worn without a corset	Art Nouveau
Rhinegraves	Wide men's coulotte breeches, close fitting at the hips and tied under the knee; richly decorated with loops of ribbon	Early Baroque
Robe	Term for women's over-dress, also called a manteau	Baroque, Rococo
Ropa	Fully tailored over-dress, resembling a coat	Spanish
Rotonde	Long, circular cut cape for women; also called a wrap	Biedermeier
Shenti	Loin cloth or hip skirt, highly pleated and decorated	Ancient Egypt
Slops	Baggy, overhanging knee or calf length breeches, often having lengthways slashes with protruding lining	Renaissance
Spencer	Short, narrow waisted jacket with lapels; sleeveless or short sleeved	Empire
Spoon bonnet	Small bonnet tied under the chin with a ribbon	Neo-rococo, Victorian
Steeple	Tall, conical women's head-dress with a flowing veil	Burgundian
Stola	Women's outer robe in the form of a shift, worn belted over the tunic	Ancient Rome
Stomacher	Lengthening of the lower bodice front into a pointed or rounded peak	Spanish, Baroque, Rococo, Biedermeier, Victorian
Surcot	Women's or men's over-garment, usually sleeveless and unbelted, often trimmed with fur	Romanesque, Gothic
Tabard	Men's knee or ankle length closed outer robe, draped in many folds, usually unbelted	Gothic
Tassel cloak	Semi-circular shoulder cape closed at the front by a cord or chain on a pair of decorative plates (tassels)	Romanesque
Toga	Outer robe of the Roman ruling class; an oval woollen cloth folded lengthways and draped artistically around the body	Ancient Rome
Toque	Small flat hat with a narrow brim or brimless	Spanish
Trunk hose	Short, heavily padded breeches tied at the thigh, often with differently coloured slashes	Spanish
Tunic	Women's or men's shift style robe sewn from two pieces of fabric	Ancient Rome, Byzantine
Wimple	A band of linen wrapped around a woman's head and chin, supplemented with a brow band (fillet) or crown	Romanesque

Index of Technical Terms